the SNOWY TORRENTS

Avalanche Accidents in the United States

1996–2004

By Knox Williams and Spencer Logan

THE SNOWY TORRENTS
AVALANCHE ACCIDENTS IN THE UNITED STATES
1996–2004

Authors: *Knox Williams and Spencer Logan*
Editor: *Blase Reardon*
Assistant Editor: *Emma Walker*
Design: *McKenzie Long at Cardinal Innovative*
Published and distributed by the American Avalanche Association

Front cover photo:
A powder cloud during a scheduled helicopter-assisted avalanche mitigation mission on a terrain feature called the Rooster Comb, which rises up above the backside of the Stevens Pass Ski Area in Washington State, February 2014. *Photo Scott Rinckenberger.*

Back cover photo:
The crown of an avalanche that occurred during control work on Mount Baker, Washington, March 24, 2012. *Photo Grant Gunderson.*

International Standard Book Number:
978-0-9984805-0-3

Printed in the USA.

The snowy torrents are like the deep sea; they seldom return their victims alive.

—*Kampf über die Gletschern*
(Battle Over the Glaciers)
by W. Schmidkunz

CONTENTS

CONTENTS

FOREWORD

***The Snowy Torrents* has been the most important source** of information on avalanche accidents in the United States for the last 50 years. Four volumes of *The Snowy Torrents* have been published, but it has been more than twenty years since the last edition. The American Avalanche Association, with assistance from the Colorado Avalanche Information Center, is proud to continue this tradition with the publication of this book. As an association, we are dedicated to promoting and supporting professionalism and excellence in avalanche safety, education, and research in the United States. This book exemplifies that dedication by examining more than 200 avalanche accidents that have occurred in the US during the eight-year period from 1996-2004.

We have learned a lot about avalanches and avalanche safety since the first volume of *The Snowy Torrents* was published in 1967. During that time, the popularity of winter sports, the number of people traveling in avalanche-prone terrain, and the sophistication of avalanche rescue equipment have all grown. Much has changed, but avalanche accidents still occur. As professional and recreational users of avalanche terrain, we still have room to improve. The case studies in this book have been carefully studied and reviewed by the authors and offer a chance for all of us to learn from others.

We learn from our experiences, both individually and collectively. John Dewey wrote, "Failure is instructive. The person who really thinks learns quite as much from his failures as from his successes." I implore you to use this book as an opportunity to learn from others and add that knowledge to your own. When you read a report, strive to stand in the shoes of those involved. Could you have made similar mistakes? What human tendencies can you identify with in a given report? Be objective and ask yourself how you would approach a similar situation differently.

The American Avalanche Association will continue to move forward with additional volumes of *The Snowy Torrents*. Individually, we must make better-informed choices, and as a community, we must continue to share these choices—regardless of the outcome—so that others may live to enjoy the snow. It is my sincere hope that future volumes will contain fewer fatal accidents and more stories about close calls with positive outcomes. This will require members of our community to report not just fatal accidents, but their close calls, as well. Tragedy averted is not solely the work of luck; it is the sum of our knowledge and experience while dealing with uncertainty.

—John Stimberis
President, American Avalanche Association

PREFACE

The stories you are about to read are true. Sadly, most of them end in death. But telling these stories is meant to promote a very positive outcome: saving lives of those drawn to the thrill of winter recreation—whether it is skiing, snowboarding, snowmobiling, snowshoeing, or climbing.

Each report in this volume contains the facts and details as provided by the survivors, witnesses, rescuers, and investigators involved in the incident. All names are real. The intent is to teach by example, both good and bad. As you read these personal stories, one fact will become apparent: people repeat some of the same mistakes over and over. If we, as educators and recreators, can help break that cycle, we can help save lives. Analyzing accidents is a valuable tool in teaching how to stay alive in avalanche country.

Avalanche safety comes about by building layers of defense. The first line of defense, comprised of knowledge and experience, is one of the hardest to acquire. Take an avalanche class. Know the current avalanche conditions from the local forecast and choose appropriate terrain for the conditions. Choose the right companions. Today's avalanche education focuses on the physical factors leading to avalanches—terrain, weather, and snowpack—and on the human factors.

Human factors that often contribute to avalanche accidents include—but are not limited to—ignorance *("I didn't know an avalanche could happen here")*, arrogance (*"I can out-ski anyone or anything"*), expert halo *("I followed him here because he had taken an avalanche class")*, and scarcity or competition *("We were in a hurry to get first tracks")*. When relevant in a fatal avalanche report, we point out the human factors that likely contributed to the accident.

The last line of defense against an avalanche is rescue gear, which is of utmost importance once an avalanche burial occurs. We are unequivocal in our criticism when people are buried and cannot be found because the group lacked rescue gear. Our message is simple: buy rescue gear, practice with it, and always take it.

And on the subject of rescue gear, in the reports included in this volume, we stress the need for carrying transceivers (beacons), probes, and shovels. Our era of accidents is 1996-2004, which was before avalanche airbags had come on the US market. Future volumes of *The Snowy Torrents* will most likely stress the added life-saving value of possessing airbags as well.

The Snowy Torrents is a publication of the American Avalanche Association, whose mission is to promote and support professionalism and excellence in avalanche safety, education, and research in the United States.

This volume of *The Snowy Torrents* is the fifth in the series. The first was authored by Dale Gallagher in 1967 and documented accidents in the United States from 1910-66. The second volume, written by Knox Williams and published in 1975, covered the period of 1967-71. Volume three came in 1984, written by Knox Williams and Betsy Armstrong for the years 1972-79. That was followed by volume four, written by Nick Logan and Dale Atkins in 1996 and covering 1980-86. Throughout the series, we looked for those teachable moments that will stick with the reader.

We would like to thank the American Avalanche Association for its encouragement and support that resurrected *The Snowy Torrents* project—after a lapse of 20 years—and made this book possible.

To our readers, we have these words of encouragement: **"Do it right, get it done, and stay on top."**

—Knox Williams and Spencer Logan, April 2017

ACKNOWLEDGMENTS

We would like to thank the hundreds of people who initially investigated and/or documented the avalanche accidents compiled in this volume of *The Snowy Torrents.* Without their efforts, this book simply would not be possible. Those individuals include survivors, witnesses, rescuers, avalanche workers, law enforcement and medical personnel, and journalists. Nearly all those people contributed to investigations during or shortly after stressful searches, rescues or recoveries, or while grieving for lost partners, co-workers, friends or family members. Many of them contributed anonymously or without acknowledgment in the initial report. That fact—and the sheer number of people involved in the 208 accidents compiled here—make it impossible to thank each individual by name. A general but heartfelt note of appreciation will have to suffice. To each and every person who contributed an image, statement, or measurement that helped document one of these accidents, thank you.

For these accounts, we relied heavily on accident investigations conducted by regional avalanche forecast centers. Other sources include media accounts of the accidents and reports written by U.S. Forest Service, Bureau of Land Management or National Park Service personnel, as well as snow safety and ski patrol workers at ski areas. Many of these documents are available online (http://avalanche.state.co.us/accidents/us/ and http://www.avalanche.org/accidents.php), while others exist only in file folders in boxes or cabinets. Several investigators provided particularly comprehensive reports, among them Doug Fesler, Jill Fredston, Kevin Heinecken, Steve Karkenan, Glenn Kessler, Gene Thompson, and Bruce Tremper.

Many people, including some of the original investigators, helped with the production of this book. They supplied additional images, clarified questions, filled in details, or commented on drafts. These include: Dale Atkins, Paul Baugher, Doug Chabot, Ethan Greene, Michael Ferrari, Rob Hunker, Janet Kellam, and Mark Moore. Our thanks to them for their invaluable assistance.

While fatal avalanche accidents are increasingly well-documented, non-fatal accidents and incidents remain under-reported. Information from non-fatal close calls and incidents provides indispensable learning opportunities for other riders and precious data for researchers. We encourage anyone involved in an avalanche to document as many details as possible using one of the forms included in Appendix D.

The AAA wishes to recognize and thank the Colorado Avalanche Information Center (CAIC) for all the time, energy, and resources they committed to collaborating on this project. This book would not have been possible without the inspiration, support, and hard work of numerous members of the CAIC staff. The CAIC has truly been an integral partner in making this publication a reality.

Thank you to our Industry Supporters who have helped make this volume of *The Snowy Torrents* a reality.

Please support your local avalanche center.

HOW TO USE THIS BOOK

We anticipate that many people will read all 208 of these narratives chronologically. However, we expect other readers will turn to individual accounts and then hopscotch between seasons, often to read reports of accidents with which they have a personal connection. To facilitate either approach, we have employed conventions that aim to provide accurate accounts of individual accidents, yet draw comprehensible connections amongst the entire series of narratives.

Sources: The primary sources for most accounts in this volume are accident reports produced by regional avalanche forecast centers. In a handful of cases, land management agencies such as the National Park Service issued the reports. In Alaska, The Alaska Mountain Safety Center conducted many investigations during the period spanned by this volume. The authors of these reports generally investigated the accident sites and interviewed survivors, witnesses, and/or rescuers. Of course, the level of detail varies depending on access to the accident site and other incident-specific factors. Published accounts of accidents in newspapers, magazines or other media often supplement investigation reports. In some cases, they are the only sources available.

Readers can assume that we based each accident account in this volume on an initial accident investigation report unless otherwise specified. Any unattributed quotes come from these initial reports. We have cited published sources and listed them in a References Cited list (Appendix E) for each season. We also cite the sources for extensive quotes from an initial report, which we typically set off as block quotes. In a few cases, we have reprinted the initial reports almost verbatim, because they are especially comprehensive or draw particularly valuable conclusions. We alert readers to these with a two-sentence header:

> *The following accident was investigated by [NAME] of [ORGANIZATION]. The results of their investigation appear here with minimal editing.*

Accident names: We identify accidents by the name of the specific location or feature where the avalanche occurred, followed by its position relative to the nearest landmark or town. For the entry titled "Hurricane Bowl, South of Aspen, Colorado," "Hurricane Bowl" is the specific location and "Aspen, Colorado" is the landmark. Specific features may be common local names for a slope or geographic feature, named runs within ski areas, or USGS names for geographic features. With the exception of ski areas, the landmark or town is a USGS place name—usually the name of a nearby town from which people often access an accident site. For accidents that occurred inside a ski area boundary or involved people who exited a ski area boundary, we use the contemporary name of the ski area as the landmark. Where possible, we have included a brief description of the accident site within the report. These conventions should make locating an accident site relatively easy using the maps or software of your choice.

Accident report sections: The standard format for each accident account includes the following sections: Weather and Snowpack Conditions, Accident Summary, Rescue Summary, Avalanche Data, and Comments. If one or more of these sections do not appear in a report, it is because we did not find sufficient information to complete that section meaningfully.

Within the Avalanche Data section, we distinguish the avalanche dimensions, the weak layer and slab characteristics, and event characteristics. The latter typically appear as a code such as SS-ASu-R2-D2-O. Each element in these codes identifies one characteristic of the avalanche; we used classifications defined in the industry-standard *Snow, Weather and Avalanche Guidelines: Observational Guidelines for Avalanche Programs* in *the United States*[1]. If event characteristics were not available in the original reports, we developed them based on available information. We classified avalanche size using both the Relative and Destructive scales when possible, though many accident reports for the period report only Relative Size. For an explanation of the codes used to describe and classify avalanche events, including size, see Appendix C.

The Comments section is where we point to factors that appear to have contributed to an accident or its outcome. It is the heart of each account. The purpose of this section is to highlight decisions, actions, and practices that readers can avoid—or adopt—in order to reduce their own exposure. We address only what seem to be the most salient factors. Accidents result from a chain of choices and actions, many of which can seem inconsequential. Chance plays a large role in their outcomes. Limited information is available for many accidents, and even in well-documented incidents, many factors go unnoticed or unreported. The comments are thus not a comprehensive accounting of an accident's causes. Where information about an accident was too sparse for thoughtful comments, we include a standard notice:

The lack of information available on this accident precludes comment.

People: We refer to the people involved in avalanche accidents in *The Snowy Torrents* by their real names wherever possible. When original investigations or news reports do not list victims' and/or their companions' names—or when those resources used pseudonyms—we have relied on pronouns or numbered the people involved, e.g. Rider 1. When a participant's or victim's age was available, we included that information in parentheses following the first mention of that person's name.

Callouts: Several factors appear consistently in the accidents in this book. We have identified nine of the most common factors using callouts in the margins. We hope these help readers identify patterns in the avalanche accidents we describe in *The Snowy Torrents.*

- **No rescue equipment:** No one in the party was equipped with transceivers, shovels, and avalanche probes.
- **Inadequate rescue equipment:** The party was missing key elements of their equipment. They were carrying either insufficient transceivers or limited shovels, or they were not carrying dedicated avalanche probes.
- **Traveling alone:** The victim was traveling alone or out of sight of the rest of the party when the avalanche occurred.
- **More than one person on a slope:** Multiple party members were on the slope, and often the avalanche caught more than one.
- **High avalanche danger:** The local avalanche center had forecast a High avalanche danger, or issued an Avalanche Warning through the National Weather Service. For the period this volume covers, the scale used in the United States defined High danger – Level 4 on a five-level scale - as "natural and human triggered avalanches are likely."

- **In avalanche runout:** The party was traveling or camped in low-angled terrain below the starting zones. In some cases, the party thought they were safe from avalanches.
- **Terrain trap:** One or more of the victims was carried into a landscape feature that magnifies the consequences of avalanches. Narrow gullies concentrate flowing snow and increase the force of avalanches. Avalanche debris can also pile deeply into gullies or abrupt slope transitions, leading to deep burials. Being swept over cliffs or into trees can cause severe injury or death.
- **"Red flag" indications of danger:** Obvious signs of unstable snowpack conditions, like recent avalanches on similar slopes, collapses or shooting cracks, or large and rapid amounts of falling or drifting snow.
- **Lack of training:** The party demonstrated a lack of practice with rescue equipment, misinterpreted snow profiles or test results, or used travel practices that were ineffective in mitigating their exposure.

In the Avalanche Data sections, we included additional marginal callouts highlighting the avalanche character. The concept of avalanche character focuses on risk management strategies for backcountry travelers. Since about 2010, it has become common in avalanche bulletins, forecasts, and education. We used character descriptions modified from those used by the Colorado Avalanche Information Center in 2016[2]. Where possible, we used the avalanche type, destructive size, and bed surface to categorize the avalanche events into one of the following characters:

- **Loose Dry avalanche:** Release of dry, unconsolidated snow. Other names for loose dry avalanches include point-release avalanches or sluffs.
- **Storm Slab avalanche:** Release of a soft cohesive layer (a slab) of new snow that breaks within the storm snow or on the old snow surface.
- **Wind Slab avalanche:** Release of a cohesive layer of snow (a slab) formed by the wind. Wind Slabs form in specific areas and are confined to lee and cross-loaded terrain features.
- **Persistent Slab avalanche:** Release of a cohesive layer of soft to hard snow (a slab) in the middle to upper snowpack, when the bond to an underlying persistent weak layer breaks. The slabs often propagate in surprising and unpredictable ways.
- **Deep Persistent Slab avalanche:** Release of a thick cohesive layer of hard snow (a slab), when the bond breaks between the slab and an underlying persistent weak layer. They are often triggered from areas where the snow is shallow and weak. The avalanches are typically very large, with average crown heights 4 feet or greater, and capable of destroying cars and breaking trees.
- **Loose Wet avalanche:** Release of wet, unconsolidated snow or slush. These avalanches typically occur within layers of wet snow near the surface of the snowpack.
- **Wet Slab avalanche:** Release of a cohesive layer of snow (a slab) that is generally moist or wet when the flow of liquid water weakens the bond between the slab and the surface below (snow or ground). They often occur during prolonged warming events and/or rain-on-snow events.
- **Glide avalanche:** Release of the entire snow cover because of gliding over the ground. Predicting the release of Glide Avalanches is very challenging. Because Glide Avalanches only occur on very specific slopes, safe travel relies on identifying and avoiding those slopes. Glide cracks are a significant indicator, as are recent Glide Avalanches.
- **Cornice fall:** Cornices form overhanging masses of snow created as the wind moves snow over a sharp terrain feature, such as a ridge, and deposits snow on

the downwind (leeward) side. Avalanches began as falling cornice, and sometimes triggered slab below.

- **Roof avalanches:** Release of the snow cover off a structure, generally as a cohesive layer (a slab). They are often prompted by warming temperatures.

Appendices: Readers will find more detailed information in the appendices of this volume, including a breakdown of accidents by state, activity, number of victims caught and killed, which callouts applied, and avalanche character (Appendix A, page 315). For unfamiliar terms and concepts, readers can refer to a glossary of terms used in *The Snowy Torrents* (Appendix B, page 329), information on avalanche event characteristics (Appendix C, page 335), and the industry-standard avalanche reporting form (Appendix D, page 339). We also include a list of references cited by chapter (Appendix E, page 347). We hope that referring to the appendices can answer most questions readers might have as they flip through this volume.

INTRODUCTION

This volume of *The Snowy Torrents* covers eight winters, from 1996-97 to 2003-04, and contains 208 reports. We documented 220 deaths in 198 different avalanches. These deaths occurred in 12 different states, including New Hampshire and New York.

This volume also includes 10 accounts of non-fatal avalanche involvements. Non-fatal accidents, unfortunately, often go unreported to avalanche centers and are sparsely documented. The data that researchers have on avalanche involvements is thus very biased to fatal accidents. This volume is no different, and that bias can make for overwhelmingly grim reading.

Between 1989-90 and 2009-10, avalanches killed an average of 25 people a year in the United States. The number of avalanche deaths varies conspicuously from winter to winter. However, the annual number of fatalities shows few significant trends since 1992, regardless of whether evaluated over five-, 10-, or 20-year periods. The number of people killed by avalanches is not decreasing significantly, despite improvements in safety equipment, avalanche education, and avalanche forecasting. Conversely, the number of deaths is not increasing appreciably, despite an obvious increase in winter backcountry recreation.

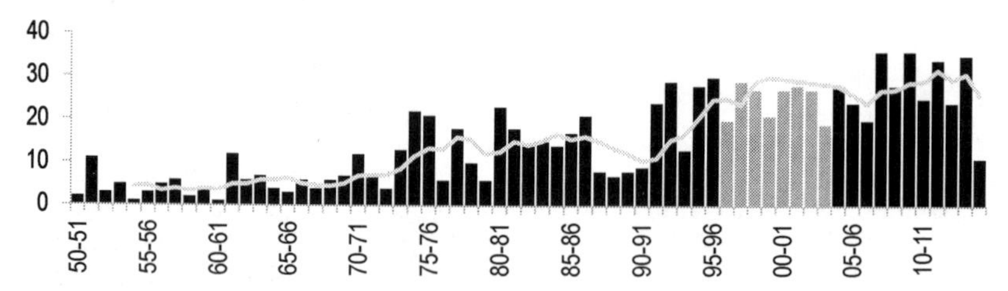

The number of avalanche fatalities in the United States for each winter, 1950-51 to 2014-15. The line indicates the five-year moving average. The years covered by this volume are in grey.

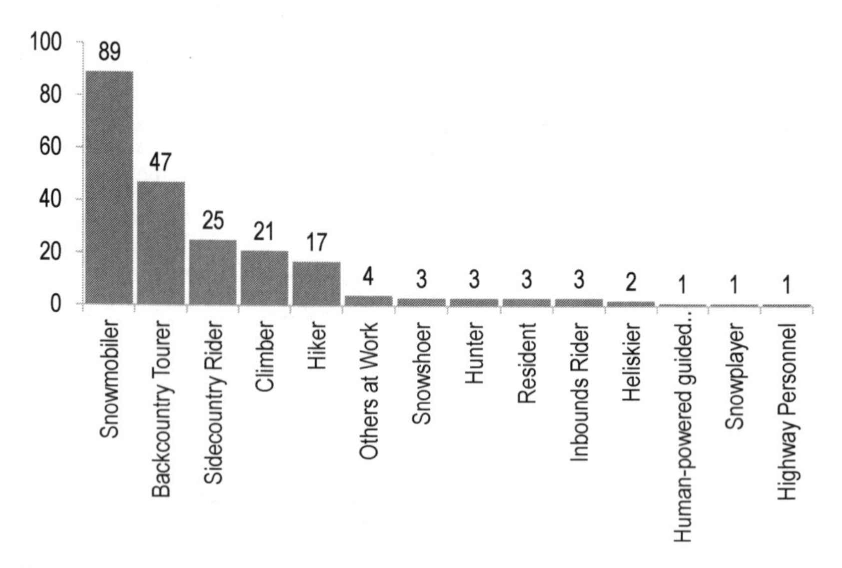

The number of avalanche fatalities by activity category.

Only a few of the people you will read about in this book were killed on the job. A few others died when avalanches overran their homes. Most people involved in the stories that follow were recreating. They chose—even if they were unaware that they were making the choice—to expose themselves to the danger of avalanches.

Of the recreationists whose deaths we document in this volume, snowmobilers make up the largest subset, with 89 deaths. These riders were killed while highmarking in avalanche terrain, riding through gullies and other terrain traps, or even following roads, unaware of the dangerous avalanche terrain around them. Many of those fatalities involve snowmobilers who were not carrying avalanche rescue gear.

Not only are snowmobilers the largest subset of avalanche deaths overall, they were the largest subset of avalanche deaths each winter. Some of this is an artifact of the classification scheme, which lumps all snowmobilers into one group but splits human-powered recreation based on equipment and intention. There may be ways to subdivide the snowmobiler category further, contrasting riders who are highmarking from those following roads. However, many riders like to boondock or sidehill off of roads as the opportunity presents itself, so differentiating them by activity or intent is difficult. There were three winters, 1997-98, 2001-02, and 2002-03, where more snowmobilers died in avalanches than all the people involved in human-powered recreation combined.

Amongst people engaged in human-powered recreation, most avalanche fatalities (47 deaths) involve backcountry tourers. These are people traveling on skis or snowboards, often with the intention of making turns on downhills or covering long distances. The second-largest group of fatalities is amongst sidecountry riders (25 deaths)—those who left a ski area for the unpatrolled and unmitigated slopes beyond the resort boundaries. We distinguish them from backcountry tourers because the two groups approach avalanche terrain differently, with different information-gathering and terrain management opportunities and challenges. Inbounds riders, who ski or snowboard within the patrolled and avalanche-mitigated boundaries of ski areas, comprise only three deaths in this volume. Climbers make up the third-largest segment, with 21 deaths. We differentiated climbers from hikers by intent, terrain, and equipment. We categorized as climbers

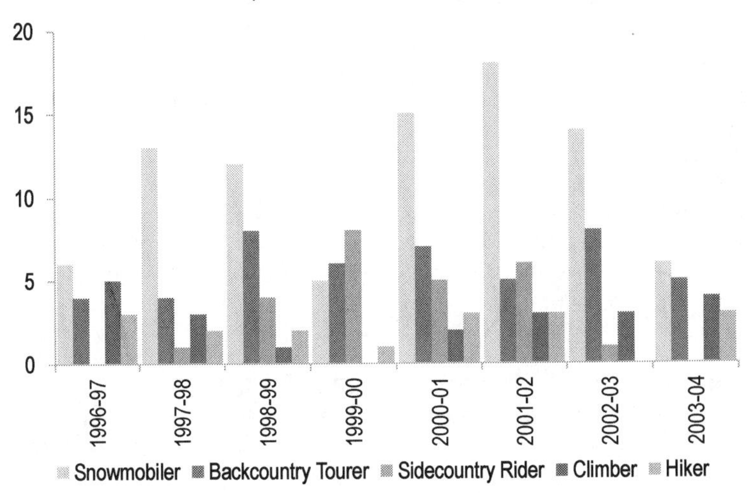

Avalanche deaths by selected activity category for each year in this volume. Appendix A —the callouts table—lists the activity category for each accident.

people oriented to peaks or specific routes, traveling in very steep or exposed terrain, or using technical mountaineering gear like ropes or ice axes.

Some people involved in accidents did not fall neatly into one category: climbers traveling on skis, hikers who scrambled into avalanche terrain, skiers who snowmobiled a distance before beginning their tour. We used our judgment to assign people to a category for the summary purposes. We strove for consistency.

Of the fatal avalanches themselves, almost 80% (158) were soft or hard slab avalanches. These are avalanches that release cohesive layers of snow—the slab—all at once. There was often a layer of weaker snow under the slab. In just over 50% (101) of the avalanches, the weak layer was a "persistent grain type" of faceted snow that can be problematic and produce avalanches for days, weeks, or even months after it is formed and buried in the snowpack. Travelers can trigger these persistent slab or deep persistent slab avalanches from a distance or the bottom of a slope. They often break wider than anticipated, catching multiple people who may have been spaced out adequately for smaller avalanches on non-persistent weak layers.

AVALANCHE TYPE	NUMBER
Loose-snow	1
Wet loose-snow	2
Wet slab	4
Soft slab	110
Hard slab	48
Roof	1

AVALANCHE CHARACTER	NUMBER
Loose Dry	1
Storm Slab	12
Wind Slab	8
Persistent Slab	90
Deep Persistent Slab	11
Loose Wet	13
Wet Slab	4
Glide	1
Cornice	9
Roof	1

The number of avalanches in this volume, by type and character.

The avalanches tended to be small or medium-sized relative to the paths (R3). The path-relative scale was in widespread use in the United States during the period spanned by this volume. Only a few of the initial investigation reports noted the destructive size of an avalanche. When possible, we assigned a size category based on descriptions of the damage, and of these, most were large (D2) or very large (D3) and could have destroyed cars (D3).

In just over half of the reports, we highlighted no (71) or inadequate (37) rescue gear as a factor in the accident. On a winter-to-winter basis, lack of rescue equipment was a factor in 40 to almost 70% of the accidents. Proper rescue equipment is not a guarantee of survival. It may not have made a difference in accidents where the victim was deeply buried or suffered severe trauma. In many other cases, proper equipment may have led to a swift rescue and a report omitted from this book. There was no clear trend of increasing use of rescue equipment through time over the period of this volume, except among snowmobilers. We determined the marginal callouts based on

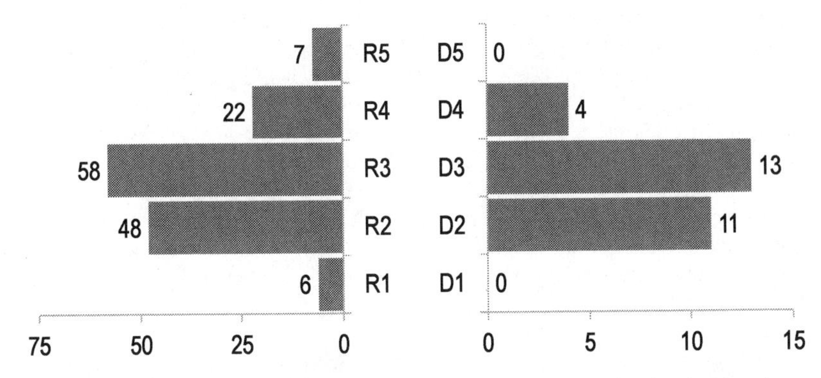

Graphs of the path-relative (R) and destructive force (D) sizes for avalanches in this volume

WINTER	NO RESCUE EQUIPMENT	INADEQUATE RESCUE EQUIPMENT	% OF ACCIDENTS WITH NO OR INADEQUATE GEAR
96-97	8	0	40
97-98	11	7	62
98-99	11	3	52
99-00	8	2	48
00-01	9	9	67
01-02	8	5	46
02-03	11	7	67
03-04	5	4	47

Counts of the rescue equipment callouts, by winter. The right column shows the percent of reports, for each winter, with a rescue equipment callout.

patterns repeated across many accidents. As such, the callouts are not a rigorous analysis, and the trends are not a statistical analysis.

The rest of this book steps beyond counts and summaries and into the particulars of 208 avalanche accidents. Each narrative highlights an incident's specific circumstances and essential details, many of which stand as examples of mistakes and misjudgments. And each story hints at the personal costs to the people involved. They can make for gloomy reading. Often, however, they also reveal the determination, creativity, and selflessness of survivors and rescuers. These narratives thus serve to illustrate what not to do, and what to strive for.

1996–1997 SEASON

19961111

TRUMAN GULCH, WEST OF BRIDGER BOWL SKI AREA, MONTANA | November 11, 1996

One backcountry skier caught, partially buried, and injured

WEATHER AND SNOWPACK CONDITIONS

Winter began in the Bridger Range of southwestern Montana when about three feet of snow fell in two late October storms. Near-surface faceted snow grains formed on all aspects in the Bridger Range during a Halloween cold spell. On November 4, three inches of new snow fell in the Bridgers and buried the near-surface faceted grains. From November 7 through 9, winds were strong from the west, with average wind speeds around 30 mph and gusts near 60 mph.

ACCIDENT SUMMARY

Two backcountry tourers and their dog were skiing in Truman Gulch on the west side of the Bridger Range. The party had climbed up the slopes of Bridger Bowl Ski Area, and then crossed the ridge into Truman Gulch. The pair noted variable snow conditions due to the recent strong winds. Both skiers carried avalanche safety gear.

Traveling alone

Around 12:30, the partners were out of sight of each other, separated by a slight ridge. The lead skier began to descend a gully full of drifted snow. He made two or three turns when the avalanche broke above him.

The avalanche quickly knocked the skier down. He lost his skis and poles shortly after being caught. He was in "total swimming mode" as the avalanche carried him about 700 vertical feet through trees and over small rock bands. He received numerous contusions, including a deep contusion to his thigh from hitting a tree.

RESCUE SUMMARY

The first skier was near the toe of the debris when the avalanche stopped. He was partially buried with only his face exposed. His head was downhill and his arms were near the snow surface. He was able to free his arms and dig himself out of the debris. He moved to some nearby trees.

The second skier was just over a small ridge and did not see the avalanche occur. When he got to the gully, he saw the avalanche crown with no exit tracks. He began a search for his partner within a "few" minutes of the avalanche. As the second skier neared the avalanche debris, he heard his partner yelling.

The pair decided that self-evacuation was not possible due to injuries and lost gear. The injured skier got comfortable and waited. The second skier climbed back up to the ridge and skied to the base lodge at Bridger Bowl where he notified the Gallatin County Sheriff's Office. Two members of the Bridger Bowl Ski Patrol and two members of the Gallatin County Search and Rescue responded to the incident. They lowered the injured skier about 300 feet to a point where a helicopter was able to land. The skier was flown to a hospital.

AVALANCHE DATA

Persistent Slab avalanche

The slab was drifted snow about one foot deep and 10 to 20 feet wide. The slab failed on a layer of near-surface faceted crystals buried under the wind-deposited snow (SS-ASu-R2-O). The slope faced northwest with a slope angle of 36 degrees.

COMMENTS

This accident included several elements common in early season conditions. Areas of wind-drifted snow, like the gully, offered sufficient snow depth to ride, but the slabs of drifted snow also sat over a thin layer of weak, faceted snow. Thus, in isolated spots, triggering avalanches can be possible or likely. A victim caught in a slide like this can be slammed into obstacles like rocks and stumps that are barely covered by the shallow snowpack.

PROVIDENCE LAKE, SOUTHEAST OF LOGAN PEAK, UTAH

19961206

December 6, 1996

Two snowmobilers caught; one fully buried

ACCIDENT SUMMARY

Two snowmobilers, both in their late 20s, were riding powerful hillclimbing machines and highmarking on an east-facing slope near Providence Lake, in the Bear River Range of northern Utah. One rider got stuck on the slope, and the other rode up to help. The avalanche broke about 200 feet above them at about 17:15 in the afternoon, and caught both riders.

More than one person on a slope

RESCUE SUMMARY

One rider was partially buried and able to free himself from the avalanche debris. The other rider was fully buried. Another party of five snowmobilers saw the avalanche and rode to a nearby warming hut where there was a cache of avalanche rescue probes and shovels. They returned to the avalanche and began probing. Another party of three riders joined shortly after. Rescuers estimated that they had to search an area "50 by 60 feet."

No rescue equipment

The fully buried rider was located and the rescuers had uncovered his airway in about 15 minutes. He was buried facing downhill, with his head about 1.5 feet deep. He was unconscious but breathing when rescuers reached his head. The rider rested in the warming hut and rode back to the trailhead.

One of the rescuers used a ham radio and reached 911 about the same time the rider's face was uncovered.

AVALANCHE DATA

Rescuers estimated the avalanche as about 300 feet wide. The slab was about 1.25 feet deep, with the majority of the slab on the hill the riders were climbing.

COMMENTS

The group did not have rescue equipment. One of the rescuers noted that a key factor was having avalanche rescue equipment nearby at the warming hut. "They were put there a couple of years ago after another close call...[and] probably made the difference between life and death." The nearby hut provided a location for the buried rider to recover, too.

19961207a

CURRANT CREEK PEAK, SOUTHEAST OF HEBER CITY, UTAH | December 7, 1996

Three snowmobilers caught and partially buried

ACCIDENT SUMMARY

More than one person on a slope

Several snowmobilers were highmarking a very steep (45-degree) slope near Currant Creek Peak between the Wasatch and Uinta Mountains, about 10 miles southeast of Heber City, Utah. One rider got stuck high on the slope. Another rider got stuck just below him on the same slope. A third snowmobiler rode up to help. The avalanche released and caught all three.

RESCUE SUMMARY

All three riders were partially buried-critical with just their hands sticking out. One rider freed his hand and eventually got himself out. He then helped dig one of the other riders out. They could not find the third rider.

No rescue equipment

The two broke off tree branches and began to randomly probe the debris. A number of other snowmobilers in the area joined the search. One of the pair who self-rescued was probing about 100 feet above where he was buried. He saw the fingers of a glove sticking out of the snow.

Rescuers dug down about three feet and found the rider blue in the face and not breathing. He started breathing on his own and eventually recovered enough to ride out. Rescuers estimate the third rider was buried about 25 minutes. He was wearing a helmet with a face shield, which was not filled with snow.

AVALANCHE DATA

Persistent Slab avalanche

This avalanche broke four to five feet deep and 150 feet wide. The bed surface was a three-week-old rain crust. The weak layer was faceted snow on top of the crust. The avalanche occurred on a steep, east-facing slope. It was a sunny Saturday, and the day after a storm.

COMMENTS

Three very lucky riders. The next report describes a similar incident that occurred on the same day and also involved multiple riders caught with no companion rescue equipment. One of those riders was not so lucky. The incidents are two of five avalanches that caught 10 people on December 6 and 7, all documented by the Utah Avalanche Center. An avalanche warning was in effect from December 3 to 6.

19961207b

BOUNTIFUL PEAK, EAST OF FARMINGTON, UTAH

December 7, 1996

Three snowmobilers caught; two partially buried, and one buried and killed

ACCIDENT SUMMARY

A group of four snowmobilers, Rick Adams (37), Todd Lomax (29), J.D. Horne, and Chad Horne, were riding together. They were highmarking a steep, east-facing bowl along the ridgeline of Bountiful Peak in the Wasatch Range, east of Farmington, Utah. Each rode the slope one at a time while the others waited below. Adams was riding near the top of the slope when the avalanche released around 11:40.

Lomax was below Adams. "There wasn't a sound at all. I just looked up and saw a wall of snow coming at us. I just yelled 'Run!' I just took off." Lomax sped downhill and outran the avalanche. He yelled a warning to the Hornes, who were on foot and working on their sleds.

The Hornes ran downhill. The avalanche caught J.D. and buried him to his waist. Chad was hit by his snowmobile, which the avalanche had sent tumbling through the air. Chad was almost completely buried, with only one hand above the debris and his snowmachine almost on top of him.

RESCUE SUMMARY

Lomax helped rescue the Hornes. None of the group carried avalanche rescue equipment. They saw no sign of Adams. They searched the debris surface and sent one person for help.

No rescue equipment

About 20 search and rescue personnel, including dog teams, arrived at the site in the afternoon and searched until dark. On the morning of December 8, searchers conducted explosive mitigation and got "spectacular" results, triggering avalanches on both sides of the initial avalanche. Searchers probed the debris for two days before the suspending the search.

Adams was recovered on December 19, 11 days after the avalanche. A group from the University of Utah's Department of Geology brought in a magnetometer. A few days prior to their search, friends of Adams had found snowmobile tread marks on a tree in the upper track. The geologists began searching a swath downhill from the marked tree. They "hit a huge magnetic spike" in a group of trees about 100 feet above the toe of the debris. They dug down five feet to find Adams's snowmobile.

They began a fine probe search from the snowmobile working uphill. The probe line found Adams 30 feet uphill from the snowmachine, under four feet of snow, lying horizontally with his head pointing upslope.

Investigators on the debris next to two of the party's snowmobiles. *Photo Bruce Tremper, Utah Avalanche Center.*

AVALANCHE DATA

The initial avalanche averaged two feet deep, 600 feet wide and started on a 40-degree, east-facing bowl which spanned the aspects from southeast through northeast (SS-AMu-R3-O). It descended about 500 vertical feet with the crown face around 9,100 feet in elevation. The debris covered an area of about four football fields and was up to 15 feet deep where it filled a gully.

Persistent Slab avalanche

The avalanche ran on a stout rain crust formed about three weeks prior to the accident. The weak layer was two to three mm of faceted snow, formed from low-density new snow that fell on top of the rain crust. The slab consisted of snow from two storms in the week prior to the accident, both with relatively dense, rimed snow.

The structure described above was capable of producing large avalanches, as exemplified by the "spectacular" results on the morning of

December 8. Specifically, one 4kg hand charge triggered an avalanche on one flank three to six feet deep and over 1,000 feet wide. The other flank broke out two to three feet deep and 600 feet wide with several 2kg hand charges.

COMMENTS

High avalanche danger

The Utah Avalanche Center issued an avalanche warning on each of the four days prior to the accident. The center rated the avalanche danger High on slopes like the one that avalanched. These riders were among the 10 backcountry travelers caught in avalanches in northern Utah on December 6-7.

This group was riding the slope one at a time. However, the rest of the party had not moved far enough from the slope and were still exposed to potential avalanches. When the avalanche released, it caught three of the four riders.

None of the riders were equipped with avalanche rescue gear. With transceivers, probes, and shovels, it is possible they could have located Adams and excavated him in time. It certainly would not have required several days of search and rescue volunteers conducting a fruitless search in potentially dangerous conditions.

19961223

CHAIR PEAK, NORTHWEST OF SNOQUALMIE PASS, WASHINGTON | December 23, 1996

Two climbers caught, fully buried, and killed

WEATHER AND SNOWPACK CONDITIONS

In the Snoqualmie Pass area of the Cascade Range, over two feet of snow fell between December 20 and 23. The new and drifted snow buried several layers of surface hoar and storm instabilities. Snowfall was light and scattered on Sunday, December 22. The weather deteriorated significantly Sunday night, with an additional seven inches of snow and 0.7 inches of snow-water equivalent falling with increasing southwesterly winds. Temperatures warmed during the day on Monday. An additional 1.3 inches of snow-water equivalent fell with strong southwesterly winds on Tuesday, December 24, with significantly rising temperatures and freezing levels.

ACCIDENT SUMMARY

On Sunday, December 22, two climbers, Robert Mattson and Matthew Ichihashi, both 19, headed out to climb Chair Peak. Chair Peak is a popular climb about four miles northwest of Snoqualmie Pass. The pair snowshoed in on Sunday to establish a base camp. Rescuers assume the pair climbed Monday morning and triggered or were caught by the avalanche Monday morning or early afternoon.

RESCUE SUMMARY

Family members reported the climbers overdue around 20:00 on Monday, December 23. King County Search and Rescue teams began searching early Tuesday morning. Deteriorating weather hampered the search. Rescuers experienced rising temperatures, increasing snowfall, and poor visibility. Avalanche conditions were dangerous, with numerous natural avalanches occurring. Authorities suspended the search after "three avalanches struck in two hours."

Clearing skies on Wednesday, December 25 allowed a helicopter fly-over. Rescuers spotted the climbers' tent on a bench above Source Lake and a faint hiking trail that disappeared into avalanche debris. They also saw evidence of an avalanche crown extending around much of the cirque to the east of Chair Peak. They concentrated their efforts in the avalanche debris and located the climbers late Wednesday afternoon by transceiver search. The transceivers were early Christmas presents. The climbers were found within 30 feet of each other, buried under 2.5 to 3.5 feet of avalanche debris.

AVALANCHE DATA

The Northwest Avalanche Center issued avalanche warnings for High danger December 20, 21, and 22. Over two feet of snow had fallen on "several weak layers" of surface hoar and storm instabilities in the area since December 20. Numerous natural and triggered avalanches were reported from the nearby Alpental Ski Area, in avalanche paths above Interstate 90, and in the surrounding backcountry Sunday and again on Monday.

High avalanche danger

COMMENTS

The victims headed into the backcountry when the avalanche danger was rated High and an avalanche warning was in effect, though whether the victims knew of the warning is unknown. In these conditions, large natural avalanches and human-triggered avalanches are likely or very likely. It is difficult to avoid being in or below avalanche terrain, so backcountry travel is not recommended. Sadly, the victims' newly-gifted beacons did them little good, because they were both buried. One hopes the beacons did not contribute to an over-confidence in their skills to manage the dangerous conditions.

FLAGSTAFF MOUNTAIN, NORTH OF ALTA, UTAH

19961226

December 26, 1996

One backcountry snowboarder caught, buried and killed

ACCIDENT SUMMARY

Flagstaff Mountain is a popular backcountry area in the Wasatch Range above the town of Alta, Utah. Greg Dres (35) was last seen around 15:00 on December 26, heading up Flagstaff in stormy weather. He failed to meet his girlfriend that night. The morning of December 27, she and friends discovered that Dres's car had been towed from the Flagstaff trailhead overnight.

Traveling alone

RESCUE SUMMARY

Search and rescue personnel began looking for Dres on December 27. Late in the day, Al Soucie, the US Forest Service Snow Ranger for Little Cottonwood Canyon, joined the crew of a Life Flight helicopter in an aerial search. They noticed a large avalanche in Days Fork, the drainage just northwest of Flagstaff Mountain. However, it was too windy to land and too late to launch a ground search.

According to his girlfriend, Dres would often boot up Flagstaff ridge, take a quick run in Day's Fork, boot back up to Flagstaff and snowboard back down to Alta. The Day's Fork slide thus became the primary search area. She also said that he always wore an avalanche beacon.

The ground search began at 07:00 on December 28. Rescuers first searched the Day's Fork avalanche debris with transceivers. The avalanche was hundreds of feet wide and debris covered several acres. Rescuers found no transceiver signal and called in avalanche search dogs.

Recovering the victim. *Photo Bruce Tremper, Utah Avalanche Center.*

Rescuers then began to search along the south side of the Flagstaff Mountain ridge, Dres's likely descent route back to the trailhead. Rescuers encountered avalanche debris below the ridge, but they assumed it was from routine avalanche mitigation above the village of Alta. They searched it nonetheless and found a transceiver signal near the toe of the avalanche debris, in the bottom of a narrow gully, about 1,000 vertical feet below the starting zone.

Rescuers found Dres fully buried, three to four feet deep. He was face-down, head oriented downhill, with his snowboard still attached to his feet. With his hands near his chest, he was unable to make an air pocket.

AVALANCHE DATA

The avalanche was a soft slab, presumably triggered by Dres on descent, moderately sized relative to the path, sliding on old snow (SS-ARu-R2-O). The avalanche started around 10,000 feet on a south-facing slope about 35 degrees in steepness. Winds often drifted snow into the starting zone, and the path funneled into a narrow gully. Investigators were unable to conduct a crown profile, but assume the crown was one to two feet deep as recent snow was drifting into the starting zone. The weak layer was probably low-density storm snow, and the bed surface a subtle rain and rime crust formed on December 25.

Wind Slab avalanche

The avalanche bulletin for December 26 forecasted "High danger on any slope steeper than 35 degrees, especially in wind loaded areas." The weather was snowy and windy with rapidly rising avalanche danger. The Utah Avalanche Center issued an avalanche warning December 27 cautioning people about widespread natural avalanche activity. No one knows if Dres checked the avalanche bulletin before leaving.

High avalanche danger

COMMENTS

There is no margin for error when traveling alone in avalanche terrain. If Dres had been with skilled partners who could effect a quick companion rescue, this accident could have been a scary, instead of tragic, experience. Rescuers found signs of asphyxia, and no signs of trauma, when they recovered Dres's body.

MOUNT INDEX, SOUTHWEST OF INDEX, WASHINGTON

19961228

December 28, 1996

Three hikers buried and killed while camping

WEATHER AND SNOWPACK CONDITIONS

The weather was "very stormy" on Thursday, December 26 through Sunday, December 29 in the Cascades and at Stevens Pass, 20 to 25 miles east of Mt. Index. The Washington State Department of Transportation study plot at the summit of Stevens Pass reported daily snowfall amounts of 15, 16, and 12 inches respectively for the 24-hour periods ending at 06:00 on Friday, Saturday, and Sunday. Water equivalents in many areas for the three days ranged from two to three inches. The extended snowfall buried a variety of weak layers including surface hoar and cold, low-density snow sitting on a thin crust.

Strong winds accompanied the snowfall. Free winds at the 5,000 and 9,000-foot levels averaged 30 to 50 mph on Friday, decreased overnight, and increased again by later Saturday. By the morning of December 28, strong west to southwest winds had drifted 24 to 47 inches or more of snow onto northeast aspects.

ACCIDENT SUMMARY

Three hikers left on the afternoon of Friday, December 27 for a weekend hike and snowshoe trip around the Lake Serene and Mt. Index area. The three men, Scott Bennett (28), Fred Petri Jr. (31), and Tim Skadan (31), were experienced hikers and had visited the area several times previously. Bennett had some equipment issues, so the three only hiked a short distance and established a base camp at around 1,400 feet.

Rescuers believe a natural avalanche released from about 4,000 feet on the northeast flank of Mt. Index either late Friday night or early Saturday morning. The avalanche hit the hikers while they were camped. They were found in their sleeping bags, with the tents "rolled up" around them.

In avalanche runout

RESCUE SUMMARY

Over the following week, several search attempts by both Snohomish County SAR and several groups associated with the families of the hikers were abandoned due to intermittently bad weather, large snowfall, and the threat of further avalanches. The searchers utilized search dogs, helicopters, and infrared heat sensing equipment.

A group of searchers, composed mostly of the hikers' relatives and friends, found the three on Saturday, January 11. Melting snow had exposed a portion of one tent. Upon recovery, the end of the tent was at the surface, and the other end was buried about six feet deep.

AVALANCHE DATA

The Northwest Avalanche Center had issued avalanche warnings for High danger at all elevations throughout the Washington Cascades near and west of the crest on December 27 and 28, and with High to Extreme danger expected by December 29.

High avalanche danger

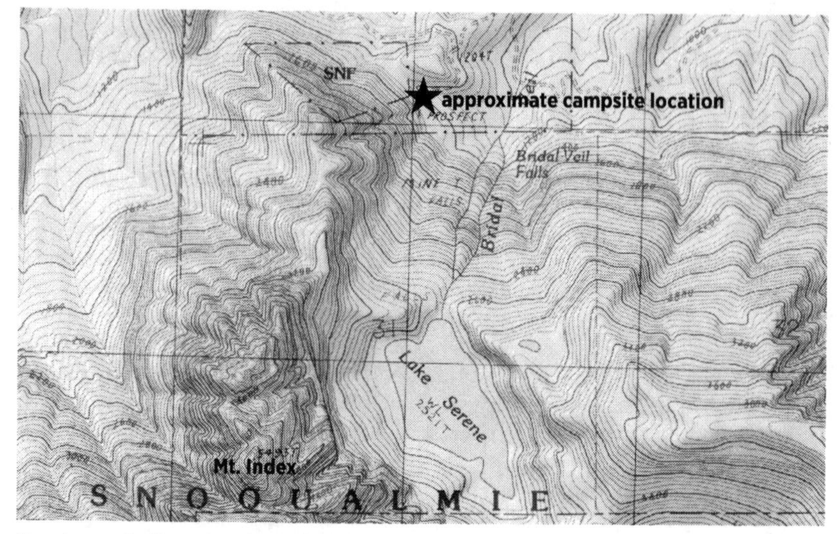

The star marks the approximate location of the campsite.

COMMENTS

No rescue equipment

The group was not carrying transceivers. Transceivers may have been of limited help, since all three hikers were buried close together, and no one could conduct a companion rescue. Transceivers could have facilitated the recovery effort several days later.

The trio's bodies were recovered on January 11. That night, a natural avalanche in Utah overran another trio of backcountry campers and killed them (19970111b). The two incidents serve as reminders that it can be difficult to determine avalanche runouts, so during periods of High avalanche danger, it's safest to avoid traveling and camping in avalanche terrain altogether.

19970101 GLENWOOD, MINNESOTA | January 1, 1997

Four snowplayers caught; two partially buried and two completely buried

WEATHER AND SNOWPACK CONDITIONS

There had been "at least a dozen blizzards"[1] in the Glenwood area of west-central Minnesota prior to January 1. Snowdrifts near the gravel pit where the avalanche occurred were about five feet deep. Sustained winds for several days prior to the accident formed a cornice and drifted snow on the steep slopes of the gravel pit.

More than one person on a slope

ACCIDENT SUMMARY

Four boys, ages nine to 14, rode snowmobiles to a gravel pit. There, they played on foot. They were sliding and jumping down one of the steep slopes when they triggered the avalanche.

No rescue equipment

One boy was partially buried, with his head and arm above the snow. He was able to dig himself out. He could "hear his friends calling for help. Knowing he could not dig them out himself, [he] ran out of the pit, got on his snowmobile, and drove" to the residence of another boy's parents. The parents called 911.

RESCUE SUMMARY

Rescuers arrived shortly after the 911 call and saw "a gravel pit filled with snow...The fallen avalanche ran parallel with the cliff and was about 200 yards long. There were no kids in sight."

Rescuers started a somewhat haphazard search. One pair spotted a glove, and dug out the second of the three boys about 25 minutes after the avalanche. "He was breathing and alive, and that gave us hope."

The first boy returned to the scene and was able to provide rescuers with last-seen locations. Several rescuers were already digging and spot probing in the area he identified. A shoveler struck the third boy in the head about 35 minutes after the avalanche. "I realized that the boy...was my son. He was talking and breathing and I knew he would be alright," one rescuer said.

Rescuers continued to excavate in the last-seen area and found the fourth boy about 40 minutes after the avalanche. He was unconscious but breathing. He was hospitalized and treated for "hypothermia and a traumatic respiratory condition."

COMMENTS

Although avalanche accidents are most common in the western United States, records include several narrow escapes like this one in the Midwest. The fact that all four boys survived is likely due to several factors: the lucky fact of one boy not being completely buried, the prompt rescue he initiated, and his memory of the last-seen locations. The fact that the initial survivor could hear his friends calling for help suggests that the debris that buried them was soft, allowing for more air spaces around the buried boys and giving them more time to be rescued.

MONTPELIER CANYON, NORTHEAST OF MONTPELIER, IDAHO | January 11, 1997

19970111a

One snowmobiler caught, buried, and killed

ACCIDENT SUMMARY

A group of three or four snowmobilers was riding in the Fox Spring area in Montpelier Canyon in southeastern Idaho. Two of the riders were on a ridgeline while a third highmarked a steep, north-northwest facing slope below a cornice. The highmarking rider triggered the avalanche around 11:30. He tried to ride out the side of the avalanche but was swept away.

RESCUE SUMMARY

No rescue equipment

The other riders searched for their friend. Other snowmobilers joined the search and probed the avalanche debris all afternoon. They found the snowmobile but not the rider. Search and Rescue was paged out around 14:00, with assistance from ski patrollers at Pine Creek Ski Area. Searchers arrived at the avalanche site around 16:00.

Three dog teams from American Search Dogs, based in Utah, arrived at the avalanche around dark. One of the dogs alerted at the base of a tree about 40 feet uphill of the snowmobile's location. A probe strike confirmed it was the buried rider's body. The rider was buried about two feet deep, wrapped around a tree.

AVALANCHE DATA
The avalanche was a hard slab, triggered by the snowmobiler. The slope faced north-northwest, was very steep, and had an "overhanging cornice at the top." The avalanche broke four to five feet deep and about 600 feet wide. Debris piled up about 10 feet deep.

COMMENTS
This accident illustrates the importance of two common avalanche safety messages: Get the gear; Get the training. This party was traveling without avalanche rescue equipment—avalanche transceiver, shovel, and probe. The lack of rescue tools made it very difficult to effect a timely companion rescue. It's not clear what avalanche safety training the party had, or whether anyone in the party identified the slope the victim highmarked as a potentially dangerous avalanche slope. Basic avalanche safety training can help recreationists to recognize and avoid avalanche terrain. In this case, the slope's steepness, the cornice, and the aspect were all signs of potential avalanche danger.

19970111b DRY CANYON, WEST OF LOGAN PEAK, UTAH

January 11, 1997

Three backcountry tourers caught, buried, and killed while camping

WEATHER AND SNOWPACK CONDITIONS

High avalanche danger

A rain crust, up to five inches thick, formed on January 1 and 2, 1997. Snowfall in the following week added about six inches of snow above the crust. The snow faceted and formed "recrystalized powder" by the morning of January 11.

A storm began January 11. About a foot of snow fell during the day. A cold front with strong northwest winds arrived around 18:00. The weather station on Logan Peak, less than a mile to the east, recorded 25 to 50 mph winds from the northwest with frontal passage. An additional foot of snow fell the night of January 11.

ACCIDENT SUMMARY
On January 11, a group of three friends, Max Lyon (38), Keith Maas (36), and Karl Mueggler (29), left for several days of backcountry skiing and winter camping in the Bear River Range of northern Utah. All three were experienced backcountry skiers and mountaineers and very familiar with the terrain around Logan Peak. They were anticipating the oncoming storm and the improving ski conditions. Sometime during the night of January 11, a large natural avalanche overran their campsite and buried all three men.

RESCUE SUMMARY
The group was reported overdue on January 13. Authorities dispatched Cache County Search and Rescue that evening. A hasty party noted avalanche debris in Dry Canyon, and a search team was dispatched at 21:00. Information from the hasty party and from witnesses who had seen the trio on January 11 helped searchers locate the avalanche debris by 22:30.

One of the trio had left his avalanche transceiver on overnight. Rescuers were able to quickly locate the burial site in thick timber about 150 feet above the toe of the avalanche debris. The trio was buried four to six feet deep, in their sleeping bags and tent. The tent was wrapped around an aspen tree.

AVALANCHE DATA

Persistent Slab avalanche

This was a hard slab, triggered naturally, very large relative to the avalanche path, and broke in old faceted snow above a crust (HS-N-R4-O). The avalanche occurred on a wide, planar slope facing southwest. Slope steepness was around 35 degrees.

When the cold front passed over the area the evening of January 11, up to two feet of new snow was available for transport. The strong northwest winds rapidly drifted this snow into a thick, dense slab. Under the slab, the combination of faceted snow above a rain crust probably allowed the natural avalanche to run "farther and faster than might have been expected" for that slope.

COMMENTS

The men located their camp in a site that seemed outside the expected runout of avalanches. Unfortunately, the site was not safe in these particular conditions. As one investigator noted: "in 20 years of skiing, in that drainage I have never seen a slide of that magnitude on that slope, although trees show evidence of having been previously hit." The accident underscores the importance—and difficulty—of placing camps well outside the potential runouts of avalanche paths, even when vegetation clues are present.

This accident occurred on the opposite side of the peak from an accident a month prior (19961206) that almost claimed the life of a snowmobiler. The bodies of three other campers were found on January 11 in Washington. They, too, had been killed when an avalanche overran their tent (19961228).

SWAN LAKE, SOUTHWEST OF RESURRECTION PASS, ALASKA | January 17, 1997

19970117

One hunter caught, buried, and killed

ACCIDENT SUMMARY

Lance Domonoske (39), and John Lesterson were hunting for shed moose antlers using snowmachines and snowshoes near Swan Lake, southwest of Resurrection Pass in Alaska's Kenai Mountains. They were both experienced outdoorsmen and familiar with the terrain, but neither had formal avalanche training.

Traveling alone

Around 12:00, Domonoske spotted a pair of antlers high on a distant slope. Lesterson did not want to go after them, so they made a plan to rendezvous at the trailhead in the evening. When Domonoske failed to show up, Lesterson backtracked. Domonoske's snowmachine was parked at the edge of a large avalanche, and Domonoske was "nowhere to be found."

Lesterson drove home and alerted the authorities. Searchers arrived around 20:30.

RESCUE SUMMARY

Domonoske was found by a search dog named Zip on January 18. Domonoske was buried face-down, about a foot below the surface and within 10 feet of the toe of the avalanche debris. He was still holding one snowshoe. Presumably, Domonoske had been traversing the slope on foot, with his snowshoes in hand. The avalanche swept him 200 to 300 vertical feet before it stopped.

AVALANCHE DATA

Rescuers and investigators described the avalanche as "large" and "wide"; it was triggered by a person on foot (HS-AFu). The fracture line was about 2,400 feet wide. The slab averaged about two feet thick. The slope angle was about 38 degrees in the starting zone. Domonoske presumably was crossing below the steeper part of the slope, on slopes around 30 degrees.

COMMENTS

Many accounts in this volume involve solo travelers who triggered avalanches and were partially or shallowly buried. In several cases, like this one and the Truman Gulch accident earlier in the season (19961111), the victim triggered a slide after splitting up from one or more partners. Traveling solo—and splitting up in order to travel solo, or even moving out of sight of partners—magnifies the consequences of getting caught in avalanches, because even partial and shallow burials can easily be fatal without a partner who can find you and dig you out..

19970125

THE FANG, PROVO CANYON, UTAH | January 25, 1997

Two climbers caught and partially buried; one injured, one killed

WEATHER AND SNOWPACK CONDITIONS

At the time of the accident, rain was falling at the elevation of the ice climb and heavy snow was falling at higher elevations.

ACCIDENT SUMMARY

The Fang (II, WI5) is an ice climb on the north-facing side of Provo Canyon, in the southern Wasatch Range. A natural avalanche hit two ice climbers around 12:45. They were swept off the climb and fell over 300 vertical feet. Doug Hall, (27) was killed by massive trauma. Scott Lee (25) was injured and hospitalized.

RESCUE SUMMARY

Another party of three climbers was about 250 feet below Hall and Lee. The avalanche passed over the second group and left them unscathed. They called 911, immediately rushed to the deposition area, and uncovered the two climbers. The two were partially buried with their rope still attached. Hall did not respond to CPR. The three extracted and stabilized Lee. Utah County Search and Rescue, assisted by Sundance Ski Patrol, arrived around 13:00 and evacuated Lee.

Wet Slab avalanche

AVALANCHE DATA

The rain saturated the new snow and a relatively small pocket of snow above the climb released, sweeping the climbers off the ice.

COMMENTS

The Fang ice climb sits below a large wooded bowl. Any avalanches in the bowl funnel straight into the ice climb.This is typical of avalanche accidents involving ice climbers. Climbers tend to be impacted by natural avalanches more frequently than other recreators.

This was the sixth avalanche fatality in Utah for the 1996-97 season—the largest number in a single winter since 1950. There were also six fatalities in 2000-01, and eight in 2005-06. During the period of this volume, Utah averaged three to four fatalities a winter.

ROCK LAKE, WEST OF CASCADE, IDAHO | February 1, 1997

19970201

Two snowmobilers caught; one buried and killed

WEATHER AND SNOWPACK CONDITIONS

Investigators described a "big snow then rain pattern all season." The day before the accident, about four to five inches of dense wet snow fell. Strong westerly winds drifted significant snow onto the slope. Skies were clear the day of the accident. Air temperatures were rising above freezing.

ACCIDENT SUMMARY

Three snowmobilers were highmarking at around 8,000 feet in elevation on an east aspect above Rock Lake in the West Mountains of west-central Idaho. The area is a popular highmarking spot for experienced riders. The slope had been wind-loaded on previous days, with estimates of up to 12 feet of drifted snow. There was a cornice at the top of the slope. Below the cornice, the slope angle was 30 degrees. There was a rollover about 250 feet below the cornice, with a short section of 45-degree slope, and then the lower 250 feet of the slope were about 40 degrees in steepness.

The snowmobilers "tested" the lower steep slope by highmarking one at a time while the other two watched from below. After making about 12 runs, each one higher until they could reach the lower-angled slopes just under the cornice, they thought it was safe. None of the riders had formal avalanche training, and none of them were equipped with avalanche rescue equipment.

No rescue equipment

Around 13:00, two riders made a run for the cornice at the same time. When they reached the cornice, the lead rider, Roger Youd (39) made his turn downhill. He triggered an avalanche about 24 inches deep. Youd realized what had happened and made a run for the edge of the avalanche. He was headed towards two trees at the top of the breakover. He gunned the sled to avoid the trees but ended up "center punching" one of them. The tree broke, throwing Youd forward over the break in the slope. That was the last his companions saw of him.

The third rider was waiting at the bottom of the slope. He saw the avalanche start and waved frantically to his friends. When he realized the avalanche was going to overtake him, he started his machine and outran the avalanche.

In avalanche runout

The lower rider had made his turn and was heading downhill, below the slab, and did not realize what had happened. He saw the third rider gesturing and turned to see "a 12-foot wall of snow overtaking me." He gunned his throttle and outran the avalanche as well.

Photo of the avalanche crown, showing two significant layers of wind-drifted snow. *Photo Jeff Halligan.*

RESCUE SUMMARY

When the powder cloud settled, the two riders began searching for Youd. They were able to locate the damaged snowmobile but no signs of the victim. Another group of snowmobilers happened on the scene around 14:30 and called 911. They remained and assisted in the hasty search.

A search and rescue team including US Forest Service personnel and National Ski Patrol members arrived around 17:00 and searched until dark. The search resumed the following morning with search and rescue dogs and teams from Boise's Idaho Mountain Search and Rescue Unit.

Searchers found Youd on the third pass of a probe line. He had been buried about 26 hours. His body was about four feet downslope from his machine, buried under about three feet of avalanche debris. He was found laying on his side with his head down slope. He had suffered significant trauma, and there was no evidence of an ice mask or frost in his helmet visor.

AVALANCHE DATA

Persistent Slab avalanche

The avalanche was about 300 feet wide. Fractures traveled another 100 feet onto a slope about 25 degrees in steepness, but that slab only moved a few inches down slope. Investigators conducted a very hasty crown profile. One described the slab composed of two layers of dense snow, with a 1/8 of an inch thick ice crust in the middle. The avalanche broke on a thin layer of "cupped" crystals in the middle of the snowpack.

The avalanche ran about 400 vertical feet on the flats adjacent to the lake. Debris covered an area of about two acres, with deposition up to 16 feet deep.

COMMENTS

Very quick reactions and powerful sleds saved the second and third riders. Youd was not so lucky, despite having similar reactions and a similarly powerful sled. The differ-

Looking south from the accident site. Visible are recent natural avalanches that ran in similar terrain as the fatal avalanche. *Photo Jeff Halligan.*

ence highlights the fact that once a person is caught in a slide, survival often depends on chance and factors a victim can do little to influence, such as whether one strikes trees or stays near the surface of the debris. A victim that suffers significant trauma and/ or a deep burial—as Youd did—may not survive even with a prompt companion rescue. Thus, the most reliable way to avoid burial, injury or death in an avalanche is to avoid being caught in one.

As in the four previous accidents involving snowmobilers during the winter of 1996-97, the riders in this case were not carrying transceivers, shovels, and probes. And as also noted earlier, that pattern diminishes through the course of this volume, as many snowmobilers adopted the practice of carrying avalanche rescue gear. However, accidents involving snowmobilers not carrying rescue gear continue to occur, including one in this same location on December 17, 2009, in which one rider was killed and a second was injured.

NEAR JACKSON, MONTANA | February 21, 1997

19970221

One snowmobiler caught, not buried, but killed by trauma

ACCIDENT SUMMARY

A snowmobiler was highmarking a slope and got his machine stuck. He was trying to get his machine out when the avalanche released. Neither the rider nor his machine was buried, but the avalanche carried him through trees. He was killed by trauma. The avalanche was about 300 feet wide.

Terrain trap

COMMENTS

The lack of information available on this accident precludes comment.

19970303 FACTORY HILL, YELLOWSTONE NATIONAL PARK, WYOMING | March 3, 1997

Two backcountry skiers (researchers at work), caught, buried, and killed

ACCIDENT SUMMARY

Two geologists were monitoring geothermal features in the Heart Lake area of southern Yellowstone National Park. Rick Hutchinson (47), was a Research Geologist with the National Park Service and was familiar with the geothermal features in the area. Diane Dustman (37) was a visiting geologist.

In avalanche runout

The pair was skiing westbound along the base of Factory Hill, a route Hutchinson frequently used to visit a thermal feature. They were traveling across a gentle slope, about 16 degrees steepness, but below a much steeper slope. The avalanche caught them in the middle of the runout area.

RESCUE SUMMARY

Hutchinson and Dustman failed to make an afternoon rendezvous with other rangers on March 4. The other rangers headed into the Heart Lake area. They discovered the pair's ski tracks going into avalanche debris about 21:00.

A larger search party began working the avalanche debris on March 5. Searchers used probe lines and search dogs. Downed timber made the probing difficult, and sulfur from geothermal features interfered with the search dogs. Searchers recovered the first body on the afternoon of March 6.

AVALANCHE DATA

Persistent Slab avalanche

The avalanche broke in depth hoar near the ground. Investigators found that the snowpack on the slope that slid was shallower than in the surrounding area, with a widespread layer of depth hoar at the base. A larger avalanche had run on that slope in December, removing much of the early-season snow cover. The shallow snowpack that developed after the avalanche was prone to faceting.

COMMENTS

Unfortunately, Persistent Slab avalanches can be triggered from below, even from flat or low-angle terrain. The failures can propagate long distances, and debris from resulting avalanches can overrun people in the runout zones of remotely-triggered avalanches. That is probably what happened here, and it will be another common characteristic of accidents in this volume. The trigger point may have been near a thermal feature, where the warm ground would have increased the development of weak faceted snow and depth hoar. While thermal features may be rare outside Yellowstone National Park, backcountry travelers can reduce the risk of being caught in remotely-triggered avalanches by avoiding runout zones when the potential for Persistent Slab avalanches exists.

LOST CREEK, EAST OF PRIEST LAKE, IDAHO | March 8, 1997 19970308

Two snowmobilers caught; one buried and killed

ACCIDENT SUMMARY

Troy Douglas (28) and friends were riding in the Lost Creek area in the Selkirk Mountains of northern Idaho. There were many groups in the area. Douglas followed a rider from another group up a hill climb. Douglas's sled got stuck, and he tried to turn it back downhill.

More than one person on a slope

According to eyewitnesses, the first snowmobile, higher on the slope, triggered the avalanche. "It caught up to [Douglas]," one witness said, "and shot him up in the air." [2]

RESCUE SUMMARY

Douglas was caught in the avalanche. "I tried watching Troy as long as I could," another witness said. "He was swimming in the avalanche" for a while. Douglas was fully buried when the avalanche stopped.

He and his party were not equipped with avalanche rescue gear. Douglas' friends grabbed sticks to probe the snow. They placed a 911 call just after 12:30. Through the afternoon, some 30 or 40 people—some snowmobilers, some neighbors from a nearby community—searched the debris field.

No rescue equipment

Douglas' body was recovered the following morning by volunteer searchers, many of whom were his friends. "We found his sled first," a searcher told the newspaper, and "five or ten minutes after that, we finally found [Douglas]."

COMMENTS

This was the fourth fatality of the 1996-97 winter involving a party of snowmobilers who were not carrying avalanche rescue gear. Many of these avalanches started when multiple riders were on the slope.

STEEPLECHASE, EAST OF ASPEN HIGHLANDS, COLORADO 19970311

March 11, 1997

One sidecountry snowboarder caught, partly buried, and injured

WEATHER AND SNOWPACK CONDITIONS

Investigators described the day of this accident as the "first significant thaw of the season." A pair of sidecountry riders was descending a relatively low-elevation slope in mid-afternoon.

ACCIDENT SUMMARY

At about 14:00, two snowboarders left the Aspen Highlands Ski Area in central Colorado, below the Steeplechase runs, to ride to the valley floor. At about 9,000 feet elevation, a 30-year-old rider triggered and was caught in a small wet loose-snow avalanche. At first it was only as wide as his snowboard and did not seem dangerous. As the wet snow continued to flow downhill, it entrained additional snow and widened to about 40 feet across. The second snowboarder watched his friend "riding the white tiger" into relatively thick aspen trees.

Loose Wet avalanche

Terrain trap

The snowboarder described the wet snow as "quicksand" from which he could not escape. It was "like being in a cement mixer," especially when he was slammed through the aspen trees. The avalanche broke trees and ripped his bindings from his board. With his feet free, he was able to "swim with the avalanche," and after a ride of about 500 feet, he was able to grab a tree with his legs as the avalanche slowed to a stop.

RESCUE SUMMARY

After the avalanche stopped, the second rider hurried down to help his injured friend. The victim was "pretty beat-up," and, by his own admission, he looked like "he had been in a bar fight with a couple of cats." The pair used their avalanche shovels as small crutches to assist the injured man's painful hobble (about 100 feet) to the road and their car. Once there, they headed to the emergency department at Aspen Valley Hospital, where the victim was admitted with multiple contusions and abrasions, a fractured rib, and a fractured lumbar vertebra (#4).

COMMENTS

The man admits he was very lucky. When his snowboard was ripped from his boots, he gained some mobility that helped him swim with the slide, but it was his helmet and his backpack that likely saved his life. During the avalanche he struck trees with his back and head, yet he was able to walk away.

Most avalanche accidents involve dry slab avalanches. This accident was an exception that exemplifies the particular dangers posed by loose avalanches composed of wet snow. Although they start small, they can rapidly entrain large amounts of dense debris, making them very difficult to escape. They can also be triggered in small patches of snow above obstacles like trees, rocks and cliffs, increasing the potential for trauma.

19970411 GAKONA GLACIER, NORTHEAST OF PAXSON, ALASKA

April 11, 1997

One snowmobiler fully buried and killed in cornice fall

ACCIDENT SUMMARY

Cornice fall

A 27-year-old Anchorage man was highmarking with his snowmobile on a steep slope along the Gakona Glacier in the eastern Alaska Range. He stopped his machine at the top of a narrow ridge near the 7,000 foot elevation level. When he stopped, the cornice he was standing on broke away and carried him and his snowmobile 1,300 vertical feet down the other side of the mountain. The cornice fall triggered a slab avalanche. The man was buried under approximately six feet of dense, wet avalanche debris. He died from severe trauma.

COMMENTS

A nearly identical accident with the same results happened in the same area on April 3, 1993.

MOONFLOWER BUTTRESS, MOUNT HUNTER, ALASKA

19970606

June 6, 1997

One climber killed by trauma

WEATHER AND SNOWPACK CONDITIONS

Reports describe the day of the accident as part of "a warm weather spell."

ACCIDENT SUMMARY

On the afternoon of June 6, Steve Mascioli (37) and his partner were climbing The Shaft, a 400-foot, ice-lined chimney that is one crux of the Moonflower Buttress route on Mount Hunter in Denali National Park. At about 17:00, the party was on the 17th pitch at about 9,800 feet elevation. Mascioli was belaying his partner, who was leading some distance above him. The leader had safely passed a large chunk of snow. Mascioli was "killed...when [the] huge, dense mass of snow dropped 100 feet onto him from a rock overhang."[3]

Terrain trap

RESCUE SUMMARY

Mascioli was killed instantly. His partner was uninjured. The partner rappelled down, retrieved their haul bag and other gear, and continued rappelling over the next day and a half, reaching the fifth pitch on June 8. He stayed there for roughly half a day to avoid more "snow avalanches caused by the warm conditions."

While waiting, he yelled and caught the attention of another climbing party camped on the glacier below. Those climbers radioed Denali National Park climbing rangers, who made preparations for a rescue. Eventually, Mascioli's partner was able to reach the other climbers and rope up with them for the descent to base camp down the Southeast Fork of the Kahiltna Glacier. Climbing rangers recovered Mascioli's body on June 11 using a helicopter and short haul technique.

COMMENTS

Alpinists often choose steep, technical routes because such routes limit their exposure to avalanche starting zones, which tend to be more extensive on lower-angled slopes. In this case, however, the warm weather increased the danger of falling snow and ice. The danger was particularly acute in the chimney feature they were climbing at the time of the accident because it funneled falling debris directly onto the victim.

Several days after Mascioli's death, two climbers named a new route on Denali's South Buttress in his honor, Mascioli's Pillar (Point 15,840).

19970705 GLADSTONE PEAK, SOUTHWEST OF TELLURIDE, COLORADO | July 5, 1997

Two climbers caught; one injured, one partly buried and killed

WEATHER AND SNOWPACK CONDITIONS

Investigators described the weather as "hot" and the snow "wet," at the time of the accident.

ACCIDENT SUMMARY

A party of four climbers summited Wilson Peak (one of several "14ers" in the San Miguel Mountains of southwestern Colorado) in the morning. They traversed towards Gladstone Peak for a second summit. The party split in half, with two climbers descending to the snowfields and John Ortega and Brendan Slevin traversing along the Wilson-Gladstone ridge. Around 14:00, Ortega and Slevin were within a few hundred vertical feet of the Gladstone summit. A rock Ortega was holding "gave way, tumbled down by me, and started a rock slide." He and Slevin were caught in the rockfall and swept to the snowfield below. The falling rocks triggered a wet slab avalanche.

Another party of climbers on Gladstone Peak heard or saw the rockfall. They had a shouted conversation with Ortega and began to descend to search for Slevin.

Ortega fell about 30 feet, was not buried, but suffered skull fractures and lacerations. He felt he "did not have much time to reach safety" and that, given the violence of the rockfall, Slevin only had a remote chance of survival. Ortega made the difficult decision to return to the ridge and descend to the Silver Pick Basin trailhead. From the trailhead, Ortega was able to call 911 and alert Search and Rescue.

RESCUE SUMMARY

Around 17:00, a helicopter flew rescuers in, including an avalanche dog and handler from Telluride Ski Patrol. The dog found Slevin before rescuers saw him. Slevin was partially buried in avalanche debris and appeared to have suffered significant trauma.

AVALANCHE DATA

Wet Slab avalanche

The rockfall and avalanche occurred around 13,800 feet on the northeast aspect of Gladstone Peak. The wet slab avalanche broke two to three deep, to the rocky ground surface. It was about 30 feet wide, and ran 300 vertical feet. The avalanche debris was four to six feet deep and contained numerous rocks.

COMMENTS

This was an unfortunate mountaineering accident. The combination of rockfall and avalanche caused serious injury to both climbers. Fatal accidents involving Wet Slab avalanches are unusual.

1997–1998
SEASON

19971109 HATCH PEAK, HATCHER PASS, NORTH OF PALMER, ALASKA | November 9, 1997

Two backcountry riders caught; one fully buried and killed

WEATHER AND SNOWPACK CONDITIONS

Hatcher Pass cuts through the southern Talkeetna Mountains about 40 miles north of Anchorage. The road through the pass is closed in the winter, but the surrounding area offers many winter recreation opportunities. It has been the site of many avalanche accidents, including two others on or just below the same peak (20011111 and 20030329). In November, 1997, shallow, early-season snow had turned into a layer of weak faceted snow at the ground. Three storms with strong wind formed a hard slab of snow over the facets. Strong winds in the 12 hours prior to the avalanche drifted about two feet of snow onto the slope. The snow available for drifting had fallen several days before the accident.

The day of the accident, rangers at the nearby state park were warning recreational users about recent avalanche activity and signs of instability.

ACCIDENT SUMMARY

Lack of training

A group of seven experienced snowboarders toured south from Hatcher Pass in south-central Alaska. The seven group members were all friends who had partied together the night before. Most had no formal avalanche education beyond awareness talks. The group had driven about 2.5 hours from Girdwood to the trailhead.

The seven ascended a ridge of Hatch Peak (4811 feet), along the eastern flank of April Bowl. They snowshoed for about 90 minutes to reach the top of the bowl. Winds along the ridgecrest were blowing 45-60 mph at the time, hampering visibility and communication.

Andy (25) dug two snow pits along the route. His first pit was along the ridge in an area of deeply drifted snow. He dug his second pit about 10 feet below the corniced ridge on the eastern side of the main face of April Bowl. From his evaluation, Andy felt the snow stability looked "good" and he communicated his assessment to other members of the group within earshot.

More than one person on a slope

Andy descended from his second pit onto the 38-degree slope below. At the same time, perhaps unknown to Andy, his friend Pat (early thirties) jumped off a cornice on the western side of April Bowl. A second party of three snowboarders arrived at the ridge as Andy and Pat began their descents. Witnesses below the bowl said they saw "two snowboarders and two dogs jump into the bowl at nearly the same time." Both riders had made about three turns when the "whole slope ripped out above them as four large plates."

RESCUE SUMMARY

As the avalanche swept Andy and Pat swept down slope, the remaining party members carefully watched. Pat was able to ride out of the western flank of the avalanche. Andy was swept over a steep convexity and out of sight. Spotted by his friend Colin as he reappeared far below, Andy was still standing and trying to ride out of the avalanche. The avalanche hit an abrupt change to a very low-angle slope. The last wave of moving debris suddenly over took Andy and buried him.

Colin fixed Andy's last-seen location in his mind. Colin rode down the bed surface to Andy's approximate position. Pat arrived within moments and both started a visual and beacon search for Andy. They picked up a transceiver signal almost immediately. Within minutes, the additional seven riders from above and three witnesses from below were on-site and digging. After 10 to 15 minutes of digging, Andy's exact location remained unknown.

Because none of the rescuers were carrying avalanche probes, Colin pulled the basket from a ski pole and started probing the sidewalls of the hole. Almost immediately, he made a positive strike about four feet beyond the western wall of the pit. Within another two minutes, rescuers uncovered Andy's head.

Inadequate rescue equipment

One rescuer, Erik, was a registered nurse. As his friends continued to remove the snow from around Andy's chest and legs, Erik cleared Andy's airway and checked for a pulse and respirations. Andy appeared unresponsive with no pulse or respirations. Several of the other rescuers were EMTs or had CPR training. The group started CPR as soon as it was possible to lay Andy flat.

As the group was excavating Andy, they sent two rescuers to alert authorities. Once notified, Alaska State Park rangers immediately contacted a medical helicopter and the Alaska State Troopers helicopter for assistance. Rangers responded to the site within minutes.

The rescuers improvised a backboard from a snowboard. They continued CPR for approximately two hours until the medical helicopter arrived and transported Andy to the nearest hospital, 15 miles away. Andy was declared dead on arrival due to cardiac arrest due to traumatic asphyxia. Additionally, some bruises were evident on his body (presumably from impacts with rocks) and one rib was broken (possibly during CPR).

The avalanche buried Andy in a crouched (standing) position with one hand in front of his face and the other extending toward his binding. Rescuers did not find a visible ice mask. His head was about four feet below the debris surface and his snowboard about seven feet deep. He was 15-20 feet from the toe of the debris. Rescuers described the debris "as being remarkably light considering the depth of the slab."

AVALANCHE DATA

Two days after the avalanche, investigators found "a pencil hard wind slab of variable depth (one inch to seven feet with an average of depth of four feet)" above a two-inch thick layer of faceted snow.

Persistent Slab avalanche

COMMENTS

In their report on the accident[1], investigators described the group as "generally comfortable with exposure and accustomed to taking risks. They weren't considered reckless, just a little loose with their travel procedures (i.e., more than one person on a slope at a time, etc.)." The riders were all proficient and "sought terrain that would challenge their skills." However, the investigators did note that the riders' "avalanche hazard evaluation skills were considerably less refined".

It appears that in this case, that gap between motivation and hazard evaluation skills caught up with the group. They recognized but misjudged the avalanche danger; that misjudgment may have had three contributing factors. One was the difficulty communicating in the roar of the wind on the ridge. A second may have been incomplete information. The group was not aware of the rangers' concerns about lingering instability; they did not talk to the rangers or to other parties that had. They did talk about the potential avalanche hazard being "high" due to the strong winds and blowing snow. But they observed "No collapsing, shooting cracks, hollow-sounding snow, or recent avalanches" as they ascended. These key clues may not have been scarce because of their route, which followed a well-compacted road and then an often-bare ridge. Investigators noted that for this group, the only major clue to potential instability was the "observation of strong winds and evidence of snow redistribution in combination with steep, leeward slopes." Those were exactly the slopes they planned to ride, and their commitment may have led them to minimize the importance of that information.

Lastly, they may have relied too much on the assessment of one member of the group. Andy's first snowpit in the deeply drifted snow was not representative of the slopes below. However, investigators commented that his second snowpit was in a "good location and contained all the critical information required to make a 'No Go' decision: a four-foot deep fresh wind slab poorly bonded to a two-inch thick layer of weak faceted snow sitting on a 38-degree slope being loaded by 45-60 mph winds." From the data present in the second snowpit, investigators concluded:

> Andy either did not dig deep enough to reach the weak layer (not likely), misinterpreted the data he found, or ignored the data because it conflicted with a preconceived notion based upon previous experience or intended purpose....In any event, Andy communicated to the group that stability looked 'good' and nobody questioned that evaluation. Had several members gathered stability information along the way and discussed the results, a different decision might have been reached.

Several other factors slowed the rescue. Everyone in the group carried avalanche rescue transceivers and knew how to use them, though some in the party had not practiced since the prior winter. They did not accurately pinpoint Andy's burial position during their transceiver search and wasted significant time digging in the wrong location. Moreover, none of the group were carrying avalanche probes, though some usually did. Probes might have helped accurately pinpoint Andy's body and may have reduced the search time by 10 to15 minutes. Once Colin probed Andy through the wall of the hole, it took only a few minutes to uncover his head. It took considerably longer to free Andy's body.

19971122

TONY GROVE LAKE, NORTHEAST OF LOGAN, UTAH

November 22, 1997

Two backcountry tourers caught; one partially buried, one fully buried

ACCIDENT SUMMARY

In avalanche runout

More than one person on a slope

Two snowboarders, a husband and wife in their mid-20s, were near Tony Grove Lake in the Bear River Range northeast of Logan, Utah. The area is popular early-season because it provides easy access to backcountry terrain. The pair were climbing on foot, ascending a low-angled slope with the intention of building a jump. The slope was below a steep, wind-loaded gully. The husband was leading when the avalanche broke on the steep slopes above them.

RESCUE SUMMARY

The pair tried to run but could not. The man jumped on his board and rode it like a surfboard. The avalanche knocked him over and buried him neck-deep (partially buried-not critical). He was able to self-rescue.

The avalanche completely buried the woman. The husband did not have a last-seen point. After looking briefly, he heard her voice and dug down to her with his hands. He exposed her airway within a few minutes, and she was not injured. She was facing downhill in an upright position, and her head was four feet below the snow surface.

AVALANCHE DATA

Investigators described the avalanche as a soft slab, 100 yards wide, with a crown height of one to four feet. It ran approximately 120 feet with a maximum debris depth of five feet. The slide started near very steep cliffs and the upper section of the gully approached 70 degrees. The majority of the crown face was 45 to 50 degrees and track averaged 38 to 45 degrees.

Persistent Slab avalanche

The bed surface was a melt freeze crust formed in October, two inches above the ground. The avalanche broke in a six inch thick layer of faceted snow above the crust. Storms of the previous several days had deposited new snow and wind drifted snow one to four feet deep.

COMMENTS

Whew. A close call that illustrates the importance of avoiding avalanche runout zones when ascending, in order to minimize a group's exposure to natural and remotely-triggered avalanches. This practice is particularly important when the potential exists for Persistent Slab avalanches. These can propagate in surprising ways and can be triggered from points outside the start zones, such as low-angle terrain adjacent to the avalanche path or the runouts below.

In this case, it's not clear whether the couple was struck by a natural avalanche or triggered the Persistent Slab avalanche remotely. Regardless, their ascent route was not in avalanche-proof terrain, and they almost paid a high price for that error.

The couple was aware of the avalanche danger. They had attended several avalanche awareness seminars. They called local avalanche forecast before their tour and knew the hazard was rated Considerable. They noticed a large natural avalanche that had released the night before on a slope above the cliffs, a red flag for unstable conditions.

"Red flag" indications of danger

In the end, the avalanche did not run very far, and the couple was caught near the flank. The debris was very soft. The soft debris allowed the husband to self-rescue, hear his wife, and dig with his hands.

KING RAVINE, MOUNT ADAMS, NEW HAMPSHIRE

19971123

November 23, 1997

One hiker caught and partially buried

WEATHER AND SNOWPACK CONDITIONS

Over November 22 and 23, the summit of Mount Washington recorded about four inches of new snow. Winds were from the southwest averaging about 25 mph. Temperatures were around 20° F.

ACCIDENT SUMMARY

On November 23, Joel Reigner (27) and Luc Parent (30) hiked up the Great Gully Trail, a steep and difficult hiking trail that ascends a major avalanche path in King Gully on the north side of Mount Adams in the Presidential Range. They were on a day hike. Both were experienced hikers and were well equipped with crampons and ice axes, but they did not carry any avalanche rescue gear. Both men assumed it was too early in the season for avalanches to be a concern.

No rescue equipment

"Red flag" indications of danger

As they ascended, they triggered numerous small "pocket" avalanches. They recognized the unstable snow, but considered the avalanches inconsequential. Near treeline, they were "slogging" through drifts up to their thighs.

The trail crossed through a gully with significantly more snow. Parent was about 20 feet behind Reigner. Parent was concerned about the amount of snow and turned back to the edge of the gully. He wanted to suggest to Reigner that he do the same, but the distance between them made communication difficult.

It was about 17:00, dark, and Reigner's headlamp had failed. Near the middle of the gully, he triggered an avalanche. It swept him past his friend, into the darkness.

RESCUE SUMMARY

The avalanche stopped on a bench after about 150 vertical feet. Reigner was buried on his left side, with his head and arm above the snow and up to four feet of debris elsewhere. Reigner yelled and could see his friend's headlamp above him.

Reigner began to self-rescue. His mouth and nose were packed with snow. His ice axe was in his free hand, and he used that to dig out his upper body. His legs took significantly longer, and he was finally free almost an hour after the avalanche.

Reigner set out to find his friend. Without a headlamp, he was unable to travel far. He excavated a snow cave and settled in for a long, cold bivouac.

After the avalanche swept past, Parent thought he heard a yell, but "dismissed it as his imagination." He was "intimidated by both the steepness [of the gully] and the possibility of starting another slide" and feared his partner was deeply buried far below. During an interview with USFS investigators, Parent "affirmed his awareness that successful avalanche rescue must be carried out by the victim's party. Nonetheless, he continued up the trail, intending to descend another trail to a cabin with a caretaker."

Parent's headlamp eventually died, too. He lost the trail below treeline and was forced to bivouac as well. In the morning, he was still unable to find the trail, and bushwhacked down the side of King Ravine. He eventually reached a major trail and hiked out. He reached the local fire station around 09:30, about 16 hours after the avalanche. "There's been an avalanche. My friend is dead," he said in shock.

Search and Rescue was dispatched. Reigner had begun hiking early in the morning, and arrived at the trailhead as the rescue party was leaving. Reigner was "cold and tired, with a large bruise on his leg, a twisted ankle, and quite a story to tell."

AVALANCHE DATA

Reigner estimated the avalanche as about six inches deep and 20 feet wide. It was probably a soft slab of recent snow, unintentionally triggered by a hiker on foot, and small relative to the slope (SS-AFu-R2).

COMMENTS

One contributing influence for this accident was the pair's initial mindset that minimized the avalanche danger. They maintained this attitude despite obvious signs they were mistaken—the small avalanches they triggered, the weather, and the wind-drifted snow. To his credit, Parent recognized the danger at the right moment —crossing the loaded gully where Reigner triggered the avalanche. Had Parent not turned back to the edge of the gully, the avalanche likely would have caught both men. Without avalanche rescue gear, the close call might easily have turned deadly.

"Both men were fortunate to escape unharmed. Not only did they survive an avalanche, but the notoriously dangerous winter weather of the Presidential Range had been fairly mild for spending an unprepared night out above treeline," investigators noted.

In hindsight, it is easy to fault Parent for not searching. The reader should imagine the fear, panic, and stress he felt, not just about the avalanche, but the dark, stormy weather and the end of a long day.

CROW CREEK, NORTH OF GIRDWOOD, ALASKA

19971124

November 24, 1997

One hiker buried and killed

WEATHER AND SNOWPACK CONDITIONS

During a cold October in the Chugach Mountains of southern Alaska, the shallow snowpack became faceted. November brought relatively warm temperatures to the area. On the day prior to the avalanche, about six to eight inches of snow fell—the first snowfall in several weeks. The storm started warm and ended cold. Gusty winds during the last few hours of the storm formed shallow drifts in leeward pockets of terrain.

ACCIDENT SUMMARY

On the afternoon of November 24, Angela Paez (34) and Bill English (mid-40s) decided to go skiing in the Crow Creek area north of Girdwood. The snow conditions were not ideal for skiing, so they decided to hike instead. The route to Crow Pass follows an old mining road for the first two miles. At the end of the mining road, the trail ascends series of switchbacks up a steep scree slope. Drifted snow typically covers the switchbacks by the end of September. Ascending the slope "requires skilled evaluation, careful route selection, and luck" because of a combination of factors: the slope angle is in the mid to high 30s, the ground cover is smooth scree that provides few anchors for the snowpack, and a gorge at the base of the slope acts as a terrain trap.

Paez and English discussed their route options when they reached the switchbacks.

> One option was to follow a windblown scree rib vertically to the high route, then traverse across along the base of the cliffs above. Another option was to try to follow the existing trail zigzagging back and forth across the slope, but because the trail was buried, this made little sense. The third option was to traverse the scree slope (approximately 600 feet horizontally) with the intent of gaining a windblown rocky rib that ran vertically along the north side (left side looking upslope). They felt that this last route would give them the least exposure and would be the most direct, but to gain this route they had to first climb upslope about 300 linear feet (to be parallel with the beginning of the rocky rib).

The snowpack along the traverse was "generally less than 12 inches deep with numerous rocks exposed." Walking was easy. English hiked first and reached the rocky rib at 14:35 p.m. He turned around to watch Paez following in his track. She was about

50 feet behind him when the slope around her started to move. The avalanche broke about 50-75 feet above her and extended about 10-15 feet in front of her.

The avalanche immediately knocked Paez down. Initially, the avalanche was "shallow and slow-moving, but quickly accelerated and gained in volume and size as it descended." Paez was in a sitting position, and "made no attempt to fight, jump, or roll to the side."

Terrain trap

English watched as the avalanche carried Paez downslope. She disappeared beneath the debris just before it spilled over the edge of the gorge. English ran downslope, following Paez's trajectory, and jumped the last 20 vertical feet into the gorge to reach the debris.

RESCUE SUMMARY

Inadequate rescue equipment

The avalanche debris made a cone about 25 feet around and six to 12 feet deep. English immediately found one of Paez's ski poles and placed it vertically in the snow to mark its location. With his shovel, English carefully dug a series of three trenches, one row above the other, horizontally across the debris. Each trench was about three feet deep. He periodically stopped and yelled into the snow. Twice, he thought he heard a faint, muffled yell in response, but he was unable to pinpoint the source, either by listening or by digging. He did not probe below or next to his trenches because he did not have a probe. Around 15:45, after about 70 minutes of systematic searching, English decided he needed help.

Getting out of the gorge was not easy, but with skillful climbing, English was able to climb the cliff. He reached his truck by 16:45 and drove to the nearest residence, approximately seven minutes away. There, he called 911. Alaska State Troopers alerted a host of other agencies: Alyeska Ski Resort, the Girdwood Volunteer Fire Dept., the Alaska Mountain Rescue Group, Dogs Organized for Ground Search, the Nordic Ski Patrol, the U.S. Forest Service, Alaska State Parks, the 210th Air National Guard, and the Rescue Coordination Center at Elemendorf Air Force Base.

Organized rescuers quickly converged on two staging areas by 18:30. Because of the dual staging areas, there was some confusion during the early hours of organization. Initial attempts to reach the avalanche site by snowmobile were unsuccessful due to deteriorating weather, poor visibility, drifting snow, and the concern of additional avalanches. Two attempts at reaching the site in an Air National Guard Pavehawk helicopter also proved unsuccessful due to 25 to 30 mph northerly headwinds and poor visibility from blowing snow. Rather than risk the lives of rescuers, the decision was made to resume the rescue effort in the morning, contingent upon better weather and visibility.

At first light, a team of avalanche specialists mitigated the slopes adjacent to the accident site from an A-Star helicopter. They triggered several small avalanches. A team of 13 rescuers and two avalanche dogs flew to the site. A dog alerted on Paez within four minutes of reaching the site. It took rescuers about 15 minutes to excavate her. She had no vital signs. Rescuers found Paez in a sitting position, her head under 30 inches of debris. There was no evidence of an air space or ice mask.

AVALANCHE SUMMARY

Due to strong winds and drifting snow the night after the accident, no fracture line was visible the day the rescuers found Paez. However, an examination of the bed surface and adjacent slopes, which had not slid, provided important information about the avalanche. The cool temperatures a month prior created a weak layer about two inches thick on top of the scree. The facets had a hand-hardness of Fist. Subsequent warm temperatures and slight accumulations of new snow settled the upper snowpack, creating a poorly bonded shallow crust layer about two inches thick and pencil hard immediately above the facets. The crust layer did not exist everywhere, but most likely did exist to the lee of the rocky ridge where the depth was slightly greater. The snow that began November 23 bonded well to the crust because temperatures were warm when the snowfall started. Moderate winds near the end of the storm drifted low-density snow onto the slope.

The slope angles varied across the slope. They lowest was 32 degrees (measured) where Paez was standing when the avalanche broke. The highest was 41 degrees (estimated) along the upper 15 to 20 feet of the starting zone, roughly 50 feet above her position. The scree slope was uniformly smooth and provided poor anchoring.

The rocky rib on which English was standing ran vertically upslope. The rib acted as a snow fence, allowing cross-slope winds to drift snow onto the slope the pair crossed.

COMMENTS

The two hikers observed no signs of instability along their route. They did not see significant wind drifting, either.

> This may have been due to the fact that they a) had been following a well beaten trail and b) had just reached a point in elevation where the wind action was more prevalent. In other words, within a few steps they went from an area of no wind slab to a small pocket of wind slab.
>
> This accident is a good example of how a little avalanche ending in a terrain trap can have deadly consequences. If the same avalanche had occurred on a slope shaped like an alluvial fan, Angela most likely would have been caught in snow that was less that knee deep, and probably could have easily stood up and walked away. [Because the debris piled up deeply in the gully] this accident is a classic example of how a small, isolated area of instability posed a disproportionately high hazard because of the unforgiving nature of the terrain.
>
> Neither Bill or Angela can be described as having a high-risk taking attitude or as being ego-involved with the route, but time was a factor in their route selection decisions as sunset was less than a couple of hours away.
>
> Angela was an experienced climber, but her avalanche training was unknown. Bill had no formal avalanche education, but had attended awareness talks over the years and had read avalanche articles on his own. Bill said that the threat of avalanches never occurred to them. The sun was shining, the trail conditions were good, and the scenery was spectacular. In that sense, they may have been lulled into thinking that everything was all right and lowered their guard. Both missed the subtle changes in the snow conditions as they reached the steeper scree slope, but this would be easy for an inexperienced avalanche person to do. They carried a pair of ski poles, which could be used as probes, and a shovel, but Bill never had any formal avalanche rescue training. He showed great courage in leaping into the gorge and carrying out a systematic search by trenching a series of ditches. Had he used the ski pole as a probe, he may have found Angela sooner, but it is unlikely this would have changed the outcome.

19971230 DUCK LAKE, SOUTH OF GUANELLA PASS, COLORADO

December 30, 1997

One snowshoer caught, buried, and killed

ACCIDENT SUMMARY

In avalanche runout

Two families were staying in a cabin near Duck Lake, about a mile south of Guanella Pass in Colorado's Front Range. At about 13:00, two men snowshoed away from the cabin. They were about 200 feet from the cabin, crossing through a small area of willows below a short, steep slope. The men heard a whumpf as the snow collapsed beneath them. An avalanche broke on the steep slope just above them. The men were about 15 feet apart, and the avalanche caught one but missed the other. It was over in seconds. One man was standing with his companion nowhere in sight. He hastily looked for his friend, without success, and then dashed back to the cabin.

RESCUE SUMMARY

No rescue equipment

The families called 911 from the cabin. The victim's friend and their wives quickly returned to the avalanche to look for the buried man. They knew roughly where to look and started digging. They did not probe the debris. It would turn out their excavation was a few feet from the buried snowshoer.

After about 45 minutes, the Clear Creek County Sheriff and another officer arrived. The sheriff took a ski pole and cut off the basket to fashion a probe pole. He had started to show the others how to use the pole when he struck the buried man.

They quickly dug out the snowshoer and began resuscitation efforts. The 39-year-old California man was buried under two to three feet of snow near the toe of the debris for nearly an hour. A Flight for Life helicopter from Denver arrived and advanced life support efforts were tried with no response.

AVALANCHE DATA

Persistent Slab avalanche

This small hard slab avalanche was triggered unintentionally by the snowshoers. It broke three to four feet deep in old snow. It traveled only 60 vertical feet, but broke 295 feet across a short, steep slope at 11,300 feet near treeline (HS-AIu-R1-D2-O). The fracture line also propagated about 200 feet further, but the slope there was not steep enough to slide.

The men triggered the avalanche from below as they crossed a low-angled slope. The gentle slope had scattered willows and a shallow, faceted snowpack. Directly uphill, the slope steepened to 36 degrees. The short but steep slope faced slightly east-southeast, and winds had drifted layers of dense snow onto the slope. Investigators measured densities up to 490 kg/m^3 in the slab.

COMMENTS

This accident occurred in the early season. The overall snowpack was shallow and weak, and looked like it posed little avalanche danger. The steep slope was drifted deeply, however, and the men triggered the Persistent Slab from an area of shallow snow below the steeper slope. This accident, like another early-season accident the same winter (19971122), demonstrates the importance of not traveling below steep starting zones, in order to minimize exposure to natural and remotely-triggered avalanches.

SAWTELL PEAK, NORTHWEST OF ISLAND PARK, IDAHO

19980103a

January 3, 1998

One snowmobiler buried and killed

ACCIDENT SUMMARY

On Saturday, January 3, 1998, a small avalanche buried a snowmobiler near Sawtell Peak, which lies east of the Continental Divide and northwest of Island Park. He and his partner were highmarking on a small slope when he triggered an avalanche. The avalanche occurred at about 15:30. His partner was not caught and went for help.

No rescue equipment

RESCUE SUMMARY

The partner alerted local authorities around 16:00. Rescuers reached the site and found the snowmobile but suspended the search around 18:00 because of poor visibility and concerns about the avalanche danger. The search resumed Sunday morning around 09:00. Searchers located the snowmobiler's body by probing, shortly before noon. The snowmobiler was buried about three feet deep, about 10 feet from where his snowmobile was found.

AVALANCHE DATA

The avalanche was about 100 feet wide and ran about 300 vertical feet. The steepest slope angle was about 36 degrees. The slope has an east aspect and is at about 9,500 feet. Because of near-blizzard conditions, it was difficult to find the crown face. However, the slope was wind-loaded, and to investigators it looked as though the avalanche fractured on a weak layer of faceted grains buried near an ice crust. The area had received about one to two feet of new snow during the previous few days.

Persistent Slab avalanche

COMMENTS

This was yet another deadly accident involving snowmobilers high marking a steep leeward slope without avalanche rescue equipment.

SHADOW LAKE, EAST OF DARBY, MONTANA | January 3, 1998

19980103b

Four snowmobilers caught; one buried and killed

ACCIDENT SUMMARY

"Three or four"[2] snowmobilers were caught in an avalanche near Shadow Lake, in the Sapphire Range east of Darby. "All but one of the snowmobilers managed to dig themselves out." Martin Vincent Litvin (53) was fully buried.

More than one person on a slope

RESCUE SUMMARY

The surviving party members and another group searched for Litvin. He was found after "four or five hours of searching."

COMMENTS

The lack of information available on this accident precludes comment.

19980103c

RIDDELL LAKES, SOUTH OF GRAY WOLF PEAK, MONTANA

January 3, 1998

One climber caught, buried, and killed

ACCIDENT SUMMARY

A party of two climbers, Chuck and Rod, left Missoula at noon on Friday, January 2. Their goal was to do a winter climb of Gray Wolf Peak (9,001 feet) on Saturday. Gray Wolf is a prominent peak near the southern end of the Mission Range. It lies north of Missoula and east of Arlee.

Friday afternoon, the pair snowshoed from the Twin Lakes / Riddell Lakes trailhead about four miles to tree line, where they camped for the night. They followed the Riddell Lakes Trail, but found it hard going, with brush and the shallow snowpack slowing them down. On Saturday morning, they left camp. After about a quarter mile of hiking, their route crossed an open, wind-loaded slope. They decided to rope up to cross it.

Rod broke trail while Chuck provided a standing hip belay from behind a large rock. Rod was about 80 feet across the slope when Chuck called that he was at "half rope." Rod called back "OK" because he was more than halfway to a couple of small trees from which he planned to belay Chuck.

Shortly after their shouted exchange, Chuck heard a whumpf and an avalanche released. Chuck pulled in some rope before it became tight, and then he gave rope slowly in an attempt to hold the belay. He held tighter as he neared the end of the rope. The rope cut on the rock as it came under tension.

RESCUE SUMMARY

Inadequate rescue equipment

The belay rock blocked Chuck's view of the avalanche. He hurried down the bed surface. He found the end of the climbing rope and followed it down, pulling as he went. He reached a point where he could no longer pull the rope and began to dig. "In his hurry, he did not check the length of rope remaining."

Chuck dug for about two hours along the buried rope. He excavated a trench about 10 feet long and eight feet deep. He then snowshoed out and drove to call for help. He reported the avalanche to Lake Country authorities at 15:00.

Because of the weather and late hour, the organized search began the following morning. It involved over two dozen people from numerous organizations, including: the Lake Country Sheriff, Lake Country Search and Rescue, Western Montana Mountain Rescue, Salish Kootenai Tribal Search and Rescue, and three of Rod's friends. Although the group met early, valley fog delayed their airlift for three hours.

Upon reaching the scene, the rescuers measured the rope from the mid-point mark and determined that another 10 feet remained to Rod. Rescuers spot probed, but only had short probes and did not get a strike. They began digging along the rope and reached Rod around 13:30, about 28 hours after the avalanche. He was buried about 12 feet deep, lying head downhill on his right side in a fetal position. Rescuers did not find an ice mask or evidence of melting around his mouth or nose. Investigators concluded that Rod died quickly from asphyxiation, though no autopsy was performed.

COMMENTS

Deeply-buried victims rarely survive unless they have an air pocket. Twelve feet is a particularly deep burial. It is unlikely Rod would have survived a burial of that depth even if the pair had been carrying avalanche transceivers. Pinpointing deep burials quickly and accurately requires extensive practice with a transceiver. Moving enough snow to uncover a victim buried that deep takes a long time, even for multiple rescuers. Chuck excavated an impressive amount of snow for a single rescuer but still had a long ways to go before he would have reached Rod.

The accident demonstrates why relying on a roped belay for avalanche safety is problematic. The pair recognized the slope as dangerous because it was wind-loaded but chose to cross it anyway. Perhaps the roped belay provided a false sense of security, with the climbers reasoning that a roped belay prevent them from being swept away in the debris if they triggered a slide. While it's not clear that would have been the case, the idea certainly proved an illusion once the rope cut.

ROCK CREEK, SOUTHWEST OF PRAY, MONTANA

19980111a

January 11, 1998

One snowmobiler buried

ACCIDENT SUMMARY

A group of seven snowmobilers were riding in the Rock Creek drainage of the Gallatin Range about 35 miles southwest of Livingston and about 25 miles southwest of Pray. Kemp O'Neill (37) and several other riders wore avalanche transceivers. O'Neill was the only one in the group equipped with shovel and probe, though he had them attached to his sled rather than in a pack on his back.

Inadequate rescue equipment

O'Neill and several of his friends got stuck on low angle slopes at the bottom of a bowl. O'Neill left his snowmobile—the one with the shovel and probe on board—and tried to free a friend's sled. One friend yelled, and O'Neill remembers that he "looked over my shoulder, and I got buried by a 10- to 12-foot wall of snow. I never knew something so white could be so black."[3]

"I tried with all I was worth to get my arms to help me," O'Neill said. "My arms wouldn't work. The snow slammed me to the ground."

RESCUE SUMMARY

The avalanche swept O'Neill about 450 feet down the slope. He was fully buried, lying on his back. "I did a lot of thinking down there," he said. "I was thinking about my wife and kids and things I meant to do. I was making peace with myself." He lost consciousness at some point in the burial.

One of O'Neill's friends, David Lanzendorf, had practiced using his transceiver the day before. Lanzendorf found O'Neill's general location with the transceiver, then used O'Neill's probe and shovel to complete the rescue in about 10 minutes. O'Neill was buried about 2.5 feet deep.

AVALANCHE DATA

The group described the avalanche as 900 feet wide and about 800 vertical feet.

COMMENTS

"Red flag" indications of danger

The group had been riding in the Rock Creek area for "nearly 20 years" and had never seen avalanches on that slope. On the day of the avalanche, the group observed, and ignored, signs of instability. "'It was snowing real heavy,' O'Neill said. [And]One snowmobiler had felt the snow "settle under him" in a large collapse. "You know better, but you choose not to pay attention" O'Neill said.

The party had only one probe and shovel, attached to a snowmobile. Fortunately, the snowmobile was not caught and buried.

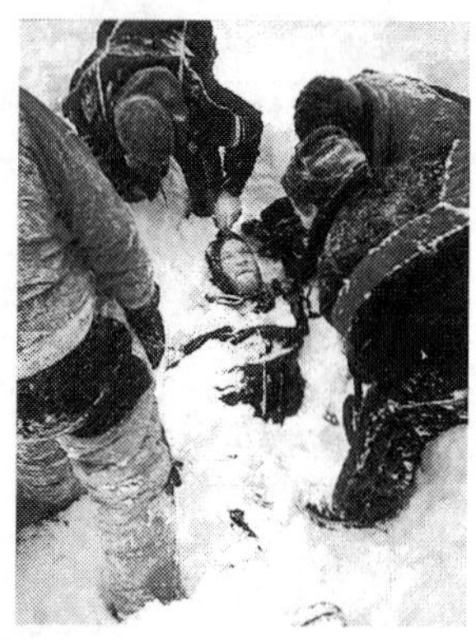

Kemp O'Neil is dug out of an avalanche by snowmobiling companions after being buried under snow for 10 to 12 minutes. *Photo Grant Asay, courtesy Bozeman Daily Chronicle.*

19980111b

BATTLE LAKE, WEST OF ENCAMPMENT, WYOMING

January 11, 1998

One snowmobiler caught, buried, and killed

ACCIDENT SUMMARY

No rescue equipment

Benjamin Frank Romios (21) was snowmobiling with four others near Battle Lake, in the Sierra Madre Range in southern Wyoming. The area is about 12 miles west-southwest of the town of Encampment. Around 14:00, Romios got his snowmobile stuck on a steep slope. An avalanche released and swept Romios up.

RESCUE SUMMARY

One member of the party left to seek help. The other three "began digging" to find their friend. Sheriff's deputies, search and rescue teams from Encampment and Saratoga, and more than 30 other volunteers arrived at the avalanche site and began probing for Romios.

Romios was found around 17:20. He had been buried under about two feet of snow for over three hours. Rescuers began CPR and rushed Romios to a medical center. He was pronounced dead a "short time later."

COMMENTS

A prompt and efficient companion rescue may have saved Romios, because he was not buried deeply. That might have happened, had Romios and his partners been carrying avalanche rescue gear that they had practiced using.

STRAIGHT FORK, EAST OF MOUNT PLEASANT, UTAH

19980117a

January 17, 1998

One snowmobiler buried and killed

WEATHER AND SNOWPACK CONDITIONS

Mid-January 1998 was very stormy in Utah. Storms began on January 9, with a rapid rise in avalanche danger and numerous avalanche accidents in northern Utah.

ACCIDENT SUMMARY

Skyline Drive is a high-elevation road that runs near the crest of the Wasatch Plateau in central Utah. The bowls and basins on either side of the are popular with snowmobilers. On January 17, Cody Dyches (23) was snowmobiling with friends in the upper end of Straight Fork, east of Mount Pleasant. Someone in the group triggered an avalanche around 17:00. Dyches was caught and buried.

RESCUE SUMMARY

Dyches' friends were unable to locate him. Search and Rescue teams brought in avalanche search dogs. The dogs alerted on Dyches' location, and searchers excavated his body around 21:30. He had been buried under about five feet of avalanche debris.

No rescue equipment

COMMENTS

January 17 and 18 were a deadly two days in the western U. S. Seven snowmobilers were killed in five accidents. All five accidents involved parties that could not conduct timely companion rescues because the victims were not wearing avalanche transceivers and the party was not carrying avalanche rescue gear. In some cases, the victims were buried deeply and may not have survived even if they'd been excavated quickly. Nonetheless, the similarities among the accidents are disturbing. Two days. Five accidents. Seven people killed. No avalanche transceivers.

UINTA MOUNTAINS, NEAR COALVILLE, UTAH | January 17, 1998

19980117b

One snowmobiler buried and killed

WEATHER AND SNOWPACK CONDITIONS

Mid-January 1998 was very stormy in Utah. Storms began on January 9, with a rapid rise in avalanche danger and numerous avalanche accidents in northern Utah.

ACCIDENT AND RESCUE SUMMARY

Damon Vernon (21) was snowmobiling with group friends in the western Uinta Mountains, near Coalville. An avalanche caught and buried Vernon around 15:00. Four friends located Vernon and dug him out, but he could not be revived.

No rescue equipment

COMMENTS

The lack of information available on this accident precludes comment.

19980118a SCOTCH BONNET MOUNTAIN, NORTH OF COOKE CITY, MONTANA | January 18, 1998

Three snowmobilers buried and killed; one partially buried and self-rescued

WEATHER AND SNOWPACK CONDITIONS

The Gallatin National Forest Avalanche Center described Sunday, January 18 as "a nice, sunny day with an unstable snowpack." Several feet of snow had fallen in a series of storms over the previous five days.

ACCIDENT SUMMARY

More than one person on a slope

Scotch Bonnet Mountain in the Beartooth Range is less than four miles north of Cooke City. On the day of the accident, a group of snowmobilers were highmarking on "fairly" steep slopes. One rider got stuck on the lower part of the slope. He and two friends were working to get his sled out when they triggered a large avalanche. The slide pulled out in two different places. Debris piled deeply at the bottom of the slope, totally burying three riders and partially burying another.

RESCUE SUMMARY

Inadequate rescue equipment

The partially buried snowmobiler eventually freed himself from the debris and rode to Cooke City for help. One of the buried riders was wearing an avalanche beacon; the first responders from Cooke City Search and Rescue quickly recovered him. He had been buried for 30 to 60 minutes and did not respond to resuscitation. Searchers eventually found the other two snowmobilers by probing. All three riders had been buried five to eight feet deep.

AVALANCHE DATA

The two parts of the avalanche were 75 and 300 feet wide. Their crowns were between two and five feet deep. The avalanche failed and slid on an ice crust near the ground.

COMMENTS

Scotch Bonnet Mountain and the adjacent Lulu Pass have one of the highest concentrations of fatal avalanche accidents in the United States. Nearly all of these involve snowmachiners, many involve multiple riders on a slope, and in all too many cases, the riders were not carrying avalanche rescue gear.

19980118b SAGE PEAK, NORTH OF HEBGEN LAKE, MONTANA

January 18, 1998

One snowmobiler buried and killed

WEATHER AND SNOWPACK CONDITIONS

January 18 was a sunny day with dangerous avalanche conditions in Montana, as noted in 19980118a. Sage Peak is also in the forecast area for the Gallatin National Forest Avalanche Center.

ACCIDENT SUMMARY
Michael Northey (24) was snowmobiling with friends near Sage Peak in the southern Madison Range. Northey was riding through a gully when the avalanche caught him. One of his friends "saw the avalanche coming and took refuge behind a tree."

RESCUE SUMMARY
Northey and his friends did not have avalanche rescue gear. His friends began to search, but had no way of finding him.

No rescue equipment

Another group of snowmobilers riding in the area witnessed the avalanche. The second group was carrying avalanche rescue gear. Because Northey wasn't wearing an avalanche transceiver, the riders in the second group used their avalanche probes to probe the debris. About 15 minutes after the avalanche, they located Northey's snowmobile. It took another half hour of probing to find Northey's body. He had was buried under about five feet of debris for 45 minutes. He did not respond to CPR.

AVALANCHE DATA
Witnesses estimated the avalanche crown as 4000 feet wide.

COMMENTS
It is common for witnesses, even very experienced avalanche professionals, to overestimate the size of avalanches. A crown 4000 feet wide would be uncommonly wide. However, the gully where avalanche caught Northey was a classic terrain trap, in which even small avalanches could have disastrous consequences.

The second group of riders conducted an efficient rescue, especially given the resources and limitations they had. Unfortunately, probing is a slow search process. By the time they had located and excavated Northey, it was too late. As the spate of fatal avalanche accidents on January 17 and 18 illustrates, not wearing an avalanche transceiver makes surviving an avalanche burial very unlikely.

LION ROCK, SOUTH OF BLEWETT PASS, WASHINGTON

19980118c

January 18, 1998

One snowmobiler buried and killed

WEATHER AND SNOWPACK CONDITIONS
The snowpack depth near the avalanche ranged from about two inches to over six feet deep in wind-drifted areas. Snow profiles near the avalanche site showed a layer of faceted snow 12 to 24 inches thick at the bottom of the snowpack. The faceted crystals were up to four to five mm in size. During the 10 days prior to the accident, winds drifted two to four feet of snow over the faceted layer, with several distinct layers within the wind slab.

Skies were overcast and it was snowing lightly at the time of the accident.

ACCIDENT SUMMARY
A snowmobiler was riding near Lion Rock, about six miles south of Blewett Pass in the central Washington Cascades. He was highmarking on a steep, 30- to 35-degree, east-facing slope at about 6,000 feet in elevation. His machine got stuck at the top of

his high mark. While trying to pull his machine around, the slope about 100 feet above him fractured to the ground. The avalanche carried the rider about 500 vertical feet and buried him in the debris.

RESCUE SUMMARY

Inadequate rescue equipment

The victim was not wearing a transceiver, and snowmobilers who responded to the accident did not have probes or shovels. They used trail marker wands to probe for the victim but failed to locate him.

Rescuers arrived at the scene the following morning. They conducted avalanche mitigation on adjacent slopes to protect rescuers. Avalanche mitigation to protect rescuers produced "climax avalanches to the ground...with every shot."

Rescuers found the snowmobiler's body that afternoon by coarse probing. The victim was buried under about three feet of debris. He was located about 60 feet below and 20 feet across the slope from his machine.

AVALANCHE DATA

Persistent Slab avalanche

The avalanche was soft, probably triggered by the snowmobiler, large relative to the avalanche path, and broke in depth hoar near the ground (SS-AMu-R3-O). It was 200 feet wide and two to four deep. It ran about 500 vertical feet.

COMMENTS

High avalanche danger

The Northwest Avalanche Center had issued avalanche warnings with High avalanche danger at all elevations for the day of the accident. It is unknown if the victim knew of the Center's warnings or the danger ratings. Investigators did not know if the victim had any formal avalanche training or if he or any of his companions observed any signs of instability or recognized their importance. It's likely there were many of these signs, given the instability indicated by the very large avalanches produced by avalanche mitigation.

19980121 SAN BERNARDO MOUNTAIN, WEST OF OPHIR, COLORADO

January 21, 1998

One backcountry tourer caught, buried, and killed

ACCIDENT SUMMARY

On January 21, a pair of backcountry riders headed to San Bernadro Mountain, which rises above Colorado Highway 145 west of the town of Ophir, in southwestern Colorado. Friends had skied the "main chute" on San Bernardo earlier that day, and their report "precipitated" the pair's plans. The pair borrowed transceivers and snowshoes. They had practiced with transceivers before but did not have formal avalanche training. They heard the avalanche report on the local radio station that morning.

The pair left the highway around 13:00. With a dog, they snowshoed three hours up the south side of the mountain to the summit.

The pair began their descent down the east face of San Bernardo Mountain. One rider was on skis; the other, a 25-year-old male, was on a snowboard. Their friends had skied the main chute that morning, so the pair opted for a route to the south/skier's right that seemed less exposed. They descended about 1,000 vertical feet through trees.

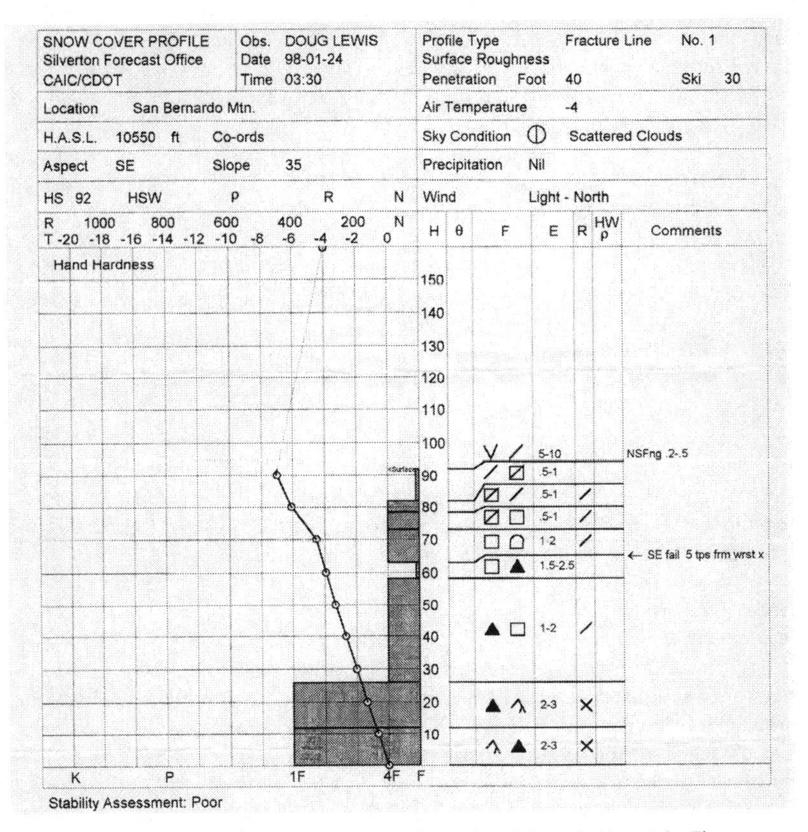

A fracture line profile of the January 21 avalanche on San Bernardo Mountain. The avalanche broke on the layer of weak snow about two feet from the ground (58 cm). *Courtesy Colorado Avalanche Information Center.*

The skier had a difficult time. He kept breaking through the upper layers of the snow pack into faceted snow near the ground, frequently falling or getting stuck.

Traveling alone

At around 11,800 feet in elevation, the pair reached the top of a chute through the trees. The snowboarder was in the lead and descended first. The skier followed but fell several times and was nervous about how much snow was around, so he exited the chute and took a break in the trees to regroup. When he was ready to ski again, the skier went back out into the chute and saw that an avalanche had happened.

RESCUE SUMMARY

The skier saw tracks out of the avalanche debris. Figuring they belonged to the snowboarder, the skier followed them down. Farther down the slope, the skier caught up to the dog and realized the snowboarder was not in the lead. The skier put his snowshoes back on and climbed back to the avalanche debris.

Terrain trap

The skier used his transceiver to locate his friend. He dug down about three feet to the snowboarder's head and shoulders, which he reached more than 45 minutes after the avalanche. The snowboarder had no pulse, was not breathing, and his lips were blue. The skier took the dog and left the scene to report the accident.

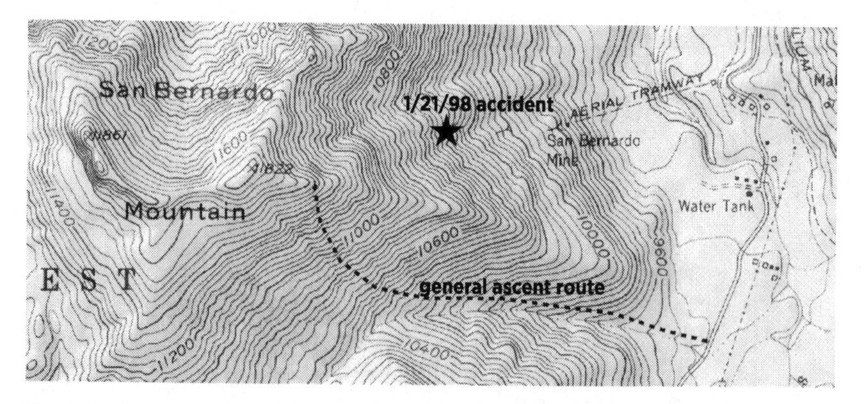

The dotted line marks the pair's general ascent route. They descended to the east, and the approximate location of the avalanche is marked with a star.

San Miguel Search and Rescue was notified after dark. They met with the skier, determined the snowboarder's location, and made plans to recover the body the following day. Telluride Helitrax assisted with the body recovery.

AVALANCHE DATA

Persistent Slab avalanche

The avalanche was a soft slab, triggered by the snowboarder, very small relative to the path, and broke in old snow (SS-ADu-R1-O). The crown was about one foot deep, and the weak layer was buried surface hoar on top of faceted snow. The avalanche started below treeline on an east-facing slope that was about 35 degrees in steepness. The avalanche ran only about 100 vertical feet, but partway down, it went over a break in slope. The snowpack had pulled out to the ground on the extremely steep, 60- to 70-degree slope. At the bottom, the avalanche debris piled deeply into an old mine prospect. The snowboarder was deeply buried in the prospect, despite the small size of the avalanche.

COMMENTS

This accident is a tragic example of the consequences of a small avalanche above a terrain trap. In this case, the debris from a small avalanche piled up into the mine prospect, burying the snowboarder more than six feet deep.

The pair separated during their descent. In many of these reports, the victims separated from their party and were traveling alone. Because of that, the skier did not realize that his friend was caught in the avalanche until he found the dog alone. By the time the skier climbed back to the avalanche, it was too late. Had they been practicing standard travel protocols, the skier would have witnessed the avalanche and could have rescued the snowboarder rapidly.

They also ignored some clues about potential snowpack instability. They ascended the more stable, south-facing terrain. Snow conditions deteriorated as the pair descended. They skier was breaking through into the faceted snow, which, although frustrating, allowed multiple opportunities to observe that there was more cohesive snow over weaker snow—"two key ingredients for slab avalanches." Had they made that conclusion, they could have avoided the avalanche terrain in the chute.

Investigators noted that "little mistakes," like traveling separate from your party or taking different routes, can have major consequences. Had the pair stayed together, the skier may have been able to conduct a swift, and successful, avalanche rescue.

INSPIRATION PASS, SOUTHEAST OF BIGFORK, MONTANA

19980124

January 24, 1998

One snowmobiler caught, buried, and killed

WEATHER AND SNOWPACK CONDITIONS

Northwestern Montana had below-normal snowfall in winter of 1997-98. Freezing rain events in late December added ice layers to the shallow snowpack. Surface hoar and faceted snow developed above the ice.

Significant snowfall began the week prior to the avalanche. The Noisy Basin SNOTEL, about 27 miles northwest of the accident scene, recorded over three inches of snow-water equivalent that week. Strong west and southwest winds drifted the snow.

ACCIDENT SUMMARY

On the afternoon of Saturday, January 24, 1998, two snowmobilers were riding in the Swan Mountain Range, southeast of Bigfork, Montana. They rode up Soup Creek from the west, and reached the crest of the range (about 7,000 feet elevation). One rider, a 21-year-old male from Columbia Falls, Montana, dropped into a southeast-facing bowl less than a mile north of Inspiration Pass. There, he triggered a large avalanche.

RESCUE SUMMARY

Lack of training

Both snowmobilers were wearing avalanche transceivers using the 457 kHz frequency. The second rider was "unfamiliar and untrained in how to use" his transceiver.

A second group of snowmobilers witnessed the avalanche and joined the search. One rider in this group also had an avalanche transceiver, but it was on the 2.275 kHz frequency that was the North American standard until the mid 1990s. That searcher borrowed the second rider's transceiver and was able to pinpoint the buried snowmobiler.

The searchers recovered the snowmobiler about 60 minutes after the avalanche. He was buried under about five feet of avalanche debris. He was "lifeless" when they reached him. The avalanche had carried him through a group of trees; his helmet was missing and his face was lacerated.

Shortly after they joined the rescue, one of the second party called 911. The ridge crest separates two counties, and both counties began to mobilize search and rescue efforts. Once the snowmobiler was found, SAR stood down and recovered the body the following day.

AVALANCHE DATA

Persistent Slab avalanche

The avalanche was triggered by the snowmobiler on a southeast-facing slope that was about 35 degrees in steepness. The avalanche was one to five feet deep and about 1,200 feet wide. The crown was "irregular in shape, running sometimes along the ridge, then down to tree outcrops, around a rock face, then back up toward the ridge." The avalanche ran about 600 feet into trees. The debris field was large and covered in "often blocky" chunks. The slab was composed of recently drifted snow. The weak layer was buried surface hoar and faceted snow, with "much denser" snow in the bed surface.

An investigator crosses part of the bed surface of the January 24, 1998, fatal avalanche near Inspiration Pass. *Photo Blase Reardon.*

COMMENTS

A deep burial and possible trauma may have lead to a tragic outcome in this accident, no matter how prompt and effective the companion rescue. However, the difficulties during the transceiver search illustrate the axiom that "the best transceiver is the one your companion knows how to use." The victim's partner learned he needed that knowledge at the worst possible moment, when his friend was already buried. Fortunately, the second party included at least one rider who knew how to conduct a transceiver search, even with an unfamiliar beacon.

A note on avalanche transceiver frequencies: The original frequency for avalanche transceivers was 2.275 kHz. In 1986, the International Commission for Alpine Rescue adopted a standard frequency of 457 kHz for avalanche transceivers. For the next decade, some manufacturers sold dual-frequency transceivers that transmitted and received on both frequencies. After the mid-1990s, the only transceivers for sale were single-frequency, transmitting on the 457 kHz standard.

Another fatal avalanche occurred in similar terrain two miles north on Gildart Peak two winters later (20000322).

BIG MOUNTAIN, NORTH OF WHITEFISH, MONTANA

19980129

January 29, 1998

One sidecountry rider caught, partially buried

ACCIDENT SUMMARY

A group of five alpine skiers exited what was then known as Big Mountain Ski Resort (Now Whitefish Mountain Resort), just north of Whitefish. They planned to ski "FAA Peak" to the northwest, and their route included descending steep chutes back into the ski area. Just before 13:00, the first skier, a 29-year-old male, descended and was "cutting across the slope…and slammed his edges into the snowpack 'to see if it might slide' and IT DID!"

The skier yelled "Slide!" and was able to stay upright as "things went down the elevator shaft." He was close to out-skiing the avalanche when he hit the groomed ski run and fell face down. Up to four feet of avalanche debris piled on top of him. He was partially buried-critical, with only his right forearm exposed.

Terrain trap

His companions thought the skier "had just skied down." Three of the five descended other chutes, triggering several more small avalanches. They skied out of the slides and continued to the bottom of a ski lift, where they reported avalanches "dumping a bunch of snow on the cat track but nothing else."

RESCUE SUMMARY

The final skier counted heads and realized one of the party was missing. He searched the debris across the ski run and saw the first skier's arm sticking out of the debris. The final skier used his ski and hands to excavate the first. The first skier's head was uncovered about five minutes after the avalanche, and it was another 15 minutes before he was completely free.

Ski patrollers arrived at the site as the first skier was freed. They cleared the site and checked the skiers over.

AVALANCHE DATA

This was a hard slab, triggered by a skier, small relative to the path, and broke at the interface with old snow (HS-ASu-R2-I). The crown was six to 15 inches deep and about 45 feet wide. The avalanche ran only 75 vertical feet. The slab was composed of snow drifted onto a layer of surface hoar. The slab had formed within the eight hours prior to the accident. The snow drifting was highly localized to slopes near a saddle that funneled upslope winds across the chutes. While conducting a crown profile, investigators estimated drifted snow accumulating at six to eight inches an hour.

Wind Slab avalanche

COMMENTS

This accident again illustrates the consequences that even small avalanches can pose. The groomed ski run at the base of the slope acted as a terrain trap and allowed the limited avalanche debris to pile up deeply enough to bury the skier. It also demonstrates the importance of several tenants of safe travel in avalanche terrain: ride one at a time, keep your partner in sight, and choose your companions wisely. None of the victim's companions saw him get caught in the slide. Three of them continued down to the chairlift unaware he was buried, despite seeing the debris pile. The last skier's presence of mind to check the small debris pile likely saved the victim's life.

19980211 MOUNT JUDAH, EAST OF SUGAR BOWL RESORT, CALIFORNIA | February 11, 1998

One backcountry tourer caught, buried, and killed

ACCIDENT SUMMARY

The summit of Mount Judah lies less than a mile and a half from Donner Pass in California's Sierra Mountains. Its western slopes are part of Sugar Bowl Resort, while its steep east face lies outside the resort boundary. Riders can reach the summit by hiking roughly 20 minutes from the resort's chairlifts.

Cornice fall

On February 11, a backcountry tourer walked out onto a cornice near the summit of Mount Judah. The cornice broke, and the tourer fell with the blocks onto the slope below. The cornice fall triggered a slab avalanche about two feet deep and 100 feet wide. The tourer was carried about 300 vertical feet and buried six feet deep.

RESCUE SUMMARY

Ski patrollers from Sugar Bowl Ski Resort responded to the accident with avalanche dogs. Two dogs alerted on the skier, who had been buried for over an hour. He had a pulse when uncovered but died from trauma sustained in the avalanche.

COMMENTS

Cornices can break surprisingly far back. While not as common as slab avalanches, cornice falls have resulted in a number of avalanche fatalities. See 19990411a for another example, and see 20020308 for another fatal cornice collapse on Mount Judah.

19980222 MORMON HILL, NORTH OF CAREY, IDAHO | February 22, 1998

Three snowmobilers caught; one buried and killed

WEATHER AND SNOWPACK CONDITIONS

A storm ended Saturday, February 21. It had dropped about a foot of snow with one inch of snow-water equivalent. The majority had fallen within 30 hours—a rapid rate of loading. Winds had been strong during the storm, drifting significant amounts of snow. The winds had eased at the end of the storm. Sunday, February 22 was a "perfect day… sunny and clear… Saturday's storm had broken and the tail end of the storm had deposited a beautiful layer of light fluffy powder snow."

ACCIDENT SUMMARY

Mormon Hill is a popular snowmobiling area in the southern end of the Pioneer Mountains, north of the town of Carey. On February 22, a group of snowmobilers was riding in the area. They highmarked a pair of northerly-facing, open bowls split by a lower-angled, treed sub-ridge.

More than one person on a slope

Ron Berry (42) got his sled stuck on the slope above the treed sub-ridge sometime between 15:00 and 16:00. He was off his sled and working to free it. Craig Hanson rode up to help Berry. Hanson had almost reached Berry when the slope avalanched. Hanson turned downhill. He had almost escaped the avalanche when it knocked him from

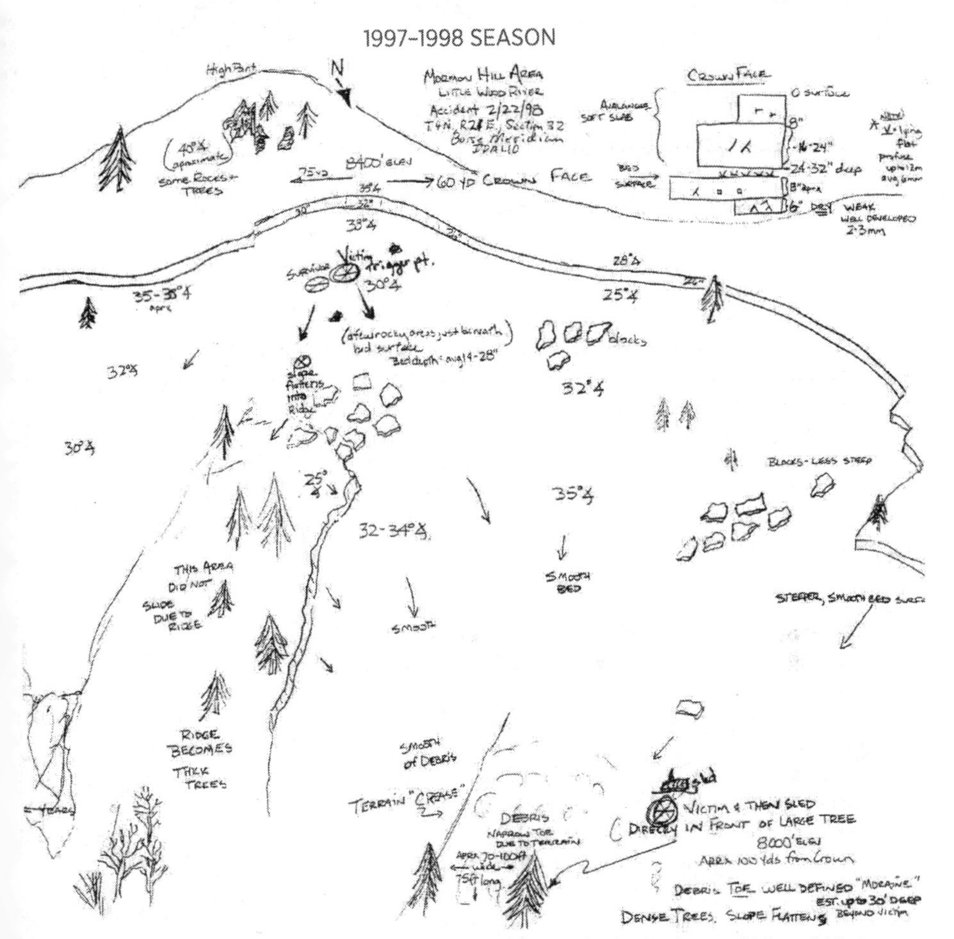

Part of a detailed diagram of the accident site from the original report, Janet Kellam, SAC.

his sled. He came to a stop, partially buried high upslope in the debris. The avalanche carried Berry down into the more westerly bowl, out of sight of the rest of the group.

A third party member was just beginning to climb when the avalanche released. He was able to turn downhill and ride to several other group members.

Lita Hanson was riding in the eastern bowl. Apparently, she was caught and tumbled along the edge of the avalanche. She was able to get back on her snowmachine, ride down, and alert other members of the group. She then continued out to alert authorities.

RESCUE SUMMARY

Terrain trap

The avalanche debris flowed into a gully at the bottom of the bowl. The gully abruptly flattened as it ran into a dense group of conifers. The debris piled deeply in the gully, with estimates of up to 30 feet of debris near the toe.

The group found Berry near the upper end of the debris, where it first entered the trees. Some, but maybe not all, of the group had avalanche transceivers and shovels. No one in the group had probes. The group dug in the area of the strongest transceiver signal. They discovered the sled first, and Berry shortly after. He had been buried in a vertical position just uphill of his sled. The party said he was four to six feet deep, and showed "no signs of life." It took them 20 to 60 minutes to find and excavate Berry.

Lita Hanson called to report the avalanche shortly after 16:00. A helicopter from Sun Valley Heli Ski transported rescuers and an avalanche dog to the site. By the time the helicopter arrived at the accident site, the snowmobilers had excavated Berry and placed him on sled, presuming him dead. The Sun Valley Heli Ski team began CPR. A medical helicopter arrived, and transported Berry to a nearby hospital.

AVALANCHE DATA

Persistent Slab avalanche

Both bowls released as slab avalanches. The slide in the western bowl, where Berry was caught, was two to three feet deep and about 120 feet wide. It broke in a well-defined layer of surface hoar, with grains up to 12 mm in size. Under the surface hoar, the bed surface was one-finger-hard old snow. The debris pile in the gully was about 70 feet wide and 75 feet long.

Most slopes that avalanched had slope angles between 30 and 35 degrees. Berry was stuck below a short section of steeper, 38-degree terrain. On the edges of the bowls, the fracture propagated onto lower-angled slopes, but the slabs did not slide far on 25-degree terrain.

COMMENTS

The group made several all-too-common errors but also made several choices that minimized the consequences of the accident. They had multiple riders on the slope simultaneously. This meant several riders were caught in the avalanche, though all but Berry were able to escape. The group responded quickly, conducting a prompt companion rescue and quickly alerting authorities to request help.

Perhaps one significant factor in the accident was the group's attitude towards avalanche danger. Investigators described the group as very skilled riders who knew the terrain well. "However, their avalanche evaluation skills did not match their riding ability… [The group was] pushing the limits by highmarking in recognizable and known avalanche terrain, the day after a significant storm and during a time of considerable avalanche hazard."

Earlier in the winter, the group had triggered and outrun several large avalanches. They began carrying transceivers and shovels after those encounters. Avalanche probes may have speeded the recovery of Berry.

19980301 RUSSELL FACE, WEST OF BERTHOUD PASS, COLORADO

March 1, 1998

Two backcountry tourers caught; one partially buried, one partially buried and killed

ACCIDENT SUMMARY

Daniel Kim (20) and Jude Fontenot (21) headed west from Berthoud Pass up a ridge that provides access to the Continental Divide. The ridge climbs steeply up the side of a southeast-facing slope known locally as the Russell Face, then reaches a broad plateau at the Divide. They hiked for several hours on snowshoes, carrying their snowboard (Kim) and skis (Fontenot). "It was euphoric," Fontenot said later. The pair stopped below the final steep climb to the ridge.

More than one person on a slope

They began their descent together on a southeast-facing slope locally known as the "Russell Face." Kim was in the lead. Three to four turns down, the slope fractured.

"When the avalanche hit me, I lost my equipment... But I was able to practice what I was told to do—kind of body-surf...and swim to stay on top of it," Fontenot said.

RESCUE SUMMARY

No rescue equipment

Fontenot was partially buried when the avalanche stopped. He briefly searched for Kim, then hiked down the "Pumphouse" drainage to the highway. At the highway, he flagged down a motorist, who reported the avalanche to the Berthoud Pass Ski Patrol.

Ski patrollers headed to the avalanche site. Much of Fontenot's equipment remained on the surface of the avalanche debris. Rescuers used these items to determine a likely path for the pair and began searching downhill. They saw one of Kim's hands above the snow.

They found Kim face-down, with his head downhill, buried about two feet deep. He had been buried for 90 to 120 minutes. Rescuers found no evidence of an air pocket around his head.

AVALANCHE DATA

Persistent Slab avalanche

The avalanche was a hard slab, accidentally triggered by the riders, medium-sized relative to the slope. It broke in old snow (HS-ASu-R3-O). It was probably initiated

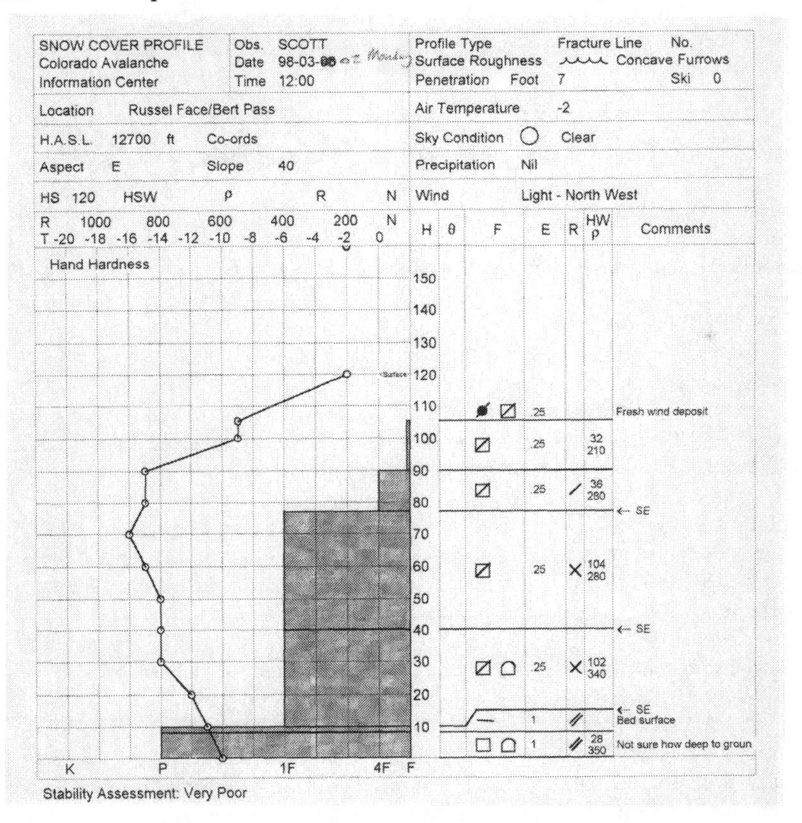

Fracture line profile from the March 1 avalanche. The avalanche broke along the top of the icy crust about four inches above the ground. *Courtesy Colorado Avalanche Information Center.*

in recent snow and then scoured through old faceted snow to the ground. The crown was three to four feet deep and 600 feet wide. The avalanche started above treeline at around 12,000 feet on a southeast aspect with a slope angle of 40 degrees. The avalanche ran 600 vertical feet.

Snow conditions the day of the accident were very unstable. The Colorado Avalanche Information Center had forecast Considerable danger with areas of High above treeline. Rescuers reported hollow, drum-like sounds in the wind-drifted snow. They also triggered a large avalanche on an adjacent slope that was only 31 degrees in steepness.

COMMENTS

One rider survived; the other did not. The survivor was able to shed his gear and actively work to stay near the surface of the moving debris. The victim was not able to release his snowboard and wound up buried partially-buried critical. The difference reinforces the importance of using releasable bindings and fighting to stay as high in the moving debris as possible. It also highlights the role luck can play in avalanche survival.

Sadly, a prompt companion rescue could have negated that difference. The surface clues led to Kim's hand above the snow. His shallow burial meant that it might not have taken long to uncover his face, even digging without a shovel. Fontenot, however, only searched briefly before going for outside help.

19980308 OPHIR GULCH, WEST OF ASPEN MOUNTAIN, COLORADO

March 8, 1998

One sidecountry rider caught, partially buried, and killed

ACCIDENT SUMMARY

Ophir Gulch is a steep drainage on the west side of Aspen Mountain. Two gullies join about halfway down to Castle Creek; the northernmost of the two is known locally as Peter Barker. The ski area boundary runs along the top of the drainage, and because the top of Peter Barker is open, it is a popular launch site for paragliders. Many riders exit the run after the top pitch, traversing north into Keno Gulch and then back into the ski area.

Kurt Olausson (43) had moved from Sweden to Colorado in the mid-1980s. He had lived in the Aspen area long enough to be considered a "local."

Traveling alone

Aspen Mountain Ski Resort scanned Olausson's ski pass around 10:30 on March 8. He probably exited the ski area into Ophir Gulch shortly after. Olausson's tracks traversed into the Peter Barker run and through a stand of aspen trees. His route cut under a steep, open clearing, and he probably triggered the avalanche from below.

RESCUE SUMMARY

No one reported Olausson overdue. Paraglider pilots first noticed the avalanche on March 8, but did not see Olausson's body until March 11. Members of the Aspen Mountain Ski Patrol reached the body that day. Olausson was found partially buried in a stand of aspen trees, and had signs of significant trauma. Unstable snow conditions prevented the body recovery until the morning of March 12.

AVALANCHE DATA

The avalanche was a soft slab, triggered by a skier, large relative to the slope, and broke in old snow near the ground (SS-ASu-R4-O/G). The crown was near 10,000 feet on a west aspect, about 400 feet below the ski area boundary. It broke across a small clearing and then uphill into a stand of aspen trees. The crown averaged three feet deep and 500 feet wide. The weak layer was faceted snow and depth hoar at the base of the snowpack. The avalanche ran 380 vertical feet through another stand of aspen trees.

Persistent Slab avalanche

COMMENTS

On March 8, the Colorado Avalanche Information Center rated the avalanche danger as Moderate.

The evidence of trauma suggests that Olausson may not have survived the avalanche even if he was rescued quickly. Traveling alone, there was no hope of rescue. There is little margin for error when alone, as many of these reports show.

Ophir Gulch has been the scene of several other serious avalanche accidents. The Peter Barker run is named for a ski patroller who was caught in a slide. On February 26, 2010, a skier fully was fully buried and seriously injured but survived, thanks to a quick companion rescue. On February 23, 2015, a fully buried skier was not so fortunate.

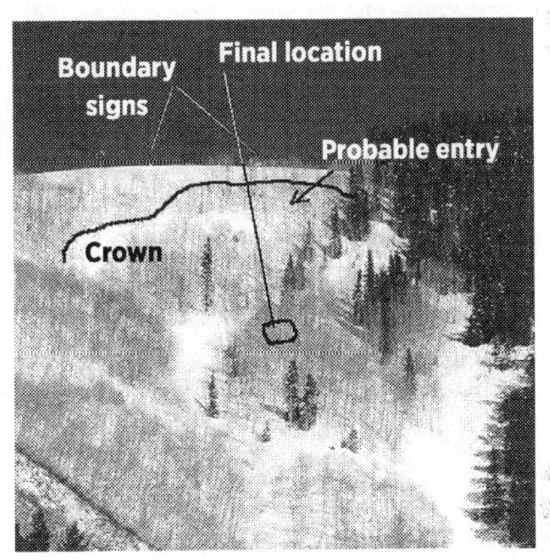

Ophir Gulch, the backside of Aspen Mountain, Colorado. The photographs were taken on March 12, 1998. *Photos Doug Driskell.*

SCOTCH BONNET MOUNTAIN, NORTH OF COOKE CITY, MONTANA | March 26, 1998

19980326

One snowmobiler caught and buried

WEATHER AND SNOWPACK CONDITIONS

The week preceding the avalanche was warm and sunny. During that period, a thick melt-freeze crust formed on most south and east aspects and at most elevations. On March 24 and 25, approximately six to 10 inches of new snow fell in the mountains around Cooke City, burying the melt-freeze crust. Light to moderate winds blew from the west.

More than one person on a slope

ACCIDENT SUMMARY

Scotch Bonnet Mountain and the adjacent Lulu Pass are popular snowmobiling areas in the Beartooth Mountains, less than four miles north of Cooke City. On March 26, riders in a group of 20 snowmobilers from Iowa were taking turns highmarking on the south shoulder of Scotch Bonnett. Mike Grevegoed got stuck. When a friend rode up the slope to assist him, the slope released. His friend was able to ride to safety, but the avalanche caught and buried Grevegoed.

Inadequate rescue equipment

RESCUE SUMMARY

The group began a rescue. No one in the group was wearing transceivers, and they had only two shovels and one probe amongst the 20 riders.

A ski from Grevegoed's snowmobile was sticking out of the snow. The group began probing there. On their first probe, they struck Grevegoed's foot, immediately downhill of the snowmobile. The group dug him out within about eight minutes. His helmet was packed full of snow and he was turning blue, but he was still conscious and breathing.

Storm Slab avalanche

AVALANCHE DATA

The avalanche crown was about two feet deep and 200 feet wide. The avalanche broke on a layer of graupel just above the melt-freeze crust. The avalanche started at an elevation of 10,400 feet on a southeast-facing slope that was 38 degrees in steepness. The average slope angle was approximately 34 degrees.

COMMENTS

This accident had a much more positive outcome than one that occurred in the same area earlier that winter, 19980l1a. And than many others that have happened in the area; Scotch Bonnet Mountain and Lulu Pass have one of the highest concentrations of fatal avalanche accidents in the United States. All too many of these – like both accidents during the 1998 winter – involve riders not carrying avalanche rescue gear and multiple riders on a slope simultaneously.

19980401 ST. MARYS GLACIER, NORTHWEST OF IDAHO SPRINGS, COLORADO | April 1, 1998

Two hikers caught; one partially buried, one partially buried and killed

ACCIDENT SUMMARY

St. Marys Glacier is a semi-permanent snowfield in the Fall River drainage of the Front Range, northwest of Idaho Springs. It is accessible year round, making it a popular day trip for residents in the Denver area. On April 1, Tamara Sylvia Cohen (38) and Roy Krumwiede hiked up the snowfield and along the top. At around 11:30, Cohen slipped and slid down the slope. She stood up and began to climb back up. She triggered the avalanche as she started back up the slope.

Krumwiede was some distance above and to the side. The avalanche broke above him and swept him down the slope. When the avalanche stopped, he freed himself from the debris quickly.

RESCUE SUMMARY

Krumwiede searched frantically. He shouted, and other hikers joined the search. After about 40 minutes, word reached the Clear Creek County Sheriff's Office and a search and rescue effort started. Rescuers found Cohen about two hours after the avalanche. One arm and leg were protruding from the snow, but her head was under about a foot of debris.

No rescue equipment

AVALANCHE DATA

The hard slab avalanche was unintentionally triggered by a hiker on foot, was medium-sized relative to the path, and slid in old snow (HS-AFu-R3-O). The crown was about two to four feet deep and almost 600 feet wide. It ran about 500 vertical feet. It started on an easterly aspect around 11,200 feet. There were "large blocks" of hard snow in the debris field.

Persistent Slab avalanche

COMMENTS

Several avalanche fatalities and numerous close calls attest to the fact that the St. Marys Glacier area is avalanche-prone backcountry terrain when snow covered. This pair was unprepared for that reality. Perhaps they did not recognize the danger because of the area's easy access. Cohen was not buried deeply, but without avalanche transceivers, it was difficult to search the large field of blocky debris quickly. If the pair had carried avalanche safety equipment, the search time could have been drastically reduced.

The Colorado Avalanche Information Center forecast was for Moderate danger near and above treeline.

RUSSELL FACE, WEST OF BERTHOUD PASS, COLORADO

19980419

April 19, 1998

Two snowshoers caught; one injured, one killed

WEATHER AND SNOWPACK CONDITIONS

The Berthoud Pass Ski Area recorded 28 inches of snowfall in the week prior to the avalanche. There were several periods of strong northwesterly winds that drifted snow. For the 20 hours prior to the accident, northwesterly winds averaged 20 mph.

ACCIDENT SUMMARY

A ridge running west from Berthoud Pass provides access to the Continental Divide. The ridge climbs steeply up the side of a southeast-facing slope known locally as the Russell Face, then reaches a broad plateau at the Divide. On April 19, Mark Hedgepath (20) and Sharon Churchwell (30) snowshoed west from the Berthoud Pass Ski Area. They reached the top of the chairlift and continued west along the ridge towards the Continental Divide.

The pair stopped for a break at the top of the Russell Face around 13:00. Hedgepath removed his snowshoes and stood them up vertically in the snow. A gust of wind blew them over the edge of the face. Hedgepath climbed down to retrieve them. A short distance below the edge, he triggered a small avalanche and was swept over a short cliff. He broke his collarbone.

Russell Face, Berthoud Pass, Colorado, April 19, 1998. *Photo Dale Atkins, Colorado Avalanche Information Center.*

Churchwell walked to the edge of the Russell Face to check on Hedgepath. They yelled back and forth, and Hedgepath warned her not to come down. Churchwell likely crept just over the edge to hear better when a second avalanche released.

The avalanche broke behind Churchwell. She was swept over cliffs and rocks but not buried in avalanche debris. She suffered serious injuries.

RESCUE SUMMARY

No rescue equipment

Hedgepath hiked down the Pumphouse drainage to the highway. He caught a ride with two doctors back to Berthoud Pass Ski Area and notified the ski patrol at 13:20.

Rescuers hiked up to Churchwell and reached her about 14:45. She was unconscious. She was flown by helicopter to a hospital, and listed in critical condition with serious head, neck, and pelvic injuries. She died in the hospital three days later.

AVALANCHE DATA

Wind Slab avalanche

This was a soft slab avalanche, triggered by the snowshoers, medium-sized relative to the path, and broke on the interface of recent and old snow (SS-AIu-R3-I). The slab was only about a foot deep, but was about 800 feet wide. The slab pulled back and released on low-angled slopes above the Russell Face.

COMMENTS

The combination of fresh snow and strong northwesterly winds created unstable conditions. The pair's planned route skirted dangerous avalanche terrain. The mishap of the wind-blown snowshoes inadvertently took them onto the Russell Face, which is very steep, with numerous cliffs and rock outcrops. The shallow avalanche swept the pair through high-consequence terrain. The accident underscores the importance of terrain choices in dangerous conditions.

About six weeks earlier, a snowboarder died in a large avalanche on the same face (19980301). A similar accident involving a dropped ski occurred on the same slope on January 29, 2017. Fortunately, the skier was uninjured.

THOMPSON PASS, EAST OF VALDEZ, ALASKA | April 20, 1998

19980420

Two heli-skiers caught; one injured, one killed

ACCIDENT SUMMARY

Thompson Pass, east of Valdez in the Chugach Mountains of southcentral Alaska, is a world-renowned skiing destination. Helicopters provide easy access to areas many steep faces, including a peak known locally as Cracked Ice. On April 20, Ian Gini (27) and Ken Hudson (33) were skiing with Alaska Backcountry Adventures. The two walked out onto a cornice near the top of Cracked Ice. The cornice broke. They fell about 200 feet down the slope below.

Cornice fall

RESCUE SUMMARY

Alaska Backcountry Adventures helicopters flew both victims to the hospital. Hudson suffered cuts and bruises. Gini was pronounced dead on arrival.

COMMENTS

Cornices can break surprisingly far back from the edge, as illustrated by this accident, one earlier the same winter in California (19980211), and others described in this volume. The victims in these accidents often fall down very steep, rocky terrain and suffer serious trauma. Keep well back from cornices.

BROAD PASS, SOUTH OF DENALI NATIONAL PARK, ALASKA | April 26, 1998

19980426

One snowmobiler caught, buried, and killed

ACCIDENT SUMMARY

Mark Slimmen (34) was snowmobiling with two friends on the southern side of Denali National Park and Preserve in central Alaska. Slimmen was highmarking a slope near Broad Pass when he triggered the avalanche at around 14:00. He turned downhill and tried to outrun the avalanche. As he accelerated over the leading edge of the slab, his machine tumbled and threw Slimmen off. "He was able to swim at first but then was buried."[4]

RESCUE SUMMARY

No rescue equipment

Slimmen's two friends watched from a nearby knoll. They watched Slimmen for as long as possible, so they had a well-established point last seen point and likely area to search. They raced forward even as the avalanche was still moving. They did not have transceivers or shovels. They searched the surface for clues, called out, and dug in likely places with their helmet visors. Unable to find him, they eventually rode back to the highway and notified the Alaska State Troopers. Troopers and National Park Service rangers flew to the site around 18:00 but were unable to locate Slimmen during a brief search. Unstable snow, gusty winds, and lack of daylight prevented an extensive search.

The Alaska Mountain Rescue Group and Alaska Search Dogs assisted in the search on Sunday. The search dogs alerted on two spots in the most likely area. Probing found the machine first. Slimmen was found around 10:30, buried under seven feet of avalanche debris. He was buried in a prone position, across the slope, near the toe of the debris. It took rescuers over an hour to excavate the body.

AVALANCHE DATA

Persistent Slab avalanche

This was a hard slab avalanche, triggered by a snowmobiler, medium-sized relative to the path, and broke in old snow near the ground (HS-AMu-R3-O). The crown was about 1.5 feet deep and 500 feet wide. The weak layer was faceted snow near the ground. The avalanche ran about 350 vertical feet.

The avalanche started at around 6,300 feet in elevation on a southeasterly-facing slope. The slope angles in the starting zone measured between 37 and 39 degrees.

COMMENTS

It is unlikely Slimmen would have survived a burial of seven feet, even if he and his friends had been wearing transceivers and carrying shovels. Apart from that error, his friends' actions exemplify good high-marking practices and prompt companion rescue. They were parked in a spot safe from the avalanche. That prevented all three from being caught. They had a last seen point, which helped the rescuers establish a primary search area the following day. And they searched for him immediately, before going for help.

19980531 WEST CRATER RIM, MOUNT HOOD, OREGON | May 31, 1998

Five climbers caught; two partially buried and injured, one buried and killed

WEATHER AND SNOWPACK CONDITIONS

A spring storm ended on May 29. About two feet of recent and windblown snow accumulated at the elevation of the avalanche, around 10,700 feet. May 31, a Sunday, was the first clear day following the storm.

ACCIDENT SUMMARY

Mount Hood is visible from Portland, and late spring is prime climbing season. On the morning of May 31, a climbing class from the Mazamas climbing club was attempting the peak. The group was among "several hundred climbers"[5] who registered and hoped to summit that day by various routes.

High avalanche danger

In the climbers' register that morning was a hand-written sign, updated by the USFS climbing ranger several hours earlier. It read "HIGH AVALANCHE HAZARD!" Rangers had posted a similar sign only one other time in the previous seven years. The instructor and several members of the Mazamas group read the sign, and the group discussed it, though there was some confusion as to when the sign had been placed.

The Mazamas group chose the West Crater Rim route, to the west of the main route, in part to avoid all the other climbing parties. They moved slightly slower than anticipated, and another party from Hood River passed them. At around 10:00, the class had reached about 10,700 feet and was traversing a 25- to 30-degree ramp. The instructor was walking unroped behind the leader of the first rope team. The climbers were sinking into the snow about six to 12 inches with each step. A slab avalanche released a hundred or more feet above them, near 10,800 feet.

Climbers heard a "rumble" or "shotgun blast" and scrambled out of the way. The lead instructor, Ethan Van Matre, was swept up. He was able to stop before being swept far down the steep slope below. The debris carried the first rope team, with Matt Pennewell (28), Amy Horne (44), and Tom McGlinn (39), about 1200 vertical feet down the mountain. The climbing rope between McGlinn and his teammates broke during the avalanche.

All but one of the Hood River team was just past the right flank of the avalanche and escaped being caught. One member was carried about a hundred feet before a teammate arrested his fall. The Hood River team continued to the summit, unaware of their close call.

RESCUE SUMMARY

No rescue equipment

Van Matre was unburied and directed the remaining two teams to a safe area. Despite ankle and shoulder injuries, he descended the slide path and began searching. He found Pennewell buried to his waist and Horne buried nearly to her neck with her arms showing. Both were injured. Newspaper accounts said Horne suffered a broken pelvis and other injures, Pennewell a broken ankle. Both required hospitalization.

Other parties joined the rescue and search for McGlinn, with about 40 climbers and rangers participating. None of the climbers wore avalanche transceivers, so searchers used shovels, ski poles, and ice axes as improvised probes in the initial search. Organized search and rescue brought in rescue equipment.

A probe line found McGlinn about 75 minutes after the avalanche. He was buried under about five feet of avalanche debris. He had suffered "severe head trauma, perhaps caused by his ice ax."[6]

AVALANCHE DATA

Wind Slab avalanche

This avalanche occurred on a southeast-facing slope. It was a soft slab, triggered by climbers on foot, medium sized relative to the path, and broke at the interface between recent and old snow (SS-AFu-R3-I). The avalanche crown was about 900 feet wide. The slab was composed of about two feet of recent and windblown snow, though the crown reached five feet deep in places. It slid on a firm sun crust on the top of the old snow surface.

COMMENTS

It is not uncommon for climbers to forgo carrying avalanche transceivers or other safety equipment. In this case, transceivers may have helped locate McGlinn more rapidly. However, the head wounds he suffered may have been unsurvivable, regardless of the length of his burial.

The group may have minimized the avalanche danger, despite the warning they read at registration. Perhaps they mistakenly believed that slab avalanches don't happen on nice days or in the late spring. Or perhaps the presence of other people, including the party ahead of them, convinced them that conditions were not dangerous. However, none of those factors—time of year, presence of other people, or previous tracks on a slope—indicates conditions are safe.

The most significant factor in this accident was the group's decision to traverse on and below steep, recently-loaded slopes that had been receiving direct sun for at least four hours. The West Crater Rim was not an appropriate route for the conditions. At least one guidebook explicitly warns of the route's exposure to large avalanches after heavy snowfall, including in the spring. The group's slower-than-planned pace compounded the poor route choice by putting them on the most exposed slopes at the worst time. The group could have avoided the accident by choosing a different route

—even the more crowded normal route—or turning around once it became clear that were moving too slowly.

19980611

DISAPPOINTMENT CLEAVER, MOUNT RAINIER, WASHINGTON | June 11, 1998

10 climbers caught; seven injured, one killed

WEATHER AND SNOWPACK CONDITIONS

Lou Whittaker, co-owner of Rainer Mountaineering, Incorporated (RMI), stated that June 11 "was the first warm up for the whole year… We've had a real wet and cold spring up here."

ACCIDENT SUMMARY

Terrain trap

Disappointment Cleaver is one of the most popular routes to the summit of Mount Ranier. At about 14:00 on June 11, a guided group from RMI was descending from the summit. The guides and clients were traveling in two rope teams, clipped into the same fixed ropes. The fixed lines protect climbers as they traverse above significant exposure, with cliff bands and very steep, icy slopes dropping towards the glaciers below.

A small wet loose avalanche hit the upper rope team. As the team fell, two upper anchors on the fixed line failed. The second rope team had time to call "avalanche!" and take a few steps before they were hit. One anchor at the bottom of the fixed line held. When the avalanche stopped, "One guide and one client were caught on the fixed line above the cliff. Three clients and one guide clung to the top of the cliff, tangled in the rocks and ropes. Three clients dangled below them on a cliff of ice and snow, while the [fourth] client [Patrick Nestler (29)] hung below a second cliff band in a waterfall of snowmelt."

RESCUE SUMMARY

A climber at Ingraham Flats, below the steep part of the route, heard screams of distress from the climbing party. That climber called authorities. On the summit, off-duty climbing ranger Mike Gauthier heard the radio call and descended to the accident site. Helicopters flew other rescuers to Ingraham Flats.

Rescuers climbed to the fallen group. They established new anchors and began raising and treating members of the climbing party. Because of the exposure to rescuers, it took them several hours to rescue and evacuate the climbers. All the injured climbers were helicoptered off the mountain by dark.

Nestler, however, had "fallen substantially farther down the cliff than the others. The fastest evacuation was to lower him off the mountain rather than raise him back to the accident site." By the time rescuers began lowering Nestler, rescuers had not "heard from him in over an hour." Nestler succumbed to exposure during the rescue.

AVALANCHE DATA

Loose Wet avalanche

The avalanche began about 400 feet above the rope teams, and investigators estimated it was 38 feet wide and 6-10 inches deep when it hit the teams.

COMMENTS

The accident illustrates the consequence of small avalanches in very exposed terrain. Despite its narrow width and shallow depth, the avalanche was powerful. The rope teams were swept off their feet and sent tumbling down the mountain when the anchors for the fixed ropes failed.

The area where the avalanche released is not known for avalanche activity. Guides did not observe any other avalanches that day. Warm, sunny conditions in the afternoon probably contributed to the danger of natural wet loose avalanches. Investigators noted that "the rule of thumb used by most climbers is to be back down [below Disappointment Cleaver] by noon." Lou Whittaker, co-owner of RMI, said that guided groups "go up and down [Rainier] at any time of the day" and that timing was not a factor in this accident.

1998–1999
SEASON

19981107 MOUNT BALDY, SOUTH OF ALTA, UTAH | November 7, 1998

Five backcountry tourers caught; one seriously injured, one killed

WEATHER AND SNOWPACK CONDITIONS

The first significant winter storm occurred on November 5 and dropped about 17 inches of snow at the Alta Ski Area. November 7 was a sunny Saturday.

ACCIDENT SUMMARY

The boundary between Alta Ski Area and Snowbird Resort runs over Mount Baldy, 11,068 feet, in Little Cottonwood Canyon east of Salt Lake. On November 7, neither ski area was open for the season. A group of five snowboarders hiked up the peak. Shortly after 12:00, the group descended the "West Baldy" ski run one at a time.

In avalanche runout

The fifth snowboarder, Jeff Clement, (21) triggered an avalanche as he descended. He was fully buried in the avalanche. The avalanche swept down and caught all four of the other snowboarders in the group.

RESCUE SUMMARY

No rescue equipment

The four friends were buried "up to their armpits in snow, but each was able to dig out." They searched for Clement, but they did not have avalanche rescue equipment and were unable to locate him. They left to seek help.

Search and Rescue responded to the avalanche, along with members of the Alta and Snowbird ski patrols. They transported one of the riders, who had suffered "leg and hip injuries," to a nearby hospital.

An avalanche dog from Alta alerted on Clement's body about two hours after the avalanche. He was buried under about three feet of avalanche debris and appeared to have suffered significant trauma. Because of deteriorating weather, rescuers postponed the body recovery until the following day.

AVALANCHE DATA

Persistent Slab avalanche

Clement triggered this avalanche, which was about 1.5 feet deep and 80 feet wide. The avalanche ran about 500 vertical feet through cliff bands and exposed rocks.

COMMENTS

Before—and after—ski areas operate for the season, the snowpack within their boundaries is equivalent to a backcountry snowpack and must be treated as such. Too often, riders familiar with the terrain bring an "inbounds" mentality to the early season snowpack and ride as if the snowpack had been controlled and mitigated. Often people do not carry avalanche rescue equipment, as in this case. "The problem was they were in a ski area, but they were faced with backcountry conditions. They are lulled into a false sense of security, but there's no control work done and this is the tragic outcome," Sgt. Gil Howard, Salt Lake County Sheriff's Office, said about this accident.

The group rode the slope one at a time. This is standard practice to minimize exposure to avalanches. Unfortunately, they did not move out of the potential avalanche terrain at the bottom. All four were caught and partially buried. Having to first rescue themselves added significant time to their potential rescue of Clements.

Not carrying avalanche rescue gear meant the group could not perform a timely companion rescue and had to request outside help. In this case, although rescuers were close by—and far closer than they would be in most backcountry accidents—they were not able to find and excavate the victim for two hours. Companion rescue offers a buried victim the best chance for survival.

LIMA PEAKS, SOUTH OF LIMA, MONTANA | November 15, 1998

19981115

One hunter caught, buried, and killed

ACCIDENT SUMMARY

The Lima Peaks are a small cluster of peaks in the Beaverhead Mountains of western Montana, just north of the Continental Divide and south of the town of Lima. Scott Bettle (37) was elk hunting with two companions in the area. Early in the afternoon of Sunday, November 15, the hunters separated and planned to meet later in the day. When Bettle failed to make the meeting, one of his partners followed his tracks. Bettle's tracks crossed a saddle and dropped into upper reaches of Sawmill Creek. About 100 feet below the saddle, Bettle's tracks led into an avalanche and never came out. Bettle had entered the path about 50 feet below the crown.

Traveling alone

RESCUE SUMMARY

One partner went for help. Search and Rescue volunteers arrived at the avalanche site around 04:00. They "heard cracking sounds" and "got off to the side until daybreak." Searchers probed the debris on Monday.

Rescuers in a probe line found Bettle around 15:00 on Monday afternoon. His body was buried where the debris "entered trees," about 100 feet from the toe. He was buried under about five feet of debris.

Three avalanche dogs worked the site on Monday, but the area was contaminated by early rescue efforts and the dogs failed to alert.

AVALANCHE DATA

This was a hard slab avalanche, probably triggered by the hunter, and broke in old snow layers near the ground (HS-AFu-R2-O). On the slope, there was a three- to four-inch-thick crust over old snow with the texture of "granulated sand." Rescuers noted that the slope "was recently wind loaded."

Persistent Slab avalanche

The crown face was about 12 inches deep and about 30 feet wide. The slope angle near the starting zone was about 35 degrees. It started on a northeast-facing slope near tree line, at an elevation of about 9,600 feet. The avalanche ran about 500 vertical feet, but "didn't seem to damage even small six-inch diameter trees."

COMMENTS

It is easy to underestimate avalanche danger in early season, when snow barely covers the ground. Often, however, isolated slopes hold all the components needed for an avalanche. In this case, a slab of wind-drifted snow, a persistent weak layer, and a slope steep enough to slide. Not recognizing these islands of danger can have tragic consequences, as in this case. See 19961111 for a similar, early season accident with a less tragic outcome.

19981230 MISSOULA LAKE, SOUTHWEST OF SUPERIOR, MONTANA

December 30, 1998

One snowmobiler caught, buried, and killed

ACCIDENT SUMMARY

On December 30, a group of four men snowmobiled southwest up Cedar Creek near Superior towards the crest of western Montana's Bitteroot Range. They were attempting to bring supplies into a mining claim across the divide in northern Idaho. Deep snow and steep sidehilling made riding very challenging.

In avalanche runout

Near Missoula Lake, the trail crossed a long, very steep sidehill described as "45-plus degrees." The group began shoveling a trail across the slope. About half a mile across the slope, the trail dipped in and out of a draw. Two of the men worked into the draw, while the other two were still behind.

Around 16:00, one man, age 26, was shoveling in the draw when an avalanche released about 800 feet above him. The avalanche hit him, carried him about 900 feet down the slope, and fully buried him.

RESCUE SUMMARY

Everyone in the party carried avalanche safety equipment. The three other men in the group used transceivers to locate their companion within about 20 minutes. He was buried under about two feet of snow. He did not respond to CPR efforts.

AVALANCHE DATA

The avalanche released on a very steep, north-facing slope. The group estimated the crown as six feet deep and 300 feet wide.

COMMENTS

This group was prepared. They carried avalanche rescue gear, and investigators noted that the group had read "the advisory from the previous weekend." They were "concerned about possible instability." Despite that preparation, the group put themselves on a very steep avalanche slope with a large starting zone high above them. The group may have been overly committed to their goal of reaching the claim, allowing that commitment to overweigh their concerns. Although they performed a prompt companion rescue, the victim did not survive the relatively shallow burial.

19990101 ROCK ISLAND LAKES, SOUTHWEST OF JACKSON, MONTANA | January 1, 1999

Two snowmobilers caught, not buried

ACCIDENT SUMMARY

The slopes around the Rock Island Lakes in southwestern Montana are popular with snowmobilers. The area lies southwest of Jackson, Montana and north of the Continental Divide. On New Year's Day, David Shepard was snowmobiling with a group of seven other riders in the area. Shepard was climbing a hill "when he saw a crack in the snow suddenly appear."[1] Shepard recalled, "it took me a little bit to understand what I was seeing."

The slab had moved about 20 feet downhill by the time Shepard reached the crown. Shepard decided his only option was to try to jump the growing crack. He gunned the engine. "I flew off my machine and did a face-plant into the other side of the crack," Shepard said. "It must have knocked me out or something, because the next thing I knew, I was 100 feet down the hill, lying next to my sled."

Another snowmobiler was caught in the slide, but managed to stay on top of the snow by "making himself big, like a snow angel and swimming," said Shepard. "He didn't wind up sliding very far."

COMMENTS

A face-plant and snow angels aren't often among suggestions for what to do if caught in an avalanche. Avalanche educators do emphasize the importance of escaping a slab, fighting to clear snow away from your mouth, and swimming—anything to keep yourself as high in the moving avalanche debris as possible, to reduce your chances of being buried. That's what these two riders did, and the face plant and snow angel contributed to their survival. So did luck.

FAIRVIEW LAKES, EAST OF FAIRVIEW, UTAH | January 2, 1999

19990102

Two backcountry tourers buried and killed

WEATHER AND SNOWPACK CONDITIONS

There was a long period of dry and windy weather in November and December. The slope that avalanched was drifted heavily through this period, leaving dense layers of snow. During a very cold period in late December, surface hoar and faceted snow developed on the snowpack surface. More drifts buried the weak surface hoar and near-surface facets in the days prior to the accident.

ACCIDENT SUMMARY

Fairview Canyon runs east from Fairview up towards Skyline Drive, on the crest of the Wasatch Plateau in central Utah. On January 2, two teenagers, Matthew Neilsen (16) and Jesse Krebs (17) left Mapleton, Utah to spend the day backcountry snowboarding. Neither teen carried avalanche safety equipment. When the two failed to return home that evening, the boys' families notified the Sanpete County Sheriff's office and then began looking for them. Family members located the teenagers' parked car near the top of the Fairview Canyon Road, on a ridge crest above Fairview Lakes. About 75 feet east of the road, they found two snowboards resting at the top of a broken cornice.

No rescue equipment

RESCUE SUMMARY

The Sanpete County Sheriff Search and Rescue Team and Ambulance Service reported to the accident site with 27 searchers. Around 03:00 on January 3, rescuers located the teenagers while spot-probing around a large tree in the runout. Searchers found the teenagers right next to each other, buried under about four feet of debris.

AVALANCHE DATA

Cornice fall

The teens had walked onto the top of a cornice. The cornice broke under them, falling onto the slope below and entraining the pair in a slab avalanche. The slab broke up to five feet deep and 100 feet wide. The avalanche ran 150 vertical feet into scattered trees. The weak layer was buried surface hoar and faceted snow, sandwiched between densely drifted and very hard (pencil-to-knife hardness) layers of snow.

The slope was about 36 degrees in steepness at the top, and faced east-northeast. It makes an abrupt edge to the flat, meadowed plateau above. The slope was drifted heavily, with two to three times the amount of snow as in the surrounding areas.

COMMENTS

The roads across the Wasatch Plateau provides easy access to small, steep terrain features. These features do not appear to be avalanche terrain, in that there are few big slopes. The benign appearance of the terrain can lure recreationists onto cornices or avalanche-prone slopes.

19990104 DRY LAKE CREEK, SOUTH OF TOGWOTEE PASS, WYOMING

January 4, 1999

One snowmobiler, caught, buried, and killed

WEATHER AND SNOWPACK CONDITIONS

The early winter in central Wyoming's Absaroka Mountains was dry, with little snow until a series of storms from December 24 to 29. The Togwotee Pass SNOTEL site recorded 4.6 inches of snow-water equivalent during the storm cycle. Forty miles to the west at the Jackson Hole Ski Area, the storm added almost five feet of snow to a snowpack only about a foot thick prior to the storm.

ACCIDENT SUMMARY

Dry Lake Creek lies on the south and east sides of Grouse Mountain, about seven miles south of Togwotee Pass. It is popular with snowmobilers. On January 4, a snowmobiler was highmarking a slope around 11:30 when his snowmobile got stuck. He was off the machine, working to get it free, when an avalanche released.

The avalanche caught and buried the rider. A second avalanche began sympathetically. It overran the first avalanche debris field.

RESCUE SUMMARY

No rescue equipment

Searchers found the snowmobiler's body about four hours after the avalanche by probing. The debris from both slides had buried him about four feet deep.

COMMENTS

Too soon, too much. This rider ventured into steep, avalanche-prone terrain within a week of a dramatic storm cycle that dropped five feet of snow on a shallow, weak, early season snowpack.

RUMBLE GULLY, EAST OF MT. BAKER SKI AREA, WASHINGTON | January 18, 1999

19990118

One sidecountry rider caught, buried, and killed

WEATHER AND SNOWPACK CONDITIONS

The Northwest Avalanche Center issued an avalanche warning on January 18. The warning described the avalanche danger as High due to heavy snowfall and strong winds. It singled out northeast slopes as prone to avalanching. The stormy conditions continued through the 18th.

High avalanche danger

ACCIDENT SUMMARY

Rumble Gully is a popular sidecountry run just east of the Mt. Baker Ski Area boundary in northwestern Washington. The gully funnels debris from large slides that release in a northeast-facing bowl about 800 feet above. The debris tends to accumulate on a bench in the gully.

Terrain trap

On January 18, a snowboarder left the Mt. Baker Ski Area and rode down a very steep (35- to 45-degree) roll that feeds into Rumble Gully. The rider triggered an avalanche and was swept about 300 vertical feet and buried deeply in the gully below.

Traveling alone

RESCUE SUMMARY

Later in the day, the snowboarder's friends reported him overdue. Ski patrollers began searching and saw faint evidence of an avalanche crown where the snowboarder may have left the boundary. Strong winds, intense snowfall, and poor visibility hindered the search. The slopes above and in Rumble Gully posed significant potential accident avalanche danger to searchers.

No rescue equipment

Ski patrol conducted avalanche mitigation to protect rescuers. Mitigation efforts triggered a very large avalanche that overran the presumed burial area and filled the gully with additional debris. Probe lines and avalanche dogs failed to find the snowboarder, and the continuing storm prevented an extended search.

AVALANCHE DATA

The avalanche was a soft slab, triggered by the snowboarder, and small relative to the avalanche path. The avalanche paths surrounding Rumble Gully feed into a gully, which creates a significant terrain trap. The avalanche triggered by mitigation was eight to 10 feet deep.

Wind Slab avalanche

COMMENTS

Avalanche conditions in terrain outside ski area boundaries can be dramatically different than conditions within the boundaries. This snowboarder left the ski area in the middle of a storm, when an avalanche warning was in effect and those differences would have been greatest. He rode by himself into a terrain trap without avalanche rescue gear. His choices cost him his life. They also potentially endangered the lives of rescuers.

Rumble Gully was the site of another avalanche accident four weeks later (19990214), when a very large avalanche released and caught two sidecountry riders.

19990119 **CASPER BOWL, JACKSON HOLE MOUNTAIN RESORT, WYOMING** | January 19, 1999

One inbounds rider caught and killed

ACCIDENT SUMMARY

At around 11:30, Michael Langer (17) was killed by a small avalanche at the Jackson Hole Mountain Resort. Langer and two friends hiked to Casper Bowl—inbounds, hike-to terrain. They snowboarded down near "Shot 10 Buttress." They knew there were large cliffs in the area. Langer was in front. He stopped, removed his snowboard, and hiked down for a better view.

Langer realized they would "cliff out" if they descended further. He let the other two know and hiked back up to his snowboard. As Langer was putting his board back on, there was a "failure of the snowpack" and a slab about one foot deep and 50 feet wide broke just above him. The avalanche swept Langer over a 300-foot cliff.

RESCUE SUMMARY

Langer's companions began screaming. Two skiers in the area heard their cries and determined what happened. One skier left to alert the Jackson Hole Ski Patrol. The other assisted Langer's companions safely down, then found Langer's body. An autopsy found "severe head trauma and internal injuries consistent with a high fall."

COMMENTS

A resort spokesperson described the avalanche as "an isolated pocket" and a "very small" avalanche. The consequences of the fall, however, were tragically severe.

19990123 **D CHUTE, EAST OF ASPEN HIGHLANDS, COLORADO**

January 23, 1999

Two sidecountry riders caught; one buried and killed

ACCIDENT SUMMARY

Skiing out-of-bounds

Between 15:00 and 15:30, Lonnie Moore (45) and Mark Furlong left the Aspen Highlands Ski Area in central Colorado. The men exited the ski area through a US Forest Service access gate. Their plan was to ski down "D Chute" to the Castle Creek road. The area is a popular end-of-day sidecountry run. From the road, riders can catch a car ride back to town.

Both men were very experienced backcountry skiers and had skied the route many times over the years. They had left their avalanche safety equipment at home. The day prior, the pair had discussed skiing down to the road and decided it was too dangerous. Earlier that day, Moore had made two runs through adjacent backcountry terrain. "The power of powder overwhelmed their sense of self-preservation," investigators wrote.

"Red flag" indications of danger

On their descent, the pair triggered several whumpfs and shooting cracks running over 100 feet from their ski tracks. They chose to keep skiing down, despite these obvious signs of instability.

D Chute descends along, or in, the track of an old avalanche path. The upper portion of the path is within the boundary of Aspen Highlands and avalanches are mitigated. About one third of the way down to the road, the pair traversed through a stand of aspen trees, from a larger sub-ridge into a small gully.

Furlong was in the lead, and saw "the whole thing break in front of him" in an avalanche. He turned to look for Moore, and could not see his friend—only avalanche debris.

RESCUE SUMMARY

No rescue equipment

Furlong climbed a short way up to the top of the debris. He used his ski poles to probe for Moore. It took him about an hour to find and uncover Moore. Furlong's efforts at resuscitation were unsuccessful. Furlong skied down to the Castle Creek road, caught a ride to town, and reported the accident around 19:00.

The following morning, the Aspen Highlands Ski Patrol retrieved the body. Patrollers mitigated avalanches along the route; one rescuer said they "literally bombed our way out there," triggering "several" additional avalanches.

AVALANCHE DATA

Persistent Slab avalanche

Terrain trap

This was a soft slab avalanche, triggered by a skier, small relative to the path, capable of burying a person, and failed in old snow (SS-ASu-R2-D2-O). During the body recovery, ski patrollers estimated the avalanche as one foot deep, 75 feet wide, and 100 vertical feet. The avalanche flowed into a narrow gully.

The avalanche occurred on an east aspect at around 9,000 feet, well below treeline. Conifers along the southern edge of the slope shade it. In the shadowed area, the snowpack was especially weak and faceted, similar to a northerly aspect. The snowpack was also shallow, with brush and trees sticking through. In their book *Snow Sense*, authors Fessler and Fredston call shady slopes with shallow snow "facet gardens."[2] The shallow snow cover and brush sticking through increase the rate of facet development and the resulting size of the grains.

COMMENTS

High avalanche danger

The Colorado Avalanche Information Center had issued an avalanche warning for that day. Avalanche danger in the backcountry was High. Both natural and human triggered avalanches were likely. The riders chose to enter avalanche terrain despite the forecast danger.

D Chute, on the left, and close up of the accident site, below the ski area boundary, on the right. *Photos Doug Driskell.*

The day before, the riders had discussed the potential to descend to Castle Creek and decided against it, because of the avalanche danger. They left their avalanche safety equipment home, not planning on leaving the ski area boundary. Despite their lack of equipment and pre-determined planning, the pair chose to ski down to the road.

On their descent, the riders ignored or discounted several signs of instability and potential avalanches, and chose to continue to descend. Whumpfing collapses and shooting cracks are "red flag" indications of potential avalanche activity.

That series of choices resulted in tragedy. It is easy to look back and highlight the choices as mistakes. However, that day, other riders—including the victim—made similar choices and found fantastic riding.

The pair might have found the same fantastic snow. Small choices in terrain selection could have avoided the steep, shady slope. With the signs of instability, they could have chosen a more conservative descent route. They could have brought their transceivers and shovels, and the rescue could have been swift. They could have followed their plan from the day before, when they decided that the avalanche conditions were too dangerous to be in the backcountry.

19990129a NEAR SPOUT SPRINGS SKI AREA, OREGON | January 29, 1999

One backcountry rider caught, buried, and killed

WEATHER AND SNOWPACK CONDITIONS

Rescuers described the snowpack as "ideal for an avalanche." There was about 18 inches of recent snow on top of "about eight feet of snow that's kind of melted and then crusted and hard-packed."

ACCIDENT SUMMARY

The Spout Springs Ski Area is located in northeastern Oregon's Blue Mountains, about 200 miles east of Oregon's Cascade Mountains. It is small, with mostly beginner and intermediate terrain, but steep slopes outside the ski area boundary drop into Looking Glass Creek on the north and Umatilla Creek to the south. The exact accident site is unknown.

David Beegle (19) and two friends were snowboarding near the ski area on the afternoon of Friday, January 29. Beegle "stopped to adjust his snowboard equipment"[3] while his two companions went on. After a few minutes, his friends came back to look for him. "When they returned, he wasn't there, but it looked like an avalanche had been through the area." The friends alerted authorities.

RESCUE SUMMARY

"Rescuers, fighting powerful wind gusts and blowing snow, had to rappel down to the avalanche site." An avalanche dog alerted on Beegle's body and it was recovered Saturday afternoon. Beegle had been buried under about three feet of avalanche debris with his snowboard still attached.

COMMENTS

The lack of information available on this accident precludes comment.

MOUNT NEBO, SOUTH OF SPANISH FORK, UTAH

19990129b

January 29, 1999

One snowmobiler caught, buried, and killed

WEATHER AND SNOWPACK CONDITIONS

There was little snowfall in the Wasatch Mountains in December and early January. The snow on the ground faceted, forming a layer of weak snow up to one foot thick. A major storm caused an avalanche cycle between January 19 and 21. Many slopes in the Mount Nebo area, in the southern end of Utah's Wasatch Range, avalanched during the storm. A small storm on January 26 partially filled in the crowns.

ACCIDENT SUMMARY

Paul Jepson (31) and Wade Hanks were riding powerfully-modified snowmobiles on east-facing slopes to the north of Mount Nebo. They were highmarking slopes steeper than 40 degrees. Hanks was working on his sled, watching Jepson highmark, when the avalanche released just before 15:30. The avalanche caught Jepson and swept him into a stand of trees. His watch stopped at 15:28.

Terrain trap

RESCUE SUMMARY

The pair did not have avalanche rescue equipment. Hanks called 911 from his cell phone at 15:55. It took Hanks about 45 minutes to find his friend. Jepson was in a treed area and partially buried. He appeared to have suffered severe trauma. Hanks attempted CPR with no response.

No rescue equipment

AVALANCHE DATA

This was a hard slab avalanche, triggered by a snowmobiler. It broke in old, faceted snow formed during the December and early January dry spell. The avalanche was 1,200 feet wide, two feet deep, and ran 800 vertical feet. It snapped and broke six-inch diameter trees.

Persistent Slab avalanche

COMMENTS

About one quarter of avalanche victims die from trauma. A very large avalanche—like this one, which snapped trees—can inflict significant damage to a human body. Being swept into trees increases the consequence of the avalanche. It is quite possible that Jepson would not have survived this accident, even if he and Hanks had avalanche rescue equipment. However, recreating in avalanche terrain without rescue equipment reduces your chance of survival.

19990130 CRAG CREST, GRAND MESA, COLORADO | January 30, 1999

One snowmobiler caught, buried, and killed

WEATHER AND SNOWPACK CONDITIONS

The winter of 1998-99 started with below-average snowfall and a shallow snowpack. The first major storm of the winter hit Grand Mesa from January 17 to 23. Winds were strong and drifted significant amounts of snow. A second storm, on January 27, also drifted "significant snow onto the subject slope." On January 30, skies were partly cloudy and winds were light.

ACCIDENT SUMMARY

Grand Mesa is a large, high-elevation mesa that lies east of Grand Junction, between the Colorado and Gunnison Rivers. It rises about 6,000 feet above the valleys on either side. A narrow spine called Crag Crest (11,189 feet) extends east from the mesa proper; it is the highest point for several miles. The steep sides of this spine drop about 500 vertical feet. The north side of Crag Crest is often wind-loaded by storms rising up the south side of the mesa

On January 30, a group of nine snowmobilers were riding on Grand Mesa. The group included Scott Voytilla (36) and Victor Monte (44). They had been highmarking in an area known as Hidden Valley, a popular area for riding on the north side of Crag Crest and east of Cold Sore Reservoir.

In avalanche runout

Around 14:00, the group traversed eastward along a bench below Crag Crest. They stopped in a stand of trees at the bottom of an open slope. Two riders, including Voytilla, broke trail across the open bench. Monte followed seconds later. Voytilla heard the group yelling and turned to look back. He saw an avalanche sweep up Monte.

RESCUE SUMMARY

The group quickly converged on Monte's last seen point and began searching. The group was equipped with transceivers, shovels, and probes. They found Monte after about 15 minutes. The avalanche had carried him about 100 feet below the traverse. He was buried face-down, head downhill, under about five feet of avalanche debris. His snowmobile was about six feet downhill from his location, with the tip of the windshield above the debris.

The group began CPR. Several members of the group rode out to alert authorities. Other snowmobilers took emergency medical services personnel into the scene of the accident. Resuscitation efforts on Monte were stopped around 15:30, and his body was towed out in a rescue sled.

AVALANCHE DATA

Persistent Slab avalanche

This was a hard slab avalanche triggered by a snowmobiler, medium-sized relative to the path, that broke in old snow (HS-AMu-R3-O). The avalanche was about three feet deep, 350 feet wide, and ran 400 vertical feet. The bottom of the slab was very hard (pencil hardness) snow. The weak layer was large, faceted snow grains. The bed surface, just above the ground, was an old layer of refrozen snow that was very smooth.

Looking east along the north side of Crag Crest. The January 30, 1999 accident occurred on the open slope in the lower right-hand corner of the photograph. *Photo Rob Hunker, 2004.*

The Colorado Avalanche Information Center had forecast Considerable danger on steep north to east aspects. The group triggered the avalanche from below, on low-angled terrain.

COMMENTS

This group was prepared and experienced. They completed a rapid and successful companion recovery. Still, they chose to traverse under a steep slope that had been recently wind loaded. The riders did spread out, minimizing their exposure to potential avalanches. Only one of the riders was caught. Unfortunately, Monte was caught low in the avalanche path. That often leads to a deeper burial.

The avalanche underscores the danger of traversing below steep slopes when the potential for Persistent Slab avalanches exists. Collapses triggered on low-angle or flat terrain, as in this case, can propagate up slope and long distances, triggering avalanches that sweep down on people from above. In these conditions, safe travel may demand avoiding even the run outs of avalanche paths.

19990206a

CUMBERLAND PASS, NORTHEAST OF PITKIN, COLORADO

February 6, 1999

Four backcountry skiers caught, one partially buried, and three buried and killed

WEATHER AND SNOWPACK CONDITIONS

As noted in the previous account, it was abnormally dry in the early months of the 1998-99 winter in Colorado's mountains. Near Cumberland Pass, early snow in November had faceted during a dry December. Winds drifted January's snowfall into hard layers and deep drifts along the crest of the slope. The last storm was several days prior to the accident. The upper 16 inches of the snowpack was soft, and offered decent skiing conditions. On February 6, the weather was pleasant, "clear sky, barely any wind,"[4] remembers one of the group, "Yeah, a perfect day."

ACCIDENT SUMMARY

Andrew Vork (20), Matthew Noddin (22), Casey McKenny (20), Josh Shifferly (22), and Joel Karinen (21), were all students at Western State College in Gunnison. Andrew Chanos (21) was a friend who came down from Greeley for the weekend. Between them, Vork and Noddin owned four snowmobiles. They decided to ride and tow the group into Cumberland Pass, northeast of Gunnison, for some sled-assisted skiing. They left from the town of Pitkin, about eight miles southwest of the Pass, around 09:00.

The group set up an impromptu base camp at the ruins of a mine below the pass. They skied at least three laps before lunch. On the fourth, Karinen and Chanos dropped the group off a little farther up the road than previous runs and went back to the mine for lunch.

Several of the men were having "a great time 'raging in the trees' below the road cut" on snowmobiles. McKenny tried to sidehill, and rolled his sled. Noddin and Vork went over to assist. While they did, Shifferly climbed on his skis toward the top of the pass. No one in the group had climbed to the pass that morning.

More than one person on a slope

After enjoying the view from the ridgeline, Shifferly saw the other three on the road, waiting for him. "I didn't want to ski right down on top of them," he said, so he made broad turns back and forth (he described them as cuts, but they were not ski cuts intended to deliberately trigger avalanches). At the bottom of the slope he fell. As he stood up, he heard Noddin yell.

> [Shifferly] pushed away instinctively. People talk about swimming in avalanches, but Shifferly couldn't, didn't. He remembers the snow flowing, pushing him along, not slamming him, exactly, but not allowing him any control, either. He remembers lunging as he went by some bushes and getting thrown behind the tree.
>
> It all happened so quickly, in just a matter of seconds. And then there he was, on his back, half-buried by snow. No sounds from his best friend, Noddin. Nothing from McKenny or Vork—Shifferly didn't know if they'd even seen the avalanche coming. Just quiet and terrible cold. The force of the avalanche had ripped off his gloves. He freed a hand, reached back and grabbed a spare pair of mittens from the top of his backpack.
>
> He wanted to be at home, on his couch with his son, watching *The Simpsons* and drinking a beer.

19990206a CUMBERLAND PASS, COLORADO

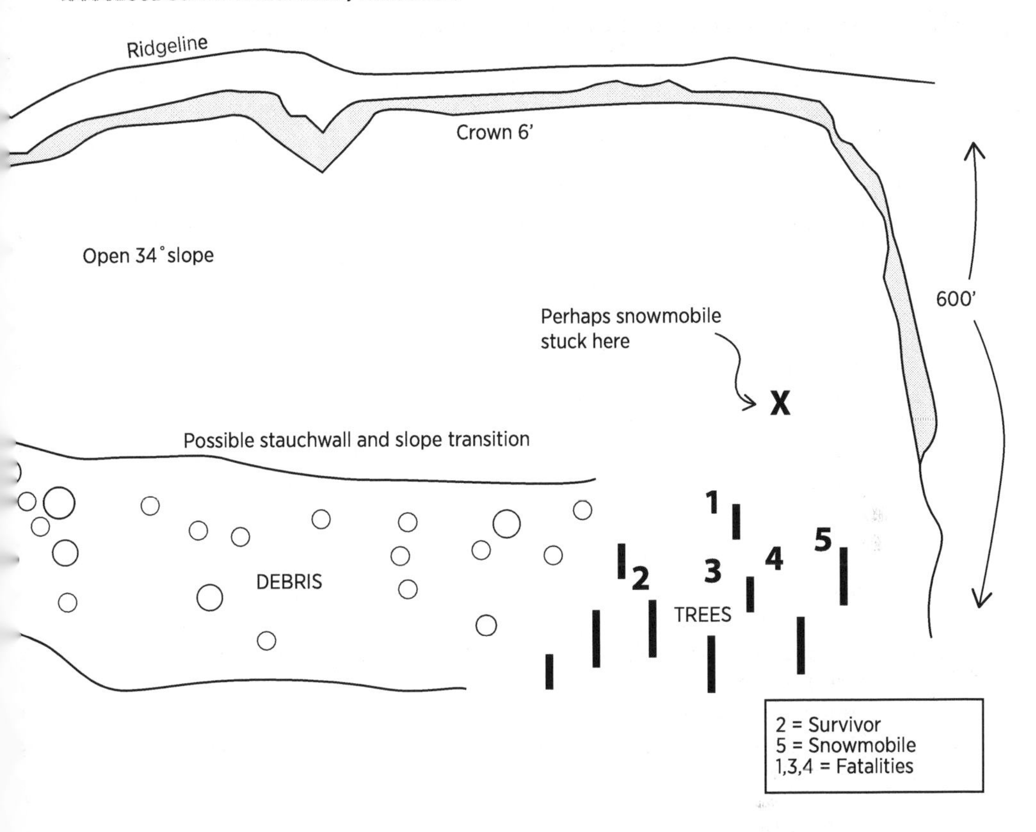

Basd on a diagram by Rob Hunker, Colorado Avalanche Information Center.

Vork, Noddin, and McKenny had tried to run away from the avalanche. All three were caught and fully buried.

"It was like looking at an eddy in a river," Shifferly remembered. "It was like I was in the calm behind the tree."

RESCUE SUMMARY

About twenty minutes after the group split up at the cabin, Chanos snowmobiled towards the pass to check on the others. He saw the avalanche and raced back to the cabin and Karinen. Both rode up to the avalanche.

Karinen remembers switching into emergency mode. He and Chanos jumped off their snowmobiles, switched their beacons to receive their buried friends' signals, and started searching the slope. But Chanos had never practiced with a beacon, and wasn't sure of what to do. They decided that he should go to Pitkin for help, while Karinen stayed and searched.

Lack of training

After Chanos left, Karinen heard Shifferly yelling. Karinen made sure Shifferly was OK and determined that it would take too long to dig him out. In proper triage fashion, Karinen continued his search. He was using an analog transceiver, searching for three signals. It was a time-consuming search.

Karinen pinpointed a signal after a few minutes. He dug about five feet deep and found Vork. Vork was not breathing, and Karinen could not find a jugular or radial pulse. Triaging again, "Karinen left Vork and continued to search. He found another signal and dug down about three feet. There was McKenny. Again, he felt no pulse at either the jugular or the wrist."

After hearing McKenny was lifeless, Shifferly "freaked out. I was claustrophobic in the hole, I needed to get out. I was like, 'Get me out of here, man!'" Karinen dug his friend out. Once free, the two resumed the search for Noddin. The first of the rescuers from Pitkin arrived at that point, around 14:45.

Chanos had reached the town of Pitkin at 14:15. The first house he stopped at was that of Charles Meredith, an off-duty Sheriff's Deputy. Meredith called county dispatch to mobilize search and rescue and then called neighbors on the search and rescue team. Within a few minutes, several Pitkin residents were riding towards Cumberland Pass as a hasty SAR team.

Noddin's body was found around 15:15. Rescuers initiated CPR. Other rescuers finished excavating Vork and McKinney, and began resuscitation efforts. None of the three responded, and rescuers discontinued efforts. They transported the bodies to the trailhead.

AVALANCHE DATA

Deep Persistent Slab avalanche

This was a hard slab avalanche, probably triggered by the skier, large relative to the path, and broke in old snow (HS-ASu-R4-O). The avalanche was about six feet deep, 1,500 feet wide, and ran about 400 vertical feet. It broke in a layer of depth hoar about one foot above the ground. The avalanche quickly scoured to the ground. Shifferly fell just above the road cut, and likely triggered the avalanche from an area of shallow, weak snow.

COMMENTS

Earlier in the morning, the group had dug a snow pit. Early reports said the group had conducted a rutschblock with a high score. The *Westword* article quoted above says the group described a shovel shear and mis-identified the test as a rutschblock. In the shovel shear test, the group identified the basal weak layer but figured "we'd seen it all this year, and it was like, 'It looks like rotten snow in the talus, like it always does.'"

The road to Cumberland Pass runs along the base of a broad avalanche path for about 3,000 feet. The group's initial runs had avoided the slope. It was later, sidehilling the snowmobile along the road, that they moved into the bottom of the avalanche path.

The group was thinking avalanche, in that they were equipped with avalanche rescue equipment. They had identified the slope as a place to avoid skiing. In their fun and excitement though, they strayed into dangerous terrain. They violated one of the fundamental rules of avalanche safety and placed four members of the party onto a potential avalanche slope at once. That proved tragic.

At the time of this accident, it was one of the two worst recreational avalanche accidents in Colorado. In 1988, an avalanche near Pearl Pass, between Aspen and Crested Butte, also killed three backcountry tourers.

LAKE MARY, SOUTH OF DONNER PASS, CALIFORNIA

19990206b

February 6, 1999

Four snowplayers caught, one partially buried, three buried, and one killed

WEATHER AND SNOWPACK CONDITIONS

Between one and two feet of dense, wet snow fell during the day on February 6. Southwesterly winds were very strong, blowing 30 to 40 mph with gusts about 60 mph. Temperatures were near freezing during the day and lowering at dusk. There was an avalanche warning, for High danger, issued at 18:00.

High avalanche danger

ACCIDENT SUMMARY

Several ski areas and numerous cabins lie on the west side of Donner Pass in the northern Sierra Nevada range. Four friends, Malcolm Hart (21), Harry Eichelberger (21), Derek Lerch (22), and Marissa Nelson (20), were staying at a cabin near Lake Mary, just south of the pass. The four were sledding. Around dusk, they decided to climb up a steep slope to the top of a small knoll.

More than one person on a slope

The east-facing slope of the knoll was deeply drifted with snow and topped with a cornice. The slope avalanched when they were a little more than halfway to the top. The avalanche caught and buried all four.

RESCUE SUMMARY

Eichelberger and Lerch said they were thrown over on their backs. Eichelberger reported that he was totally pinned but had a small airspace around his mouth and nose. He ate snow to enlarge the space. He yelled.

Lerch was able to get an arm up and push his hand above the snow surface. He heard Eichelberger yelling, and was able to punch an arm towards him and touch. Presumably both were able to get sufficient air exchange through the hole Lerch had punched to the surface.

Several hours passed. Around 21:00, Eichelberger decided he had to claw his way out or he would die. He finally struggled free. On the surface, he tried to dig out Lerch but was unsuccessful. He saw the lights of a cabin across the lake and made his way there through the heavy snow.

No rescue equipment

The Dartmouth Outing Club (DOC) was staying at the cabin. Club members called 911. Fifteen of the club members returned to the avalanche with Eichelberger. "Armed with shovels and broom handles for probes," the group found and excavated the other three snowplayers.

Donner Summit Fire Department began a rescue around 22:10. A hasty search team, including Sugar Bowl Ski Patrollers and an avalanche dog, rode snowmobiles to the site. By the time the fire department rescue team arrived, the DOC rescuers had found and excavated Hart and Nelson.

Hart and Nelson were found face down. The DOC members said Hart was responsive when first uncovered but lost a pulse shortly after. The fire department rescuers began CPR and advanced life support. Hart was transported to the hospital in Truckee, CA. The E.R. staff continued resuscitation for several hours until Hart was pronounced dead.

Nelson was responsive to painful stimulus only. She was hypothermic, with a core temperature later determined to be 76°F. She was also transported to a Truckee hospital. Field interventions prevented a further drop in her core temperature. Nelson was released from the hospital the following day "in good condition, but with little memory of her ordeal."[5]

AVALANCHE DATA

The slope failed when the group was about halfway up. The avalanche was about 50 feet wide. The path was only about 40 feet long and ran out across the lake.

COMMENTS

This group was not prepared for avalanches. They were not thinking about avalanches. They were out sledding, enjoying a snowy weekend of fun.

That only one of the group died is a combination of several fortunate events. Lerch's airspace allowed both him and Eichelberger to avoid suffocating. Eichelberger's renewed determination got him free. The Dartmouth Outing Club improvised an effective rescue and saved Lerch and Nelson.

19990206c LITTLE WILLOW CANYON, EAST OF DRAPER, UTAH

February 6, 1999

One snowshoer caught, buried, and killed

ACCIDENT SUMMARY

Persistent Slab avalanche

Aaron Bruder (24), Steve Parkins (24), and Justin Heil (22) headed up Little Willow Canyon east of Draper, south of Salt Lake City for a day of snowshoeing. Around noon, the group was traversing a slope. "Heil told his friends he 'had a real bad feeling about being up there' and decided to turn back."

Heil headed downhill. He was in a creek below his two friends when an avalanche released. Heil was fully buried.

RESCUE SUMMARY

No rescue equipment

Brudder and Parkins rushed to the avalanche debris. They could not find their friend. They hiked down the canyon and called the police from a nearby residence.
About 30 members of Salt Lake County's Search and Rescue Unit and avalanche dogs headed up to the avalanche. They "battled blizzard conditions" and low visibility to reach the site. Shortly after they began searching, the search dogs alerted on Heil around 18:00, over five hours after the avalanche.

COMMENTS

Yet another group that was unaware of the danger of avalanches and unprepared for the accident. Yet another group whose enjoyable day in the mountains turned tragic.

RUMBLE GULLY, EAST OF MOUNT BAKER SKI AREA, WASHINGTON | February 14, 1999

19990214

Two sidecountry riders caught, buried, and killed

WEATHER AND SNOWPACK CONDITIONS

Over 20 feet of snow fell at Mt. Baker in the 14 days between January 28 and February 11. Three more inches of snow fell the night of the February 13.

ACCIDENT SUMMARY

Rumble Gully is a popular sidecountry run just east of the Mt. Baker Ski Area boundary in northwestern Washington. The gully funnels debris from large slides that release in a northeast-facing bowl more than 500 feet above where riders typically enter the gully. Despite its popularity, the route into the gully can be dangerous: "This route traverses at least eight different avalanche paths across the bottom third of the slopes, with a terrain trap below and with people hiking the ridge line above the traverse." In addition, riders can hike up to the ridgeline above the gully, where they can access several other bowls.

On February 13, as the prolonged storm wound down, riders began entering Rumble Gully for the first time in two weeks. Poor visibility kept traffic low. The morning of the 14th was clear, drawing more riders into the backcountry areas near the ski area, including Rumble Gully.

At 12:19, a 12- to 15-foot-deep slab released about 100 feet below the ridge. The massive slide traveled approximately 1500 vertical feet and 3,000 to 4,000 feet slope distance down the gully, leaving debris piles six to 30 feet deep along the entire length of the gully. One person—snowboarder Justin Parker (19)—was in its path. At least 20 people watched Parker try to outrun the slide, including his father.

When the avalanche released, Shawn Riches (25) and a friend were finishing their run in the gully. They were almost into the lower-angle runout zone. They either heard or saw the snow rushing down on them. Riches turned left; his friend turned right. The slide overtook Riches; his friend escaped.

RESCUE SUMMARY

Inadequate rescue equipment

Volunteer ski patrollers were amongst the witnesses to the avalanche. They immediately reported the avalanche and closed the traverse into the gully until searchers could safely enter. Three ski patrollers performed a hasty search and transceiver search of the debris in the upper basin. Two patrollers then descended about 1,000 vertical feet and did the same in the lower basin.

The proximity to the ski area meant numerous people were immediately available to help search for missing riders. Over 120 people volunteered, including ski area guests, instructors, and patrollers. Ski patrol split them up and organized probe lines.

A probe line found Parker relatively quickly. He was buried about nine feet deep, almost vertically oriented. Rescuers reached his airway about 80 minutes after the avalanche. He was pulseless and not breathing. They could not begin rescue breathing until he had been fully excavated. Rescuers transported him to the first aid room. They stopped revival efforts about two hours after the avalanche.

The search in the lower gully for Riches proved frustrating. Surface clues provided a consistent line of travel. Searchers found one of Riches' skis speared into the snow on the hillside 52 feet up out of the gully. The ski was approximately 100 yards from his last seen point. Searchers also found his Riches' hat 100 yards down the gully from the ski and his glasses another 100 yards downslope from that hat. Probing in the area of the clues resulted in numerous strikes that, after digging, revealed three- to six-inch diameter sections of broken trees. Because of rising temperatures and the threat of additional avalanches, rescuers ended probing efforts around 15:00. Two avalanche dogs arrived from Whistler Blackcomb, in British Columbia. With support from Bellingham Mountain Rescue, the dogs worked the lower basin debris until about 17:50. They did not find Riches, and authorities suspended the search until summer. His body was recovered "substantially later," either in the summer of 1999 or the following summer.

AVALANCHE DATA

The hard slab released naturally, was maximum relative to the path, capable of destroying a substantial amount of forest, and broke in old snow (HS-N-R5-D4-O). The crown was 12 to 15 feet deep and 450 feet wide. It ran for about 1,500 vertical feet. The avalanche flowed into a shallow gully, leaving debris six to 30 feet deep along most of the path. The avalanche may have run on a thin layer of facets above a rain crust that formed six weeks earlier. During the prolonged storm prior to the accident, very large cornices developed on the ridgeline above the gully, and it is possible that a cornice collapse triggered the avalanche.

COMMENTS

This was a massive, and likely unsurvivable, avalanche. Weather conditions made the area obviously avalanche prone and dangerous. Over 20 feet of snow fell in 14 days prior to the February 14, with significant wind transport. Fresh powder and a sunny day made the area very attractive to riders without much avalanche knowledge. At least eight backcountry travelers had skied or snowboarded down the slope before it released.

The combination of dangerous yet attractive conditions proved deadly. As tragic as this accident was, it is fortunate that only two sidecountry skiers were killed. There was potential for many more riders to be on the slope simultaneously.

Another sidecountry rider was killed in an avalanche in Rumble Gully four weeks before this accident (19990118). The two accidents led to the development of a proactive education effort for sidecountry riders and requirements that skiers and snowboarders leaving the ski area carry avalanche rescue gear and not ride alone.

19990306 ARASTA CREEK, SOUTH OF VIRGINIA CITY, MONTANA

March 6, 1999

Two snowmobilers caught; one buried

ACCIDENT SUMMARY

More than one person on a slope

A group of snowmobilers was riding in southwestern Montana's Gravelly Range, south of Virginia City. They were highmarking on an easterly aspect in the Arasta Creek drainage. By 11:45, riders in the group had climbed the slope forty times. One rider went for another lap. Next, two riders started up, one after another.

The lead rider began his turn and "felt the 'ground' begin to shake like an earthquake and chunks of snow started rising up all around." He accelerated towards the northern edge of the avalanche.

At the bottom of the slope, the group watched the lead rider get bucked off his sled. He disappeared under the moving snow. About 300 feet later, the rider resurfaced. Using swimming motions, he was able to reach the edge of the avalanche and was not buried.

With the first rider safe, the group turned to look for the second rider and saw him and his machine disappear near a small group of trees about 100 yards directly up from their position. The second rider, a 21-year-old male from Ennis, was not seen again as the snow continued to slide. When the avalanche stopped, the six searchers hurried up to the trees, the last seen spot.

RESCUE SUMMARY

Inadequate rescue equipment

The group was not equipped with transceivers. There were only two shovels among them. Those without shovels began digging in the snow with their hands.

One of the group members was digging with her hands and returned to her sled to get gloves. As she climbed back towards the trees, she noticed about two inches of a snowmobile ski sticking out of the debris. All the searchers converged on the buried sled. One grabbed a small stick and began probing, and struck the second rider's leg.

The searchers dug down and pulled the second rider from the snow. He had been buried about 20 minutes. They found him head down, about three feet deep, and still "on his snowmobile." He was cyanotic and not breathing. They cleared his airway and gave him several rescue breaths. He resumed breathing immediately.

AVALANCHE DATA

Persistent Slab avalanche

This was a hard slab, triggered by the snowmobilers, large relative to the path, and broke in old snow (HS-AMu-R4-O). The crown ranged from two to 15 feet deep, and was about 600 feet wide. "There were huge chunks of snow, the size of washers, dryers, and even refrigerators, in the debris pile from the wind loaded slab." The avalanche broke in faceted snow near the ground. "Pulling out a fistful [of the faceted snow] was like holding good-sized diamonds. There was no bonding at all."

COMMENTS

Previous tracks on a slope do not indicate it is stable and safe to ride. Even 40 tracks.

Investigators noted:

> Luck played a bigger part in this avalanche than it should have. First, these snowmobilers were not adequately prepared. They had no beacons, no probes, and only two shovels (which is better than none, and probably saved the victim's life). They were playing on a slope that was obviously "pregnant" with snow, and they broke two cardinal rules of safe snowmobiling; "Only one rider on a slope at a time" and "Never ride above your partner".
>
> This story had a happy ending, when it could have just had an ending.

19990312 ALYESKA SKI RESORT, GIRDWOOD, ALASKA | March 12, 1999

Two inbounds riders caught, partially buried

WEATHER AND SNOWPACK CONDITIONS

Resort officials said almost four feet of snow fell in the two days prior to the avalanche. Two feet of snow fell in the 24 hours prior.

ACCIDENT SUMMARY

Cornice fall

Alyeska Ski Resort sits above the town of Girdwood, in southcentral Alaska. Around 14:30, a large, ridge-top cornice collapsed. The ski runs immediately under the cornice were closed, and avalanche mitigation had been conducted earlier in the day. The cornice triggered a large avalanche that "roared" down into the ski area.

"We started seeing it," said snowboarder Dustin Edmondson (14). "We started screaming, saying, 'Go! Avalanche!' It was huge."[6] Witnesses said it sounded like thunder and felt like an earthquake.

The avalanche ran over 1,000 feet into the resort's open terrain.

RESCUE SUMMARY

The avalanche caught two inbounds riders. Natasha Latta was partly buried. Edmondson and George Tauriainen (16) were just outside of the avalanche, and rushed to help Latta. Using hands and snowboards, they freed her within minutes. Mary Ann Nickles was buried up to her neck and was dug out by another snowboarder.

Alyeska Ski Patrol organized as many as 200 searchers, many of them volunteers, and six avalanche dogs. Probe lines worked the debris for about six hours, until authorities cleared the scene with no reports of missing persons.

COMMENTS

Inbounds avalanches on open ski terrain are very unusual in the United States. Natural avalanches are rarer yet.

19990321 TURNAGAIN PASS, WEST OF PORTAGE, ALASKA

March 21, 1999

13 snowmobilers caught; two partly buried, two injured, six buried and killed

The following accident was investigated by Doug Fesler and Jill Fredston of the Alaska Mountain Safety Center, Inc. The results of their investigation appear here with minimal editing.

WEATHER AND SNOWPACK CONDITIONS

In the fall of 1998, snowfall in the Turnagain Pass area of Alaska began in early October and continued for much of the month. The snowpack was sufficiently deep for winter recreation by late October. The snowpack maintained a normal depth into January of 1999. Then, during late January and early February, a dry and very cold spell brought minimum temperatures of -10 to -30°F. This created a widespread layer of facets and surface hoar that became a buried weak layer when snowfall resumed toward the end of February. Snow fell almost daily from late February through March 20.

March 21 dawned clear, warm, and windless. As temperatures rose through the day, avalanche potential also rose. Observant drivers on the Seward Highway coming from Anchorage would have noticed numerous fresh avalanches on the mountain slopes visible from the highway.

ACCIDENT SUMMARY

Turnagain Pass, at 900 feet elevation, is the high point on the Anchorage-to-Seward Highway. The slopes of the Kenai Mountains that surround the pass provide extensive opportunities for winter recreation. Snowmobilers are restricted to the west side of the highway, while the east is set aside for backcountry skiers and snowboarders. On Sunday, March 21, the parking area was jammed to capacity with 100 to 150 snowmobiles, with overflow parking lining the sides of the highway.

Three significant avalanches released in the two hours prior to the fatal avalanche. At about 14:00, a natural avalanche released on the east face of Pyramid Peak, about two miles to the north, out of view of almost all the snowmobilers. At about 14:30, a second natural avalanche released in an area called the Knob, which is a natural ramp that snowmobilers use to access the western ridge that overlooks Turnagain Pass to the east and Seattle Creek to the west. This area is also to the north of where the fatal avalanche would occur, and it was a close call for two snowmobilers. Brent Snow and his wife were at the base of the path when it released. Unable to get his machine started, Snow jumped on his wife's machine. As they sped out of the runout zone, the powder cloud dusted them with snow. They escaped unharmed. When they returned for Snow's machine, they found it partly buried by debris at the toe of the slide. This slide was large—four to six feet deep by a half-mile wide—and was also observed by several skiers on the east side of the valley.

"Red flag" indications of danger

Unfortunately, few of the other snowmobilers in the area observed or heard about these two slides, or if they did, they failed to recognize the importance of the message.

The third avalanche released at about 15:45, about a half-mile to the south of the Knob. It may have released naturally or been triggered by riders nearby. In either case, no one was caught.

Several riders closely observed this last slide. They had been highmarking. Moments later, this group of riders gathered near the runout of the most recent slide to talk over what they should do. Three members of this group were Ken Seagle, Dan Demers (37), and Aaron Arthur (29). They talked about the hazard and decided they had better "pack it in"—but first they wanted to make one more climb. The time was 16:00 when they started up the large slope that lay to the south of the Knob and to the north of the third avalanche that had run 15 minutes before.

What followed was pure chaos—ride-for-your-life chaos.

Seagle, Demers, Arthur, and a fourth rider were climbing, and numerous other riders were also on the slope when it fractured. The fracture line propagated half a mile across the top of the slope, and it was six feet deep. Ken Seagle was climbing the rider's left (south) side of the slope, which also was along the edge of the last avalanche from 15 minutes earlier. He was halfway up when he looked over his shoulder and saw the whole mountain to the north avalanching. He turned his machine to the left and rocketed toward the debris of the earlier slide and was successful in escaping onto the pile of snow blocks that were four to five feet in size. At 50 mph, he was airborne more than in contact with the snow.

More than one person on a slope

To Seagle's right (north) and about halfway up the mountain was Dan Demers, who had gotten his snowmobile stuck and was helpless when the avalanche broke above him. He and his sled were tumbled about 1,700 feet slope distance (500 feet vertical) down the mountainside. Seagle could see Demers' snowmobile, which was partly buried but totally destroyed. Seagle rode to the area to search. A man with a probe joined him a few minutes later and began probing in the area of the snowmobile. He eventually struck Demers, about five feet uphill from his snowmobile. Demers' head was 5.5 feet beneath the surface, and it took several more minutes to dig him out. Demers had been buried for about 40 minutes. He did not respond to CPR administered by a nurse who happened to be on the scene.

Aaron Arthur was in the process of making a long traverse from south to north and was about three-quarters of the way up the north side of the slope. He had just entered a very steep section of snow—later measured at 48 to 50 degrees—when the avalanche fractured about 300 feet above him. Witnesses quickly lost sight of Arthur and his snowmobile as they were carried downslope. Later in the day, Arthur's snowmobile was found 600 feet vertical below its last-seen point, but rescuers could not find Arthur.

In avalanche runout

Four men—Ray and Rex Richards, Fred Maranville and Steve Estes—were watching Arthur from their vantage point at the top of the Knob. They realized the avalanche was going to overrun their location. The Richards brothers and Maranville managed to get their machines started and sped off as the slide bore down on them. Estes, unable to start his machine, opted instead to run north toward some nearby mountain hemlocks. The powder blast hit him almost immediately. With a vise grip on a tree, he was able to hold on and was only dusted by the passing powder cloud.

The other three, Ray and Rex Richards and Fred Maranville, powered over the southern edge of the Knob and were hit by the avalanche almost immediately. They were knocked off their snowmobiles and violently tumbled about 600 vertical feet down the mountainside. When the snow came to a stop, Ray lay dazed on the surface, suffering from a concussion and facial cuts. He was four feet downslope from his broken snowmobile which was lying on its side, skis pointing uphill.

Ray remembered seeing a snowmobile hurtling through the air just before being hit by the slide. It may have been Fred Maranville's machine. Maranville came to rest 30 to 40 feet above Ray, but he was underneath his overturned snowmobile. He had a badly injured leg but managed to crawl out and establish contact with the others. Rex Richards and his machine ended up 50 to 60 feet below Ray, but were out of sight below a mound of avalanche debris. Rex had suffered a broken nose and lacerated face. His snowmobile had landed upside down with only its ski tips showing. Broken glass, anti-freeze, and blood covered the snow. Ray, Rex, and Fred were extremely lucky not to have been killed.

The avalanche continued its downward rush and slammed into other groups lower on the slope. Victor Jones (37) had been idling below the Knob on the north side of the slope when the avalanche hit him. The force carried him and his snowmobile 1,700 feet slope distance and completely buried both. It wasn't until Wednesday, three days later, that rescuers recovered his body from under seven feet of snow.

Jones' riding partner, Ray Debor (35), was approximately 150 feet downslope from Jones, heading downhill, when he was hit from behind. Debor never knew the slide was coming. He and his snowmobile were carried to within 70 feet of the toe of the slide where his machine was buried to the windshield while Debor was still sitting on the seat, buried to his knees and uninjured. There were two other two members of this group: Shane Brown, (25) and Brian Kirk (24). They were at the bottom of the slope,

19990321 TURNAGAIN PASS, ALASKA

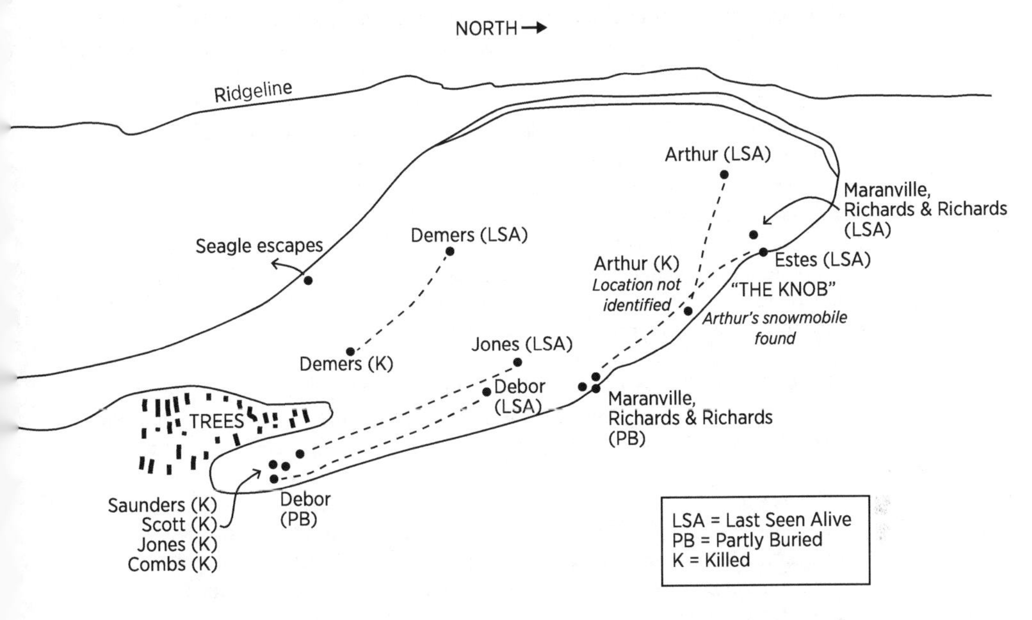

Based on a diagram by Doug Fesler and Jill Fredston, Alaska Mountain Safety Center.

roughly 150 feet below Debor. When they saw the slide coming, they had time to drive to safety and were merely dusted by the powder cloud.

Two other men, Chris Scott (24) and Jodi Combs (26) were riding together in the lower portion of the slope when they were hit and knocked off their snowmobiles. Scott's snowmobile came to rest with its handlebars and seat out of the snow, but there was no sign of Scott. Similarly, Combs was knocked off his machine and completely buried as well. Sunday evening, rescuers recovered Scott's body from under seven feet of snow. He had been buried 18 feet from his snowmobile. Monday afternoon, rescuers found Combs' body also under seven feet of snow, but he was separated from his snowmobile by 132 feet.

The sixth and final deceased victim was Jeff Saunders (29). His whereabouts at the time of the avalanche was not known, but rescuers found his body seven feet deep and about 50 feet from his snowmobile.

Evidence indicates that the avalanche was quite turbulent right to the end of the runout zone. Jeff Piakowsky (17) shot a video of the avalanche from Tincan Ridge, on the other side of the highway. It shows six to eight other snowmobilers fleeing the slide. The total number of victims caught and the number of close escapes will never be known.

RESCUE SUMMARY

Inadequate rescue equipment

Immediately after the dust settled, witnesses responded from all directions and came into several areas of the avalanche debris zone. Additionally, numerous 911 calls were made to alert rescue authorities. The debris covered an area that was roughly half a mile by a quarter mile, with debris typically deeper than 10 feet. For the first couple of hours, searchers worked independently.

The first organized rescuers to arrive on the scene were the Alaska State Troopers and the Girdwood Fire Department, followed shortly by Chugach Powder Guides, Alaska Mountain Rescue Group, Alaska Search and Rescue Dogs, National Ski Patrol, Mt. Alyeska Pro Patrol, US Forest Service, and Alaska Mountain Safety Center. Several helicopters were on site and were used to transport rescuers to the site. An aerial scene safety assessment was done before putting rescuers on the snow. Nightfall came at about 19:00, and the rescue was called off until daybreak. The site commander felt this was the only way they could gain control of the scene and determine how many people were unaccounted for.

On Monday, roughly 200 people searched the area for more than 12 hours. The bodies of Jodi Combs and Jeff Saunders were found under seven feet of snow by coarse probe lines.

On Tuesday, under deteriorating weather, the search continued for the remaining two victims, again using probe lines and using a snowcat to scrape snow from probable burial areas. Neither man was found.

On Wednesday, the weather went from bad to worse with heavy, wet snowfall and 30 to 40 mph winds. An all-out effort with 450 rescuers proved successful in finding the body of Victor Jones, who was also buried seven feet deep, like several of the other victims.

On Thursday, Friday, and Saturday, about 40 to 50 friends and relatives of the final missing victim, Aaron Arthur, continued to search without results. After that, Arthur's family asked all searchers to stop because they did not want them to be put at further risk. Arthur's body was eventually recovered, but no details were provided.

It is interesting to note that several rescue dogs worked the debris area but were ineffective. There were likely several reasons for this—the density of the debris, deep burials of most of the victims, and scent contamination from hundreds of rescuers.

AVALANCHE DATA

Deep Persistent Slab avalanche

This very large avalanche was triggered by numerous snowmobilers riding on a broad, open, southeast-facing slope. The crown was at an elevation of 2,800 feet and was half a mile wide. The avalanche fell 1,750 feet vertical. Slope angles at the crown varied from 32 to 39 degrees across the wide starting zone; however, one rollover below the crown was measured at 48 to 50 degrees. The slope's alpha angle was 23.5 to 24 degrees.

The depth of fracture averaged six feet, but at one point it was measured at 7.5 feet. The weak layer was facets that had formed during the clear, cold spell of late January into early February. This layer was 0.25 to 0.3 inches thick.

The debris field was mostly eight to 10 feet deep, but in areas it reached depths of 15 to 20 feet. The avalanche was classified as HS-AMu-R5-D4-O. It likely reached speeds of 80 to 100 mph.[7]

COMMENTS

Only four documented avalanches in US history have killed more people than this catastrophic slide in Alaska, where the death toll could have easily been higher. The signs that "something big" could happen were present in the form of three large avalanches that had released in the previous two hours. Most of the people in the area—snowmobilers, skiers, and probably a few snowboarders—had not seen the previous avalanches, and therefore were not aware of how dangerous the snowpack had become.

But some of the victims had their warning with the avalanche that released 15 minutes before the larger fatal avalanche. One group talked it over and decided to make one last climb before packing it in. It was the wrong decision.

The snowpack was primed for big avalanches. A layer of facets had formed more than a month earlier, and this potential weak layer covered a vast area. Then the weak layer got buried by the next storm, and as the storms continued, the mass of slab snow increased its stress on the weak layer. It took only one rider to find the sweet spot—sour spot?—at which point the fracture ripped through the weak layer, spreading across the entire slope within seconds. The weight of the slab and the speed at which it moved brought forces that the human body cannot withstand. Six died; it could have been worse.

NELCHINA GLACIER, SOUTHWEST OF NELCHINA, ALASKA

19990403

April 3, 1999

One snowmobiler caught, buried, and killed

ACCIDENT SUMMARY

Odman Schmalzried (40) and a friend were highmarking slopes near the Nelchina Glacier, in the Chugach range of southcentral Alaska. Schmalzried was near the top of a highmark when the avalanche released. He "flipped over backward and was carried down by the avalanche."[8]

RESCUE SUMMARY

No rescue equipment

Rescuers, including Alaska State Troopers, arrived at the site and conducted a search for Schmalzried that evening. Citing bad weather, the potential for a deep burial, and very limited resources, officials suspended the search on the night of April 3.

On April 4, family and friends continued the search. They found Schmalzried's body around 16:00 by probing. He was buried under about four feet of avalanche debris. His body was found "near the toe of the slide not far from his snowmachine."

COMMENTS

If Schmalzried and his friend had avalanche safety equipment, a lengthy search with outside help may have been unnecessary. Without transceivers, shovels, and probes, a rapid and successful rescue relies mostly on luck.

ST. MARYS GLACIER, NORTHWEST OF IDAHO SPRINGS, COLORADO | April 6, 1999

19990406

One backcountry skier caught and buried

ACCIDENT SUMMARY

St. Marys Glacier is a semi-permanent snowfield in the Fall River drainage north of Idaho Springs. It is accessible year round, making it a popular day trip for residents in the Denver area. Around 10:30 on April 6, a pair of backcountry skiers stood on top of the steep slopes above the lake. They planned to ski through chutes to the lake below. On his first turn, the first skier triggered a shallow avalanche that caught and carried him through or over the cliffs below.

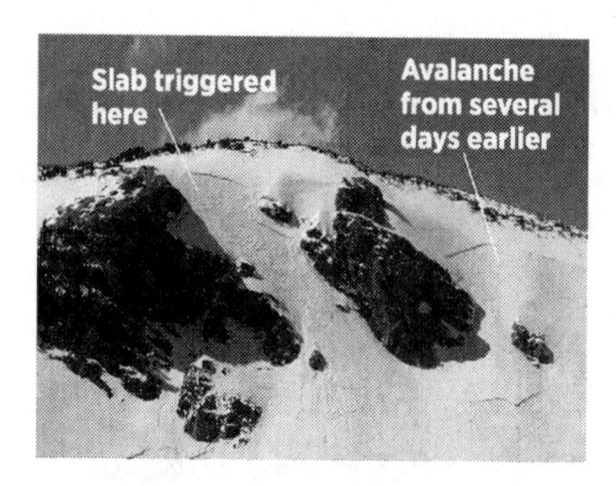

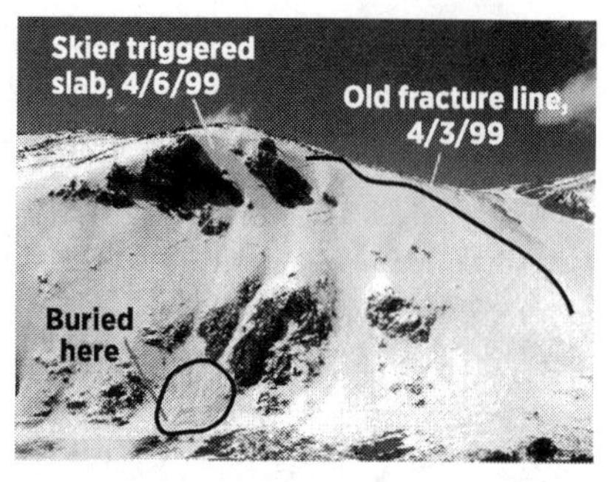

The skier triggered the avalanche in the central chute. On the left is a close-up of the starting zone and crown. The right photo shows the whole avalanche path. A large avalanche that ran several days before the accident is visible to the right of the chute. *Photos Dale Atkins, CAIC.*

About 500 feet south of the avalanche, two backcountry snowboarders were getting ready to hike up hill for another run. The pair had decided not to tackle the glacier area in favor of riding in the less-steep terrain just south of the lake. They saw the avalanche and watched the skier disappear under the snow just before the snow quickly piled up at the base of the steep slope.

RESCUE SUMMARY

No rescue equipment

The snowboarders immediately rode down through the trees toward the lake and rode a shallow traverse towards the avalanche. The pair ran the last few feet onto the debris. At the point they had last seen the skier, they saw a pair of glasses on the debris. They quickly started digging.

The snowboarders had picked the right spot and soon reached the buried skier. They uncovered his face within five minutes of the avalanche. The skier was buried face-down, under about one foot of debris. The victim's friend carefully skied down the bed surface of the avalanche to help get his friend out.

While the skier was being rescued, the Sheriff's Office was notified and local rescue teams responded.

Battered but okay, the two skiers retreated to their vehicle and avoided rescuers.

AVALANCHE DATA

Persistent Slab avalanche

This was a soft slab avalanche triggered by a skier, small relative to the path, that broke in old snow (SS-ASu-R2-O). The avalanche was about one foot deep and 75 feet wide at the top. The bed surface of the avalanche was old, frozen snow. The slab was recent snow that had fallen several days prior. Below the initial chute, the avalanche spread wider and entrained additional snow. The avalanche flowed 580 vertical feet, through some chutes and small cliffs, funneling the debris into a relatively deep debris pile.

COMMENTS

The skier was very lucky to be uninjured and to be rescued so swiftly. The avalanche carried him through rocky and cliffy terrain. The ride could easily have caused serious or even fatal trauma. He and his partner were not carrying avalanche safety equipment. Without a surface clue, the luck to be buried close to the surface, and the prepared snowboarders, the outcome of the avalanche could have been tragic.

YELLOW MOUNTAIN, SOUTHWEST OF OPHIR, COLORADO

19990407

April 7, 1999

One backcountry tourer caught, partially buried, and killed

ACCIDENT SUMMARY

Yellow Mountain is a ridge with several summits near 13,000 feet; it lies southwest of the town of Ophir. On April 7, a group of eight backcountry tourers headed to the Magnolia avalanche path, a north-facing slide path on the north end of the ridge.

The group split into two parties. The first five skiers descended to a bench. On the bench, Ryan Harnett (31) decided to wait for the other three skiers. The other four from the first party skied down to the road and to their shuttle vehicle.

Traveling alone

While alone, Harnett triggered and was caught in an avalanche.

Down at the road, the four skiers saw the powder cloud from the avalanche. They assumed it was blowing snow. They drove to the bottom of the path and realized they had seen an avalanche. Fearing the worst—that the avalanche had buried all four of their friends—they began a search.

RESCUE SUMMARY

The four searchers quickly located Harnett with transceivers and a visual clue. One of his hands was above the avalanche debris. His head was less than one foot deep, and they quickly had his airway exposed. They began CPR. About this time, the first of the three other skiers arrived and confirmed that they were not caught.

The group notified San Miguel Search and Rescue at some point during the search for Harnett. Shortly after 13:00, a local heli-skiing operation, Helitrax, flew ski patrollers and avalanche dogs from Telluride Ski Resort to the avalanche site. The skiers and SAR personnel continued resuscitation efforts for about an hour before Harnett was pronounced dead.

AVALANCHE DATA

Persistent Slab avalanche

This was a soft slab avalanche triggered by a skier, medium relative to the path, that broke in old snow (SS-ASu-R3-O). The crown was up to five feet deep and about 600 feet wide. The avalanche ran about 1,200 vertical feet. The slab failed well below treeline.

COMMENTS

The skiers were experienced backcountry travelers. They carried avalanche rescue equipment. They searched and found Harnett quickly. The speed, equipment, and experience did little to help Harnett. He was traveling alone when he triggered the avalanche, which, as many of these reports demonstrate, leaves little margin for error. Rescue arrived after he had been buried for a period of time. The avalanche carried him through about 400 feet of brush and rocks, and rescuers thought that he sustained significant trauma.

19990415 POWER CREEK, NORTHEAST OF CORDOVA, ALASKA

April 15, 1999

One worker caught, buried, and killed

ACCIDENT SUMMARY

Construction on the Power Creek Hydroelectric Project, near Cordova, in southcentral Alaska, began in the fall of 1998. By the spring of 1999, workers were building a bridge for access to the hydroelectric plant. On April 15, Gary Stone (46) was working in an excavator at the bridge site. Around 12:15, a very large avalanche released from about 2,000 feet above the construction site. The avalanche caught and pushed the backhoe and temporary bridge about 50 feet upstream. The excavator was severely damaged. Stone was thrown from the cab.

In avalanche runout

RESCUE SUMMARY

"Various...emergency rescue agencies" responded to the avalanche site. Three additional avalanches ran into the canyon during the initial search, including one that narrowly missed searchers and deposited another 15 to 20 feet of debris on the accident site. Stone's body was eventually found wedged between the excavator and the temporary bridge.

COMMENTS

Most accounts in this volume describe accidents that involve people recreating. They chose to place themselves in avalanche terrain in dangerous conditions. In some cases, the victims of these accidents and their companions did not have the knowledge or training to recognize the danger posed by the terrain and conditions. In many others, various incentives, influences, miscommunications, and/or cognitive biases led the groups to misjudge the danger and sometimes, to ignore warnings.

Workplace accidents, like this one, are different. Workers may be directed into dangerous avalanche terrain in dangerous conditions by their supervisors. And workers face additional pressures not experienced by recreationists, such as the fear of repercussions from employers for not performing assigned duties.

Fortunately, workplace accidents are also better investigated. The details in the Alaska Occupational Safety and Health Review Board (Docket 99-2131) report on this accident make for interesting reading. In this case, the workplace factors compounded a dangerous work location and environment.

In March of 1999, Whitewater Construction Company contracted with avalanche forecaster David Hamre. Hamre evaluated the construction site and wrote, "In summary, your project site has a high risk level from avalanches if work activities continue in the present configuration." He recommended a program of forecasting and mitigation.

"Notwithstanding Hamre's report and recommendations, Whitewater did not develop a written avalanche safety plan, did not provide avalanche safety training to employees, and did not hire an avalanche forecaster," court documents stated. In April 1999, Whitewater began some internal processes to address avalanche safety. With little internal experience and no outside help, the processes were plagued by miscommunication and ineffective implementation, eventually leading to a worker's death.

JACK RIVER CANYON, SOUTHEAST OF CANTWELL, ALASKA

19990416

April 16, 1999

Seven snowmobilers caught, four injured, and one killed

ACCIDENT SUMMARY

A large group of snowmobilers was riding a popular 60-mile loop through southern Alaska's Talkeetna Mountains that starts and ends near Cantwell. The "Big Notch in the Mountains" ride runs up Jack River Canyon, over Caribou Pass, back to the highway near Broad Pass, and back to Cantwell along the Parks Highway. The avalanche caught them around 16:00 while they were in Jack River Canyon.

"Generally the trail is on the creek bottom, and you're normally not in avalanche danger unless you choose to do some highmarking or go up into the high mountain draws," said Bob Gilbertson, owner of Backwoods Lodge [in] Cantwell, "I've been in there, and I've seen avalanches on the high slope."[9] Those times, the slides did not reach the bottom, he added. "My immediate reaction is that these people were off the trail or highmarking or just exploring the high canyons and draws."

"They saw a small slide coming down and the next thing they knew, it was on top of them, a big one."

RESCUE SUMMARY

In avalanche runout

The avalanche caught five to seven of the riders. A newspaper article said "a few of them were completely buried, and a couple of them got themselves out and started digging the others out."

Search and rescue worked well into the night to stabilize and evacuate the injured riders. Two of the injured men were flown out by helicopter early in the evening. Two more seriously injured patients were flown out later. The body recovery for the missing snowmobiler was conducted later.

COMMENTS

It's not clear from newspaper accounts the conditions prior to the accident, nor how the party triggered the slide.

MCGINNIS MOUNTAIN, NORTHWEST OF JUNEAU, ALASKA

19990427

April 27, 1999

One unguided heli-skier caught, partly buried, killed

WEATHER AND SNOWPACK CONDITIONS

There was an "unusual thaw" from April 16 to 18. That left a pencil-hard melt-freeze crust on the snowpack surface. The crust was buried by about three feet of snowfall from April 19 to 26. Winds were strong from the southeast during the storm. April 27 dawned clear and calm, with "dry, perfect powder" on northerly faces.

ACCIDENT SUMMARY

A group of five skiers and snowboarders chartered a helicopter to take them to the summit of Mount McGinnis, near Juneau. They were unguided. "McGinnis is a 4,228-foot peak that juts up on the west side of the Mendenhall Glacier. It is a popular heli-skiing location because it's so close to Juneau."[10] The weather was good, so several groups were flying in the McGinnis area.

The group made four runs on the broad, rolling apron of the north face of McGinnis. Around 10:30, starting their fifth run, Matthew Brakel (33) decided to snowboard the short and steep pitch from the summit. Two of the skiers descended and waited on the ridge below. The other two waited high on the ridge.

The summit pitch is short, "smooth, about 45 degrees...has an easy escape route onto the ridge...and appears to run out onto the broad, low-angled north apron." However, just below the slope an "almost imperceptible side slope causes the runout to bend 90 degrees to the left...and down a broad, ever-steepening gully that ends in 460-foot-high rocks and cliffs."

Brakel was two turns down the face when it avalanched. The avalanche was wide, and quickly swept him out of sight. The avalanche flushed Brakel over the cliffs and into a deep ravine. Over 1,000 vertical feet below the summit, the avalanche left Brakel partly buried and critically injured with his feet and a hand visible.

Terrain trap

RESCUE SUMMARY

Brakel's companions began a rescue and descended the avalanche path. Katrina Winchell (32) was one of two riders on the high ridge. She immediately began descending the bed surface of the avalanche. "A strong, confident, and fluid rider, she followed rapidly; but did not know there were rocks and cliffs below. She went over them and was killed in the fall."

The helicopter pilot "noticed the avalanche as he flew away, and radioed for help." The pilot flew over the avalanche debris and saw both Brakel and Winchell. He flew back to the ridge, picked up the three remaining riders, and ferried them to the avalanche debris. They cleared avalanche debris from Brakel and began CPR on both Brakel and Winchell. Two nearby, guided heli-ski parties arrived by 10:55 and assisted. Winchell was flown out at 11:10, and Brakel at 11:35 after paramedics arrived on scene. Both were pronounced dead from "multiple trauma injuries."

AVALANCHE DATA

Persistent Slab avalanche

This was a soft slab avalanche triggered by a snowboarder, medium-sized relative to the path, capable of burying and destroying a car, and that broke in old snow (SS-ARu-R3-D3-O). The slab was up to three feet deep, and about 230 feet wide. The avalanche ran about 2,000 vertical feet.

COMMENTS

"This is a deceptive slope," investigators wrote, with an apparently easy escape route and seemingly minor consequences. Unfortunately, the consequences were actually severe, and instead of a gentle runout, a large avalanche carried Brakel down unsurvivable terrain.

Investigators suggested that Winchell responded too fast to the avalanche. "You will need a few moments to evaluate safety before deciding whether and how to proceed."

The remaining party members, pilot, and other groups carried out a fast rescue. The two patients were quickly evaluated, transported, and flown from the field in potentially dangerous and challenging terrain.

ULTIMA THULE PEAK, WRANGELL-ST. ELIAS NATIONAL PARK, ALASKA | April 30, 1999

19990430

Three climbers caught, one buried and killed

ACCIDENT SUMMARY

Three Canadian climbers flew into the University Range in Wrangell-St Elias National Park for a multi-day mountaineering trip. All three were experienced mountaineers. Jim Haberl (41) had summited K2 in the Himalaya and published several books on mountaineering. With him were Keith Reid (39) and Graeme Alan Taylor (36). They planned to climb an unnamed, 10,950-foot peak known locally as "Ultima Thule."

According to Park Service rangers and Alaska State Troopers, who interviewed Reid and Taylor later, the men were breaking trail on skis in calm weather on a cold morning. At about 7:00, they were traversing a moderately-angled slope when a 100-foot-wide, three-foot-deep slab of snow let go.

More than one person on a slope

Haberl, according to the Park Service, was about 30 feet in front of Reid and Taylor. Reid and Taylor, according to troopers, were caught in the "broad, but slow-moving slab"[11] but were able to swim free.

Haberl, however, was swept over a cliff that sat below the 20- to 30-degree slope.

Terrain trap

RESCUE SUMMARY

It took several hours for Reid and Taylor to climb down around the 1,000-foot cliff. They found gloves, a hat, and "bloody snow" in the debris. The two excavated Haberl's body from about three feet of avalanche debris. He had sustained "severe" head injuries in the fall.

Reid and Taylor activated an Emergency Locator Beacon loaned to them by their pilot. The beacon alerted park authorities, who contacted the pilot. He flew the survivors out, then returned with the them the following day to retrieve Haberl's body.

COMMENTS

The limited accounts of this accident don't include details about the snow conditions on the slope or the group's decisions. However, several broader points stand out. One is the cliff below the moderately-angled slope the men were crossing. It magnified the consequences of any slide on the slope. It is very difficult to avoid terrain like that when mountaineering, so decisions about conditions and timing become all the more critical. With their experience, this group understood that as well as anyone. The accident underscores the importance—and difficulty—making the right choice every time one enters consequential avalanche terrain.

19990514 BLUE LAKE, EAST OF SITKA, ALASKA | May 14, 1999

Two hikers caught, partially buried; one killed

ACCIDENT SUMMARY

More than one person on a slope

Blue Lake is a popular recreation destination six miles east of Sitka, on Baranof Island in the Alaska panhandle. The road that reaches the reservoir traverses the base of a steep, southeast-facing slope. Just before the lake, the road lies in the runouts of several avalanche paths that fall 1500 feet or more from the ridge above.

Loose Wet avalanche

On May 14, Alton McAllister (22) and Niko Metashvili (20) hiked to Blue Lake. After reaching the lake, the two decided to climb a mountain above Blue Lake Campground. Around 12:15 pm, a natural, wet loose-snow avalanche released above the two hikers.

RESCUE SUMMARY

No rescue equipment

The avalanche carried McCallister a short distance and left him partially buried and slightly injured, with cuts and bruises. He yelled for help and was able to find Metashvili quickly. The slide had carried Metashvili approximately 900 feet down a narrow chute and partially buried him. He sustained major "head and neck"[12] trauma during the avalanche and was reportedly dead when McCallister found him.

A USFS employee was working at a campground nearby. He heard the avalanche "when it broke loose" and then heard McAllister yelling for help. The USFS employee radioed police at 12:19 to report the avalanche.

Several other small avalanches narrowly missed hitting rescuers as they evacuated McCallister and lowered Metashvili's body to the road. About ten minutes after reaching the road, a large natural avalanche overran the recently-vacated accident site and deposited debris within 20 feet of a hearse parked in the runout of the avalanche path.

COMMENTS

The natural wet loose-snow avalanches that struck the hikers and endangered rescuers are a frequent springtime danger. They occur after warm temperatures, clear skies and direct radiation weaken near-surface snow by introducing meltwater. The accident occurred midday, when this instability would be near or at its peak on a southeast facing slope.

The accident was unusual in that the victim was killed by a natural avalanche, which is true in only about one in 10 fatal avalanches. Nearly all fatal avalanches are triggered by the victim or someone in their party. The accident itself, however, resulted from factors that are all too common. Investigators noted that "Poor route selection, bad timing, and underestimating the hazard were major contributory factors in the accident."

In this scenario, avoidance was the best strategy. The hikers chose to travel across a slope that was very avalanche prone. Had they correctly assessed the hazard, they could have traveled on safer ridges and avoided the dangerous slopes during peak instability, or saved their climb for earlier on another day. The avalanche flushed Metashvili through terrain that caused significant trauma. An avalanche transceiver would not have changed the outcome.

Metashvili's death was last in a deadly winter in Alaska. The 1998-99 season saw 13 avalanche fatalities in the state, more than double the average of six for the decade.

1999–2000
SEASON

19991126 LONE MOUNTAIN, BIG SKY RESORT, MONTANA

November 26, 1999

Two backcountry skiers caught; two buried, and one killed

WEATHER AND SNOWPACK CONDITIONS

Big Sky Resort is located in the Madison Range of southwest Montana. In 1999, the resort's area included most of the north- through east- to south-facing slopes on Lone Mountain, 11,166 feet elevation. That year, southwest Montana had a rather dry fall, and by late November, the only skiing to be found was in pockets or gullies on northerly-facing slopes at higher elevations. This shallow snow cover was well into the faceting process, creating a weak basal layer.

On Wednesday, November 24, the most significant snowfall to date began. From November 24 to 26, 12 to 16 inches of high-density snow fell. This was accompanied by west winds of 10 to 15 mph, gusting into the 30s. This dense new snow, along with wind-drifted snow, more than doubled the total snow depth.

ACCIDENT SUMMARY

On Friday, November 26, five backcountry skiers began skinning up from the base area, with plans to ski the bowl on Lone Mountain. Two members of the group were Jack Gilliam (26) and Matt Kirkland (23). The ski resort had not yet opened for the season, so no avalanche control measures had been taken by the Big Sky patrol. One patroller warned the group not to go.

Beginning at Lower Morning Star, their route went up Upper Morning Star to ski Dobe's. They were aware of a potential avalanche danger and were equipped with beacons and shovels. Some of them had skied this slope several days earlier, before the recent new snow load.

More than one person on a slope

At Dobe's, the group picked their way up the slope by linking small rock outcroppings to reduce their exposure. At12:45 they reached a spot where they had to cross a 100- to 150-foot-wide, 37-degree slope to another rock island. Visibility was poor, since it was snowing quite hard. Crossing one at a time, Gilliam was first to go. He was almost across when Kirkland started his traverse. On Kirkland's fourth step, the slope avalanched, with the crown breaking about 75 vertical feet above him. Both men were swept about 250 vertical feet down a steep gully. The debris piled into a terrain trap formed at the edge of a rock glacier.

Terrain trap

RESCUE SUMMARY

The other party members headed down to the debris pile. Two other skiers in a different group had witnessed the slide and aided in the rescue. Right away, the searchers spied a gloved hand and uncovered Kirkland. He had been buried about five minutes with his head two to three feet beneath the surface. He was okay.

The rescuers made a transceiver search and pinpointed where Gilliam was buried—6.5 feet deep. The group was able to dig him out in about 10 minutes, and then they started resuscitation efforts. An off-duty professional ski patroller arrived about this time and coordinated the rescue and CPR efforts. Unfortunately, the resuscitation was unsuccessful.

AVALANCHE DATA

The avalanche released on a north-facing slope, at an elevation of 10,500 feet. The crown was 16 to 20 inches deep and 150 feet wide. The avalanche broke on the ground and fell approximately 300 vertical feet. The slope angles ranged from 37 degrees at the triggering location to 44 degrees at the crown. The avalanche was classified as SS-ASu-R3-D2-G. The stratigraphy was storm snow on top of a faceted layer at the ground. The weight of one or both of the skiers collapsed the weak layer, which resulted in slab release.

Persistent Slab avalanche

COMMENTS

This group did a lot right: carrying (and being experienced with) avalanche rescue gear, crossing dicey slopes one at a time, and carrying out a quick rescue. But the overriding factor in this accident was poor judgment about the snow stability. They faced a very recent slab—created by several days of falling and blowing snow—that loaded a persistent weak layer—facets at the ground. Thus, the avalanche danger had worsened substantially over several days since they last skied this area. It is not known whether the group discussed this reality.

Additionally, this small avalanche shows the danger of terrain traps. On a smooth, open slope, this avalanche may have been harmless. But the terrain trap caused all the debris to pile on top of itself, creating a deadly deep-burial situation. The rescue itself was flawless, but the deep burial was the killer. The take-home point: Avoid crossing above terrain traps whenever possible.

DIAMOND PEAKS, WEST OF CAMERON PASS, COLORADO

19991214

December 14, 1999

One backcountry skier, caught, buried, and killed

WEATHER AND SNOWPACK CONDITIONS

Cameron Pass is a popular recreation area about 55 miles west of Fort Collins, Colorado. At the summit of the pass, a parking lot gives easy access to the Diamond Peaks area less than a mile to the west. This area offers good skiing in steep terrain, but it has been the site of several avalanche accidents over the years.

Little weather data is available for this incident. The snowpack varied from two to three feet deep, which was probably near normal for mid-December. The day preceding the avalanche, an estimated eight inches of snow had fallen.

ACCIDENT SUMMARY

On the morning of Tuesday, December 14, three Colorado State University students left Fort Collins for a day of skiing on Diamond Peaks. The three men were Danny Samelson (21), Evan Stafford (20), and Peter Owens, (20). Samelson, on telemark skis, and Stafford and Owens, with snowboards, climbed from the parking lot to a prominent bench just above timberline. Above the bench, the terrain steepens, and almost all of it is avalanche prone. At this point, Samelson continued climbing toward the South summit of Diamond Peaks while his friends remained on the bench to build a jump. They lost sight of Samelson, but a short time later they heard a "whooshing" sound

Inadequate rescue equipment

and looked up to see an avalanche running on the slope south of their location. The time was 13:30. None of the group was equipped with beacons or probes: they only had shovels for building their jump.

They had not seen Samelson get caught, but they also did not see him anywhere on the slope. They climbed up to search the debris for any clues. Two other snowboarding friends joined them briefly, then left to get help. With no last-seen area, the remaining pair randomly probed the deposition area with snowboards and shovels.

RESCUE SUMMARY

The two snowboarders who left to get help made it to the highway and flagged down a Colorado Department of Transportation plow driver. That man went to his highway barn and notified both the Larimer County Sheriff's Office (to the east) and the Jackson County Sheriff's Office (to the west).

The two County Sheriff's Offices got the call at 14:55. At 15:20, the first searchers from the Jackson County (west) side of the pass arrived at the parking lot. They were led up to the avalanche site by the two snowboarders who had come down to report the avalanche. This hasty team searched some of the debris with probe poles but without success. Darkness came soon, and the authorities postponed the search because of poor visibility and additional wind loading, increasing the avalanche hazard.

The morning of Wednesday, December 15, members of the Diamond Peaks Patrol and Larimer County Search and Rescue were on site to continue the search. After determining that rescuers could safely work the debris area, a team with several rescue dogs began work. Within 10 minutes, a dog alerted, and seconds later a probe found Samelson's ski boot. Shovelers dug out his body from beneath two feet of snow. It was later determined that trauma, specifically to the spinal cord, had been the cause of death.

AVALANCHE DATA

Persistent Slab avalanche

After completing the rescue, several members of the patrol and the Search and Rescue team climbed to the crown area of the slide to gather data. The slope faced east, and the avalanche released at an elevation of 11,500 feet and fell 400 vertical feet. The slope angle at the crown was estimated at 45 degrees. The debris field was about 40 yards top to bottom, 60 yards wide, and averaged five feet deep.

Overall, snow depth in the area of the crown averaged 38 inches. The crown itself was 24 inches deep and released on a layer of old snow 14 inches above the ground. The snow beneath the bed surface was heavily faceted, especially in the bottom six to eight inches. In places, the avalanche scoured the snow to the ground. The avalanche was classified as SS-ASu-R2-D2-O. A smaller, sympathetic slide had released adjacent to the fatal slide.

COMMENTS

Avalanche awareness was not part of this group's skill set. No one had any rescue gear other than shovels. Apparently, the group had given no thought to avalanche safety. These factors likely wouldn't have come into play were it not for the victim's poor route selection. Two investigators reconstructed his route by following his ski track once he left his friends. It appears the victim climbed up a slight ridge to a point where he turned left (south) and cut directly across a slope that was steeper than 40 degrees—and triggered the fatal avalanche.

SOUTH ARAPAHO PEAK, NORTHWEST OF ELDORA, COLORADO | December 18, 1999

19991218

Two hikers caught; two partly buried, and one killed

WEATHER AND SNOWPACK CONDITIONS

South Arapaho Peak is a 13,397-foot mountain in the Front Range of Colorado and is most easily approached from the small town of Eldora. On the day of the avalanche, a cold front moved over Colorado's Front Range, bringing an abrupt and nasty change to the weather. By late in the day, a full winter storm was raging in the backcountry; snowfall, strong winds, and blowing snow were creating difficult travel, poor visibility, and increasing avalanche danger.

ACCIDENT SUMMARY

On Saturday, December 18, Justin Colonna (23) and a friend—both students at the University of Colorado in Boulder—attempted a winter climb of South Arapaho Peak. They abandoned their effort in the face of the intensifying storm.

On their descent, they decided to take a shortcut that would save at least several miles and would get them out of the storm faster. The pair walked into a shallow depression that narrowed and steepened just above treeline. The snow-filled gully looked to provide a quick, easy descent to the trail below. The rocky, grassy slopes along sides of the gully were much steeper.

Terrain trap

At about 15:00, the two were separated by about 15 feet when they triggered a small slab avalanche. Colonna's friend was on the edge of the slide and was carried only about 30 feet. When he turned around, Colonna was gone. The survivor was puzzled: he felt his friend could not have been caught, but there was no sign of him. He searched the avalanche for about 90 minutes without success. Finally, he retreated in darkness, and at 17:00 used an emergency phone to report the avalanche to the Boulder Sheriff's Department.

More than one person on a slope

RESCUE SUMMARY

That night, search crews hiked some five miles into the area of the slide and looked for Colonna until about midnight. The search resumed at first light Sunday with 25 searchers from Rocky Mountain Search and Rescue, Alpine Rescue, the Boulder Sheriff's Department, and the U.S. Forest Service returning to the area on snowmobile, cross-country skis, and snowshoes. Colonna's companion, along with rescue dogs, aided the search. While some of the rescue team searched the slide area, others checked out summer cabins and other shelters in the area in case Colonna survived the avalanche and found a place to stay the night.

Their daylong effort was hampered by deep snow, winds up to 30 mph, blowing snow, and subfreezing temperatures. By late Sunday, the search had produced nothing and the avalanche danger had worsened, so the recovery effort was suspended for the day. During the next week, rescuers continued to search both the debris and surrounding areas without success.

The following summer, on June 10, 2000, searchers finally found Colonna's remains—1,200 feet higher in elevation and a mile and a half away from the avalanche site.

AVALANCHE DATA

Wind Slab avalanche

The avalanche was a combination soft and hard slab that ran 500 vertical feet. It released in a south-facing gully loaded by west and northwest winds. At the fracture line, the slope angle was 36 degrees, but the gully steepened further downslope. The fracture line depth ranged from about six to 14 inches and was about 70 feet across. The weak layer was a soft two- to three-inch layer of small faceted grains.

Significant portions of the debris were less than a foot deep, but in many areas the debris piled up four and five feet deep over logs, willows and boulders. In the gully, snow was up to 10 feet deep in spots.

COMMENTS

The best guess is that the avalanche caught Colonna too, but he was unable to see, hear, or otherwise communicate with his companion. Disoriented, possibly injured, he probably climbed back to the pair's original route, searching for his companion, and wandered into the storm.

This inexperienced pair waited too long before abandoning their quest. Poor visibility and rapidly rising avalanche danger made a safe retreat difficult, if not impossible. The two men just wanted off the mountain. They may have given no thought to avalanche danger, or perhaps they thought that such a shallow snow cover could not avalanche.

In this incident, triggering the avalanche did not kill the victim, but it was a distraction that led the two men to get separated in stormy conditions, with each perhaps searching for the other. Only one made it out; the other succumbed to the storm. See 19971123 for an account of an accident that involved several similar factors: avalanche in a gully, darkness, and separated companions.

19991221 QUANDARY PEAK, SOUTHWEST OF BRECKENRIDGE, COLORADO | December 21, 1999

One backcountry skier caught, partly buried, and killed

WEATHER AND SNOWPACK CONDITIONS

A very dry start to the winter in Colorado (one of the driest in 50 years) left little snow on high elevation slopes and gullies during November and early December. What snow that did remain—primarily on north-facing terrain—turned to depth hoar. On December 10, the Breckenridge ski area reported a paltry 16-inch base, and the total seasonal snowfall up to that date had been only 34 inches. But the weather pattern changed, and from December 10 through 21, 30 inches of snow fell, with 18 of those inches falling from December 18 to 21.

The latter stage of this storm system also brought strong winds and cold temperatures (0 to 10°F), which created widespread soft- and hard-slab conditions. Observers in Colorado's northern mountains reported widespread collapsing and shooting cracks. On Monday, December 20, the Copper Mountain Ski Patrol remotely triggered a very large slab—2,000 feet across and five feet deep—on a high elevation, southeast-facing bowl while approaching the path from above. This site was five miles northwest of Quandary Peak.

High avalanche danger

The Colorado Avalanche Information Center had issued an avalanche advisory, rating the avalanche danger as "Considerable, but with areas of High danger on north to southeast-facing slopes above timberline." That advisory concluded with the statement, "Be very careful in the backcountry, for the Colorado mountain snowpack could easily ruin one's Christmas."

ACCIDENT SUMMARY

Quandary Peak is a popular 14,265-foot peak in the Tenmile Range south of Breckenridge. The easy summer trail to the summit is popular in the winter as well, and it attracts skiers whenever the snow cover is good. However, heading off-trail either to the north or south leads to numerous steep, rugged gullies that are a challenge to anyone who ventures there.

On December 19th, Michael Barrett (25), from the Denver metro area, told his sister in Illinois he was going to climb a 14er, but he failed to say where. Early on Tuesday, December 21, he told friends he was going backcountry skiing, but again he did not say where. Friends and co-workers reported him missing on the 23rd. On the 24th, the Broomfield Police Department issued a statewide missing persons report, and late on the 24th, a Summit County Sheriff's deputy noticed Barrett's vehicle parked at the trailhead for Quandary Peak.

Traveling alone

RESCUE SUMMARY

On Christmas morning, the Summit County Rescue Group mobilized a search effort. They came in on the southeast side of Quandary Peak and saw that five avalanches had spilled off the ridge. But lady luck was with searchers that morning; very early in the operation, a searcher happened across a tiny, torn piece of a topographic map. Moving 100 yards farther upslope, he came across another small piece of a topographic map. Minutes later they spotted Barrett's body farther upslope. Searchers found the man buried in the avalanche debris. A leg protruded from the snow. The victim had died of massive trauma.

AVALANCHE DATA

No one witnessed the accident, but it appears Barrett likely triggered a very small hard slab avalanche at the top of a steep, narrow gully on the southeast side of the peak.The crown was one to two feet thick, and it released at an elevation of 13,400 feet. The narrow avalanche fell 1,880 vertical feet, almost reaching the valley floor. The victim was hurled down the very steep, rocky gully. He was buried by debris at the bottom of the last small cliff band about 300 vertical feet above the Blue Lakes road.

Storm Slab avalanche

This avalanche was classified as HS-ASu-R2-I.

COMMENTS

The victim frequently traveled solo in the mountains. Avalanche educators regularly point out that this habit adds an element of risk, in that there is no one available for rescue in case of an accident. In this case, a companion would not have made any difference in the outcome: any fall down this chute would have been fatal. But a companion may have been able to provide advice, such as "Don't go there!"

There is one more detail of this accident that left the rescuers perplexed: Both of the victim's alpine touring (AT) boots were stripped from his feet. Boots only come off a victim when they are worn very loose. Some people loosen their boots for ascending, so was the victim ascending? Or perhaps traversing the starting zone when he triggered the avalanche? Scouting it? Or had he dropped off the main trail, which follows the ridgeline, in order to get on a leeward slope out of the wind? That seems a likely answer. Whatever the victim's rationale, his routefinding choices put him into avalanche terrain with unstable snow and a very dangerous runout.

19991226 SKYSCRAPER MOUNTAIN, HATCHER PASS, NORTH OF PALMER, ALASKA | December 26, 1999

One snowmobiler caught, buried, and killed

WEATHER AND SNOWPACK CONDITIONS

Hatcher Pass (3,900 feet) is situated in the Talkeetna Mountains north of Palmer. In the winter the road is closed, but the area is popular for motorized and non-motorized recreation. Skyscraper Mountain (4,500 feet) sits immediately north of the pass. The road crosses the pass at 3,900 feet elevation, and immediately to the north sits 4,500-foot Skyscraper Mountain.

The first snows of the winter season came in September, and this early snowfall remained on the ground and formed a basal layer of faceted snow (depth hoar). The data on storms between September and early December was not documented, but the week before Christmas was stormy. The Hatcher Pass area received three to six feet of new and wind-loaded snow, and this triggered a widespread natural avalanche cycle, with releases on all aspects.

On December 26, winds gusting to 75 mph were causing extensive blowing snow and slab formation at the time of the accident. Snow plumes were constant throughout the region, including on the ridges of Skyscraper Mountain, which would be the accident site.

Lastly, the temperature rose dramatically over the 24 hours prior to the accident—from near 0° F to 48° F at the time of the accident.

ACCIDENT SUMMARY

It was the day after Christmas, and despite fierce winds and near-blizzard conditions, people were out in force at Hatcher Pass. All three of the parking areas were full. One of the numerous snowmobile riders was Keith Coyne (37). Coyne was a local—and a very experienced rider—who was familiar with the terrain. He was one of six or seven riders who were lined up to highmark a steep slope on Skyscraper Mountain, a slope that rose about 600 feet above them. Coyne was the first to go. The time was 11:30. He had no transceiver or other rescue gear.

No rescue equipment

Coyne made it a few hundred feet up the slope, then ground to a halt and got stuck. He climbed off his machine and was hanging onto the handlebars when a small slide broke out below him. That snow began moving downhill, and witnesses reported that about 10 seconds later, a larger avalanche fractured several hundred feet above Coyne. This larger slide hit Coyne and carried him and his machine back down the slope. The other snowmobilers waiting below turned, fled, and escaped the avalanche, though initially there was some doubt about whether all had escaped.

RESCUE SUMMARY

Approximately twenty people from the surrounding area immediately began searching for Coyne, and at least one person rode to Hatcher Pass Lodge to request help. The debris pile was deep and easily exceeded 10 feet in most areas. There were no visual clues of Coyne or his machine. At the time, there was some confusion as to whether there could be other buried persons, as well. One or more of the first responders had their beacons in transmit mode, so searchers unnecessarily dug several large holes in the debris, thinking they were near a victim.

Lack of training

The search continued for two to three hours before Alaska State Park rangers marked the perimeter of the slide and then cleared the site because of the danger of additional avalanches. Soon after, a second slide did indeed release on a slope next to the searchers. Numerous other natural and human-triggered avalanches occurred during the next several hours, including a large natural release at 14:30 on nearby Marmot Mountain, which covered the uphill lane of the road with a foot of debris. By this time, law enforcement officers were asking an estimated 100-150 recreationists to clear the area in order to avoid further accidents—and in hopes that unclaimed vehicles would help establish the number and identity of buried victims. It was later determined that there were no other missing persons, leaving Coyne as the sole victim.

After the rescue attempt was called off on December 26, a formal rescue was organized for the 27th, using the Motherlode Lodge as a staging area. Alaska Department of Transportation and Public Facilities artillery was used to mitigate the avalanche hazard on the approach and accident site. Authorities fired approximately a dozen rounds bringing down at least two slides, one of which covered the accident site (roughly 150 feet by 150 feet) with an additional four to eight feet of debris. Roughly 75 probers and two dog teams, transported by about 25 snowmobilers, searched the area all day in moderate snow accompanied by 35 mph winds. Three snowcats with blades were used to trench the area where debris depths exceeded 24 feet. Searchers then probed the trenches and side walls. Participants in the search included Alaska State Troopers, Alaska State Parks, Alaska Search and Rescue Dogs, Alaska Search, Rescue, and Recovery Team, Nordic Ski Patrol, Mat-Su Motor Mushers, Glacier Snowcat, Alaska Mountain Rescue Group, Alaska Mountain Safety Center, the Red Cross, and numerous individuals, including Coyne's family and friends.

At 17:30 on December 27, Coyne was located by probers midway down the runout zone. He had originally been buried under seven to eight feet of snow, which was itself covered by four to six feet of additional debris from the artillery-triggered slide. Searchers found him on his back, head downhill, diagonal to the fall line, with both arms stretched out in front of him, pointing towards the snow surface. The visor on his helmet was up.

AVALANCHE DATA

The southeast side of Skyscraper Mountain consists of a large, tundra-covered bowl which benches out, and then from the bench, a very steep slope drops down to the road at the valley floor. The avalanche occurred on the lower slope, which is about 300 feet wide by 700 feet vertical, with slope angles around 40 degrees near the top. Avalanche dimensions were not recorded.

Storm Slab avalanche

COMMENTS

The avalanche danger was high on this day, due to the amount of storm snow and wind-transported snow. Further proof of the high danger was the natural release later in the day of the 26th, and the slides released by artillery on the 27th. Simply put, it was not the right day to be highmarking in avalanche terrain.

High avalanche danger

Nonetheless, the victim and the other riders waiting their turn to highmark did not let the weather and snow conditions deter them. The victim, with no transceiver, was certainly not prepared for an avalanche encounter. The fact that the victim had no beacon became a moot point; even with a beacon, he would not have survived the deep burial that resulted.

A final factor to consider is the dramatic temperature rise in the 24 hours before the avalanche. Could that have contributed to the avalanche release? A rising temperature in a dry snowpack affects the slab's stiffness, but does not necessarily make it weaker. In this accident, the rapid loading effects of a significant snowfall (in excess of three feet in the days before December 26) and strong winds causing heavy blowing snow were the primary factors that created a high avalanche danger. Any temperature effect would be strictly a second-order effect.

20000111 SQUARE TOP, WEST OF CANYONS VILLAGE AT PARK CITY, UTAH | January 11, 2000

Two sidecountry skiers caught, buried, and killed

WEATHER AND SNOWPACK CONDITIONS

West-to-southwest winds had been blowing in the Wasatch Range of Utah on January 10 and 11. The winds had transported enough recently-fallen snow to load north- through east-facing slopes along the Wasatch crest.

ACCIDENT SUMMARY

On January 11, Park City residents Greg (47) and Loren (41) Mackay were skiing at a resort northeast of Park City that was then named The Canyons (now Canyons Village at Park City). Friends described the husband and wife as very good skiers who looked for powder but never seemed reckless in this pursuit. At about noon that day they were seen at the backcountry access gate near the top of the Ninety-Nine 90 chairlift. There, a ski patroller discouraged them from leaving the ski area that day. The Mackays went anyway.

The couple then skied and hiked about a mile west across a saddle to a 9,770-foot peak that is a popular backcountry location for skiers and snowboarders. The local name for the peak is Square Top. It is steep, with slope angles of 37 to 38 degrees, and is known avalanche terrain. At some point in their descent, they triggered an avalanche that buried them both.

RESCUE SUMMARY

When the Mackays failed to pick up their son Connor (3) from day care on Tuesday afternoon, Sheriff's deputies and several friends began looking for the missing couple. That night, a friend found the Mackays' car in the Canyons parking lot. This find triggered a search of the Canyons' ski terrain through the night, yielding nothing.

The following morning, during a helicopter search of the terrain surrounding the ski area, rescuers saw the avalanche on Square Top, with ski tracks going in and none coming out. About 45 search and rescue volunteers and ski patrollers then went to the site. The rescuers concentrated their search down the fall line from the ski tracks entering the fracture line, but found no visible clues or beacon signals. A probe line began working uphill from the toe of the debris and soon had success.

Searchers first found a ski, then a body, and then, about 20 minutes and 60 feet farther uphill, the second body. Neither body showed obvious signs of trauma, so it appeared death was by suffocation. The woman was buried about 18 inches deep; the man 3.5 feet deep.

AVALANCHE DATA

This avalanche was classified as a HS-ASu-R4-D3. It released on the northeast side of Square Top at an elevation near 9,700 feet, and the slope angle was about 37 degrees. The crown was three to five feet deep and 600 feet wide, and the avalanche fell 1,000 feet vertical. The slide mostly ran on a firm bed surface but gouged into a layer of faceted snow in places.

Deep Persistent Slab avalanche

COMMENTS

This sad accident left the couple's 3-year-old son parentless. This couple seemed unaware of the risks they were taking, even after the ski patroller at the backcountry access gate had urged them not to go.

A little avalanche education would have gone a long way here, starting with the attitude that "sidecountry is backcountry." Had the couple abided by the basic rules of safe backcountry skiing, the outcome would have been better, even if the avalanche had still occurred. Specifically, they could have started with 1) having beacons, shovels, and probes and 2) skiing one at a time. If they had followed these two tenets, there would have been one buried victim and one rescuer, instead of two helpless buried victims.

No rescue equipment

EXTERMINATOR, CRYSTAL MOUNTAIN RESORT, WASHINGTON | January 16, 2000

20000116

One skier caught, buried, and killed

WEATHER AND SNOWPACK CONDITIONS

Weather conditions at Crystal Mountain in the southern Cascades on Sunday morning, January 16, 2000, could best be described as horrible on the upper mountain and very stormy and windy on the lower mountain. At 06:00, sensors near the top of the Rainier Express Chair at 6,800 feet measured winds at 20 to 30 mph with gusts to 40; by about mid-day, winds there had increased to 30 to 50 mph with gusts to over 70. Wind gusts over 100 mph were also recorded at the break-over tower on Rainier Express around mid-day.

The gale-force winds, along with snowfall and blowing snow, limited the ski patrol's use of chairlifts to access the upper mountain for avalanche hazard mitigation. They had run the High Campbell lift very early in the morning but after that relied on snowcats to transport mitigation teams to the rest of the upper mountain. Despite the extensive avalanche mitigation work, the ski area did not open any of the upper lifts to the public because of the deteriorating weather conditions.

ACCIDENT SUMMARY

At approximately noon, the wind holds for all upper lifts were continuing. Chair 1 (also known as Miner's Basin Lift) ran parallel to the Exterminator run and lifted skiers to a midpoint on the mountain. (Note: Miner's Basin Lift was removed some years later, and the Mount Rainier Gondola now runs on a similar line, but the gondola goes all the way to the summit of the mountain.) A ski patroller stationed near the top of Chair 1 noticed two skiers had crossed a rope line and were climbing up the Iceberg Gulch run to access higher terrain, which was normally serviced by the closed Rainier Express Chair.

The patroller yelled at the two skiers, warning of avalanche danger and trying to turn the party around. The party continued to climb. The skiers were climbing into avalanche terrain that was being heavily loaded with storm snow—terrain that patrollers had not been able to access for avalanche hazard mitigation.

Inadequate rescue equipment

The two men were Gordon McWilliams (50), a former ski patroller, and John Christiansen (42). Both were strong, experienced skiers. They both owned avalanche transceivers but had not brought them this day. The two men climbed about 1,000 feet above Chair 1 and reached the ridgeline at the top of Iceberg Gulch. They traveled along the ridge east to a small knob (Exterminator Point) above the Snag Chutes, a pair of shallow gullies on the Exterminator run.

The two men had a bite of lunch and discussed the avalanche danger. They had seen a couple of other skiers hiking in the area but had not seen avalanches. As Christiansen later related, "We knew the risks—not only the risk of avalanche, but that it was quite windy and visibility was poor. We talked about that at some length." After watching the other skiers go past without triggering anything, the two agreed to go down one at a time.

The time was about 13:15. McWilliams went first; Christiansen kept watch. "Gordon was the leader and he went off first and was caught in a very large avalanche, a wind-blown slab up to 70 yards across and a couple of feet deep," Christiansen said. "I lost sight of him. I didn't realize how big a slide this was, and was hopeful that he had either skied out of it or had been able to stay on the surface or out of the slide. I spent some time searching for him, hoping that he had either skied down a ways and was hiking back to me, or was reporting me missing down below."

Another party observed the avalanche. They were employees at the mountaintop restaurant who had been transported there that morning by snowcat. Around noon, they were told that the upper lifts would not open, so they should return to the base area. They were instructed to ski down Lucky Shot, an intermediate run, to avoid any avalanche danger. However, they instead skied and boarded toward Exterminator and Snag Chutes. Although they did not see anyone caught in the slide, they were aware of other skiers in the area. After the avalanche, they proceeded downhill toward the base area, rode the lift up to the midway area, and reported the slide they had witnessed, as well as the fact that they had seen other skiers in the area, to the patroller stationed there.

RESCUE SUMMARY

At around 13:30, the Ski Patrol Director, the Snow Safety Director, and a patroller were en route to the mountaintop via snowcat to re-evaluate the avalanche danger and assess whether to conduct further control work if the winds moderated and allowed for an afternoon opening. They got the radio report of the avalanche, and the patrol director and the ski patroller immediately skied toward the Snag Chutes area. They also requested the dispatch of additional avalanche rescue resources. The Snow Safety Director got explosives from the mountaintop magazine and followed behind. They arrived at the site in poor visibility because of the high winds and blowing snow, but they could easily see the fracture line. They assessed the remaining avalanche danger before proceeding down the bed surface to begin an initial search. Upon skiing downhill, they encountered Christiansen looking for his friend. The patrollers talked with Christiansen and got the story of what had happened.

The initial responders began a hasty search on this very large path. It was difficult to get additional rescue resources to the site because the strong winds kept the Mountain

Top lift from running. Despite that challenge, three avalanche dogs and approximately 40 other rescuers arrived on the scene within the hour and worked the large avalanche path, searching for surface clues and probing likely burial sites in the deposition. The main search effort was concentrated in the avalanche's runout zone, which included a dense band of cedar trees at about 5,200 feet. The larger trees all had mounds of debris piled on their uphill sides.

Meanwhile, several ski area personnel canvassed the base of the ski area, hoping to find that the potential victim had survived the avalanche and was waiting for his friend near the base. Also during this time, rescuers brought Christiansen back to the top of the avalanche path to once again identify the last seen area, which could hopefully yield more specific information and quicken the search. The amount of wind-drifted snow complicated the search; it made it hard for the rescuers to determine what was avalanche debris and what was not.

Finally, at about 15:25, a young avalanche dog named Rocket alerted strongly at the very toe of the debris. Rocket's handler probed the spot and struck the victim. McWilliams was buried three and a half feet deep. He had no pulse, and it was readily apparent that he had suffered multiple blunt trauma injuries as he was carried down the heavily-treed path. Ski patrol immediately applied life support procedures including airway ventilation and CPR. A ski patrol doctor pronounced the victim dead at the scene, and a subsequent autopsy confirmed that blunt trauma injury was the cause of death.

The search continued for another hour since it was unclear if anyone else had been caught. However, after finishing exhaustive search efforts with dogs and probers, and receiving no further reports of missing recreationists in the ski area, the search-and-rescue effort was concluded in impending darkness at about 16:30.

AVALANCHE DATA

Persistent Slab avalanche

The slide released at approximately 6,200 feet elevation on an east-northeast-facing slope and fell approximately 1,000 vertical feet. It was classified as HS-ASu-R3-D3-O. Slope angles measured just above the fracture line and on the bed surface were 38 degrees. Fracture line depths ranged from less than a foot on the northern flank of the slide and two to four feet near the top and south flank.

Another incident confirmed the high avalanche danger on this day and complicated the rescue efforts. At about the same time the Snag Chutes avalanche occurred, a backcountry party triggered an avalanche across the valley from the ski resort. This slide partly buried a skier, who suffered a broken femur. Multiple calls came into the Crystal Mountain Ski Patrol for assistance in rescuing this backcountry avalanche victim. Initially, there was no confirmed location. Given the poor visibility and stretched resources committed to the McWilliams rescue effort, the ski patrol decided not to initiate a second search. Subsequent reports eventually confirmed the victim's location. With that important new information, seriousness of the injury, remote location, and severe weather, the patrol responded to this accident while still in the midst of the McWilliams rescue. They safely recovered the victim of the backcountry avalanche and transported him to the patrol room.

COMMENTS

The search for powder unfortunately has always and may always lead to avalanche deaths. Knowledge, experience, good decision-making, and survival/rescue gear collectively help save lives. The two men involved in this accident had the knowledge, experience, and decision-making skills to safely travel in the backcountry, though they did not carry their rescue gear that day. But they made a poor decision by crossing the rope into uncontrolled terrain, which was effectively backcountry terrain with danger-ous avalanche conditions. It was that decision that was fatal, because rescue gear would not have saved McWilliams in this avalanche.

Several days after this accident, John Christiansen spoke with a Seattle Times report-er. He said he had been struggling to glean some reason out of what happened that Sunday, some lesson to hang onto. "I've been skiing and ski mountaineering since I was a boy, and I read the papers, and I read about events like this. And often, people want to know why, and what went wrong, and who's at fault," he said. "Both Gordon and I love the out-of-doors, and love the experience of being immersed in that envi-ron-ment," he said. "And it's an unfortunate reality that there's a risk that you take in that sort of activity. And Gordon paid the ultimate price." A price, it should be noted, that he would not have paid had he and Christiansen not ignored the closure.

20000123 JONES PASS, SOUTHWEST OF BERTHOUD PASS, COLORADO | January 23, 2000

Three snowshoers caught; two partly buried, one buried and killed

WEATHER AND SNOWPACK CONDITIONS

November of 1999 was a particularly dry month in Colorado, and the early-season snow cover in the Colorado Rockies was thin, weak, and riddled with facets. December brought slightly-below-normal snow to the Front Range, but the backcountry snow cover continued to be shallow and weak. Then January 2000 brought a series of storms that resulted in above-normal snowfall for the month; the last two weeks of the month were most impressive—snow fell every day in all mountain areas.

The January snowfall led to a snowpack that consisted of a weak layer of depth hoar just above the ground, then a month-old and somewhat harder slab layer in the middle, topped by the load of recent storm snow. The snowpack was primed for an avalanche and was just waiting for triggers.

From January 19 through the morning of the 23rd, Berthoud Pass and Winter Park Ski Resort both measured 22 inches of snowfall.

ACCIDENT SUMMARY

Jones Pass is located in the Front Range of Colorado and is a popular area for snow-shoers, skiers and snowboarders. It gets a lot of weekend use because of its easy access from the Denver metro area. The main winter recreation area is a high basin that is easily reached by a short uphill trek on a summer road.

On Sunday, January 23, three Denver residents went for a day of snowshoeing in the area of Jones Pass. The trio included husband and wife Christopher (29) and Nicole (27) Crippen from Denver, and Tracy Lynn Cooper (26), who had recently moved to Denver from Houston. On rented snowshoes, they walked into the basin. They carried no avalanche rescue gear.

No rescue equipment

At about 13:30, they were crossing a steep, east-facing slope above the Jones Pass summer jeep road. The slope was dotted with pine and aspen trees. The group was spread out with some 20 to 30 feet between them. Nicole Crippen was in the lead, followed by Cooper and then Christopher Crippen. The avalanche broke more than 100 feet above them, catching all three. Nicole was buried to the waist, and her husband Christopher was swept into a tree and buried to the shoulders. Cooper was carried farther downslope and totally buried.

RESCUE SUMMARY

Minutes after the avalanche, another skier rounded a corner on the Jones Pass road, saw the avalanche (which had run across the road), and heard Nicole Crippen calling for help. This man quickly made a 911 call on his cell phone. The Alpine Rescue Team and the Clear Creek County Sheriff's Office got the call at 13:33. Eventually, about 40 searchers from various agencies would participate in the rescue.

Meanwhile, the Crippens were able to dig themselves out of the debris, and they were joined by other skiers and snowshoers in the area, all of whom began the search for Cooper.

After the Search and Rescue teams began to arrive, several probe lines and several dogs worked the debris area, which was eight to 10 feet deep in places. The dogs were ineffective, either because of so many searchers in the area, or because of the deep burial. About two hours after the avalanche, a probe line located Cooper's body under six feet of snow. She had not survived this deep burial.

AVALANCHE DATA

Persistent Slab avalanche

This avalanche released on an east-facing slope at an elevation of 11,310 feet. Vegetation included several lone trees and at least one group of four trees. The slope angle at the crown varied from 34 to 38 degrees. Fracture depth was three feet at its deepest. The avalanche released as a slab. Once set in motion, portions of the avalanche scoured out a mid-pack layer of hard slab, and where that occurred, the avalanche removed a 10-inch-deep layer of depth hoar and ran to ground.

The avalanche was about 80 feet wide at the crown but widened to 150 feet partway down the slope. It was classified as SS-AIu-R3-D2-O.

COMMENTS

Lack of training

All evidence points to three young people with little or no awareness of avalanche dangers. The avalanche danger was High, a fact they may not have been aware of. They carried no rescue gear, and their route traversed an avalanche path that would have been obvious to trained eyes. Many people that day had used the summer road that crossed the lower part of this slide path without incident. The slab was not triggerable from that location, most likely because of a compacted snow cover on the level road. However, the avalanche was easily triggered when the snowshoers traversed directly across the steep upper track or start zone, resulting in a collapse of the weak layer and a deadly avalanche.

High avalanche danger

The Colorado Avalanche Information Center posted avalanche warnings for the Front Range from January 23 to 28. During this period, three fatal avalanche accidents occurred.

20000125a STEEP GULLIES, WEST OF ARAPAHOE BASIN SKI AREA, COLORADO | January 25, 2000

One sidecountry snowboarder caught, buried, and killed

WEATHER AND SNOWPACK CONDITIONS

High avalanche danger

The account of the fatal accident two days prior at Jones Pass (20000123) includes a summary of the season's snowpack development. An avalanche warning issued by the CAIC was in effect for backcountry areas of the Front Range on January 25. The warning area included the backcountry terrain surrounding Arapahoe Basin ski area, which had received 37 inches of snow from January 19-25.

ACCIDENT SUMMARY

The Steep Gullies are a series of steep, rock-lined chutes about a quarter mile west of the Arapahoe Basin ski area boundary. They are frequented by skiers and boarders who access the area via a gate in the Arapahoe Basin boundary and who often do several laps a day, hitchhiking back up US Highway 6 to return to the ski area.

Terrain trap

The area is known for being dangerous, and that's part of the appeal—if you can ski it or ride it, you are pretty good. These narrow gullies present formidable terrain traps that funnel snow down their guts, and if caught by a slide, there are few chances for escape.

On Tuesday, January 25, at about 12:30, two snowboarders, Corin Rowe (21) and Grayson Jones (21) crossed the roped ski-area boundary (not through the access gate) and headed toward the Steep Gullies. The pair had already made one run in that area, during which they triggered a small slide. They had no avalanche rescue gear.

No rescue equipment

On their second trip down, Rowe triggered another slide and was swept out of sight down the gully. Jones attempted to find his friend, but seeing no clues, he quickly decided to go for help. There was another group of three snowboarders nearby who also helped in the initial search, again without success.

RESCUE SUMMARY

Rescuers were dispatched to the accident scene at 13:05 and arrived there by 13:20. The highway was closed for several hours as search teams worked at the base of the slide. The rescuers brought in avalanche dogs, and soon one alerted. Rowe was uncovered at 14:18. He had been buried with one hand only about eight inches beneath the surface, but he had obviously suffered severe trauma, bashing into rocks and trees during the fatal slide.

AVALANCHE DATA

Persistent Slab avalanche

The avalanche released at an elevation of 12,100 feet in a northwest-facing gully, and it fell 1,600 feet vertical. The crown was two to three feet deep and 180 feet wide. It broke to the ground and removed the recent storm snow, the mid-pack layer, and the depth hoar in the bottom layer. The avalanche was classified as SS-ARu-R3-G.

COMMENTS

The Steep Gullies are backcountry terrain, regardless of their proximity to a ski area. These riders apparently disregarded the dangers they might face in such terrain, perhaps because it was so close to a ski area boundary. And also, perhaps, because of their youth and inexperience. It was Rowe's first winter in Colorado, and the pair probably knew little about avalanche danger in general, let alone about the inherent danger presented by the depth hoar so common to the Colorado mountain snowpack.

Basic avalanche safety education may have helped them to recognize the danger. It might have helped them to see the small slide they triggered on their first run as a sign of dangerous conditions. And they did not carry rescue gear, which slowed rescue and recovery efforts.

For Grayson Jones, the survivor, the ordeal was not over after searchers found Rowe's body. The two men, perhaps unwittingly, had ducked under a boundary rope instead of leaving the ski area through a backcountry access gate. The Colorado Skier Safety Act allows skiers and snowboarders to legally pass from a ski area into the backcountry, but requires them to do so through a gate, where signs inform them that they are leaving the ski resort and that avalanche dangers may lie beyond. Ducking a rope was a violation of the act, punishable by a maximum fine of $300.

The day following the avalanche, Grayson Jones was brought before Judge Ryan, who asked Jones if he had anything to say for himself. Jones responded, "You can do anything to me, but nothing will come close to losing a friend." Judge Ryan agreed that there was no fine equivalent to having a friend die, and he waived the charges. Instead, the judge ordered Jones to make a charitable donation of $150 to the Colorado Avalanche Information Center.

HURRICANE BOWL, SOUTH OF ASPEN, COLORADO

20000125b

January 25, 2000

One backcountry skier caught, buried, and killed

WEATHER AND SNOWPACK CONDITIONS

The account of the fatal accident two days prior at Jones Pass (20000123) includes a summary of the season's snowpack development in Colorado.

High avalanche danger

ACCIDENT SUMMARY

Hurricane Bowl lies on the west side of Richmond Hill, about 4.5 miles south of Aspen. Most of the bowl is less than 30 degrees in steepness, but it funnels into a very steep, narrow gully about 1,000 feet below the ridgeline. A road crosses below this funnel as it climbs from Castle Creek toward the Little Annie Mine; most of the road is snow-covered in the winter.

Carl "Chip" Johnson (37) was an Aspen area resident and an experienced backcountry skier. On Tuesday, January 25, Johnson was skiing with friends in the backcountry terrain on Richmond Hill outside the boundary of Aspen Mountain Ski Area. Toward the end of the afternoon, Johnson's girlfriend realized she had forgotten her backpack at the top of Aspen Mountain. They made a plan for her to catch a snowmobile ride back to the top of the ski area to retrieve her pack while Johnson skied down to the cars, which were near the bottom of the Little Annie Basin road. They planned to rendezvous at the parking area between 16:30 and 17:00.

Traveling alone

After his girlfriend left, Johnson was skiing alone. His route took him into the narrow gully below Hurricane Bowl, about a half-mile from the parking area. He probably was near the bottom of the gully when he triggered an avalanche that released well above him and buried him.

Terrain trap

RESCUE SUMMARY

When Johnson failed to show up, his girlfriend summoned help from some local residents. She and a friend then snowmobiled from the parking area back to the top of the slope, intending to find and follow the victim's tracks. Along the way, they met an Aspen Mountain ski patroller who was snowmobiling home from work. Those three rounded up one other friend to help search, and they set out to find Johnson's ski tracks. They had beacons, probes, and shovels.

One man followed the victim's tracks into the narrow gully, which had a steep, north-facing slope. Johnson's ski tracks disappeared into avalanche debris. The other three rescuers approached from the bottom. When they realized what had happened, they instructed Johnson's girlfriend to get additional help while the other three started the search. She called the Pitkin County Sheriff's Office at 17:45.

No rescue equipment

A beacon search was unsuccessful, so the trio started probing the center of the gully. Standing three across, the trio could easily cover the narrow gully bottom. They made a strike after 20 minutes of probing. They found Johnson upside down, in a headstand position. His head was buried under six feet of snow. They attempted CPR without success. The victim's mouth and nose were plugged with snow.

Members of Mountain Rescue Aspen arrived to help evacuate the body. By that time, it was dark and snowing moderately.

AVALANCHE DATA

Persistent Slab avalanche

The avalanche released on a 38- to 40-degree slope that faced north-northwest and was well below treeline at about 10,200 feet elevation. The avalanche fell about 100 vertical feet and was 150 feet wide. The fracture line was about 2.5 feet deep, and the avalanche ran to ground. The terrain was a classic terrain trap, and the avalanche debris filled the gully eight feet deep.

This avalanche was classified as SS-ASu-R2-G. Prior to this accident, other observers in the Richmond Hill area reported that the lower half of the snowpack consisted of faceted grains (sugar snow) and depth hoar (advanced faceted grains).

COMMENTS

One of the first tenants of backcountry riding is "Don't ski alone." Another is "Carry avalanche rescue gear, even near ski areas." Had Johnson abided by these principles and descended with his girlfriend, as originally planned, he might have survived the slide.

But Johnson's truly fatal error was skiing into a narrow gully with steep sidewalls. In terrain features like these, debris from a small slide can pile up deeply on its victim. Viewed from this perspective, even a companion equipped with beacon, probe, and shovel may have not been able to save the victim's life in such a deep burial.

20000126 EYAK LAKE, EAST OF CORDOVA, ALASKA

January 26, 2000

Seven buildings damaged or destroyed; five people caught; one killed

WEATHER AND SNOWPACK CONDITIONS

Cordova, Alaska, is a fishing town that sits on the rocky eastern shore of Prince William Sound, a large inlet of the Gulf of Alaska. No roads lead in or out, making it reachable only by boat or plane. There is, however, a road leading from town to the airport 13 miles east. At Mile 5.5, along a loop between the main road and the shore of Eyak Lake, is a cluster of houses and buildings. These structures also sit in the shadow of the Heney Range, which rises about 2,000 feet above.

Snow had been falling for much of the week prior to the accident. The heavy, wet snow had piled up six feet deep. On the morning of Wednesday, January 26, winds of 50 mph were causing whiteout conditions. The heavy snowfall and gale-force winds had also brought the avalanche danger to the tipping point on the mountain slope above the houses and buildings along Eyak Lake.

ACCIDENT SUMMARY

It was about 09:45 when several people heard a rumble, and within seconds, a massive avalanche slammed into the homes and buildings. Jerry LeMaster (50) had been shoveling snow and had just come inside his house when he heard the sound; a split second later, the back wall exploded, and he was buried in the rubble. His partner, Martha Quales (63) was also somewhere inside the house.

A few houses away, Wes Burton was in bed nursing a recent knee injury when he heard a rumble; then the electricity went off, and then the whole house moved. His girlfriend, Christal Czarnecki, was taking a shower when the room went dark, the water shut off, the whole room shuddered, and everything came crashing off shelves and out of cabinets. The first floor of their house had disintegrated; the second floor, where Wes and Christal were, remained somewhat intact, sliding about 20 feet over the rubble of the first floor and ending up on top of their car, which had been parked in the pulverized carport. They were uninjured.

Kirk Gunnerson lived on the other side of LeMaster and Quales' house. He was talking on the phone when he was hit with what felt like a bomb blast. He was thrown forward as his house blew apart. Amazingly, he was neither buried nor injured.

In addition to the three houses, the avalanche also destroyed a construction company warehouse, and did lesser damage to several other houses.

RESCUE SUMMARY

The accident site was several miles from downtown Cordova. Emergency dispatch in Cordova logged its first 911 call at 09:56. More calls followed, coming from homeowners, plow drivers, motorists, and other witnesses. Dispatch notified the police and fire department of a massive avalanche at Mile 5.5.

When rescuers arrived, they saw an area of destruction the size of a city block. Their first task was to bring a sense of order to the scene: Whose houses were hit? Who was accounted for? Who was missing?

By talking to witnesses and survivors, the rescuers determined that only LeMaster and Quales were still missing, so that they focused on the wreckage of their house. Rescuers began shoveling snow and pulling apart the wreckage, as well as calling out into openings to see if there was any response. At about 12:30, they found the body of Martha Quales amid the debris of the living room.

They continued their search for LeMaster, but it was slow work. LeMaster was a member of the volunteer fire department, so rescuers tried paging him to make his beeper sound. Every so often, they'd order all cell phones, radios and backhoe engines silenced so they could listen. They were holding another paging test at 14:55 when they first heard LeMaster. It took another 30 minutes of digging into the snow and pulling away scraps of debris before they could free him. He was pinned next to the furnace, which itself had held up a fallen door and a beam. That jumble created the air space that kept him alive.

AVALANCHE DATA

This avalanche was classified as HS-N-R5-D4. It was approximately 1,000 feet wide and piled debris up to 30 feet deep.

COMMENTS

An excellent account of this avalanche can be found in Chapters 1 and 11 of Jill Fredston's *Snowstruck*[1].

The 5.5 Mile area outside of Cordova had a history of avalanches going back more than a century. Indeed, a photo taken of the area in 1907 showed a broad treeless swath at that very area, the result of periodic large avalanches that swept it bare. Following the disaster of 2000, the city of Cordova's political leaders called in Doug Fesler and Jill Fredston as consultants to recommend what should be done with the area. As it turned out, their recommendation to condemn the area took traction with the city council. Additionally, the Federal Emergency Management Agency (FEMA) came on board with a plan to purchase damaged properties in the "red zone" at pre-avalanche prices and to pay the cost of moving houses that had not suffered heavy damage to new locations. Before the following winter, all intact houses had been moved, and the area had been declared a high-hazard zone with building banned for perpetuity.

20000201 BIRD FLATS, WEST OF GIRDWOOD, ALASKA

February 1, 2000

Three workers caught; two partly buried, and one killed

WEATHER AND SNOWPACK CONDITIONS

In the last week of January, about 70 inches of snow fell in and around Alyeska Ski Resort, near Girdwood, southeast of Anchorage. The snowfall was part of a series of storms that pounded southcentral Alaska in late January 2000. This same storm cycle led to the destructive and fatal avalanche that struck near Cordova on January 26 (20000126).

ACCIDENT SUMMARY

The Seward Highway links Anchorage, Girdwood and towns on the Kenai Peninsula. The Alaska Railroad and a major powerline share a common route with the highway along the high-tide mark of Turnagain Arm, an inlet of the Gulf of Alaska. Above this infrastructure rises a series of avalanche paths that can drop enormous amounts of snow to the valley flats and simultaneously block the highway and railway and disrupt power transmission.

On Monday, January 31, several avalanches released and blocked the highway. Work crews were headed that way to plow through the slides when another avalanche nearly wiped out the highway avalanche forecaster in his truck. He retreated and decided it was too dangerous to bring in the plows, so the highway between Anchorage and Girdwood remained closed until road crews could work safely. And then things got even worse.

An avalanche ran over the highway southeast of Girdwood. Three vehicles turned around at the debris, but before they could escape, another slide hit and partly buried two of the cars. Now nine people were trapped. A rotary plow could not cut through the slide debris because of broken trees in the snow, so the motorists spent a cold, sleepless night in their cars. To add to the overall mess, power was knocked out between Anchorage and Girdwood sometime during the night, perhaps because of another avalanche.

The next morning, February 1, there was a lull in the storm. The Air National Guard in Anchorage sent a helicopter to rescue the nine motorists trapped south of Girdwood. They also flew others who had been stranded in Girdwood for two to three days back to Anchorage. Equally importantly, the lull allowed the highway avalanche crew to fly over the area to see if explosives could be dropped in avalanche zones, which would reduce the danger before sending in the plows. It also allowed Chugach Electric to fly to find the powerline break.

The powerline break was easy to spot: the air/powder blast from one of the natural slides had destroyed one of the transmission towers, and repairing the damage would have to wait until the avalanche danger had abated.

But there was nothing to stop the helicopter mission to bomb the hillside's chutes to trigger avalanches from any remaining snow. That mission released nothing of any size, so avalanche forecasters for the Transportation Department and the Railroad deemed it safe to begin clearing the 10 to 15 foot deep snow piles from the highway.

But the fair weather lasted little more than an hour. The wind quickly picked up, blowing snow back into avalanche start zones. Bill Mowl, an Anchorage district transportation superintendent, later commented, "When we started, it was dead calm. An hour later, it went to hell."[2]

An avalanche spotter was put in place to observe the start zone of the avalanche path above the work area, a chute named Five Fingers. Three bulldozers began clearing snow off the highway. At 12:30 the avalanche released. A few seconds later the spotter screamed "Avalanche!" into the radio. But how do you move three bulldozers to safety in seconds? You don't.

Larry Bushnell saw it coming. All three operators spun their bulldozers to face the mountain and lifted their blades in the air to absorb the brunt of the avalanche. Bushnell was belted in his seat. "I could hear the windows starting to crackle and shatter. Then one popped and so did the others. There was so much pressure."[3]

He turned his face to the left, taking the force of the pounding snow with his right side. The blast of air ripped off his glasses and radio headset. "At one point, I couldn't breathe," he recalled. "I was gasping for air. I thought I was a goner. It didn't move the dozer, but I felt like I was being ripped out of it." When the snow settled, Bushnell was cemented in the cab with snow to his chest.

He looked over at the Caterpillar that had been working 50 feet to his right. It had vanished. The snow had pummeled that bulldozer so hard it was pushed several hundred feet onto the Turnagain Arm mud flats and flipped over. The driver, Kerry Brookman (53), was buried in snow, but he was able to stick his hand out and wave at people nearby. It was a signal that he needed help.

Brookman was in bad shape. The avalanche had rolled his 35,000-pound D6 Cat out onto the frozen mud flats and crushed the cab. The avalanche had ripped off his snowsuit. He was cold, in shock, and was suffering from internal injuries that would later become apparent. Brookman was airlifted by helicopter to Providence Alaska

Medical Center in Anchorage, and spent all afternoon in surgery for a crushed pelvis, other internal injuries, and bleeding. Surgery could not save his life; Brookman died that night.

AVALANCHE DATA

Wind Slab avalanche

This avalanche released at an elevation of about 2,800 feet and fell to sea level. An air blast likely accompanied the high-speed snow, which increased its destructive potential. The avalanche was classified as HS-N-R5-D4.

COMMENTS

Avalanche forecasting is far from an exact science. Forecasters at ski resorts, heli-ski operations, in the backcountry, and on highways and railways are faced with daily—even hourly—decisions. They combine data on terrain, weather, and snowpack to assess avalanche danger levels. Based on that information, they can use explosives to lessen or eliminate the danger, but with full knowledge that explosive mitigation is also not an exact science; it may work 99% of the time, but 99% is not 100%. Lastly, there is always pressure—sometimes enormous pressure—to get a ski area or highway open. On this day, the helicopter bombing mission produced very little and gave the forecasters an indication that the danger had diminished.

Therefore, it is hard to find fault with the decision to proceed with the snow-clearing operation. A small window of opportunity opened with a break in the storm. However, when the wind resumed, that window slammed shut. Blowing snow began reloading the avalanche starting zones, and the avalanche danger increased by the minute. At that point, the forecasters needed to recognize conditions had change for the worse and a decision to halt the operation was warranted.

20000219a

ST. CHARLES CANYON, WEST OF ST. CHARLES, IDAHO

February 19, 2000

Two snowmobilers caught; one buried and killed

WEATHER AND SNOWPACK CONDITIONS

In mid-February, sustained snowfall and a powerful wind event hit the Bear River Range, west of Bear Lake in southeast Idaho. The snowfall started about February 10, and about four feet of snow accumulated over the next nine days. On the 14th, a significant wind episode produced average winds of 30 mph from the west-southwest but with gusts estimated at nearly 100 mph. On the 19th, the Utah Avalanche Center's Logan-area forecast—which covers the southern end of the Bear River Range—was still warning of the lingering threat of unpredictable hard slabs.

ACCIDENT SUMMARY

More than one person on a slope

St. Charles is a small town on the shores of Bear Lake in southeast Idaho. St. Charles Canyon is one of several canyons that leads west and provides access to the Bear River Range. On Saturday, February 19, two snowmobilers were riding on the slopes in the Middle Fork of St. Charles Canyon. At about 13:40, they were highmarking in a narrow gully below a steep, wind-loaded bowl. One rider became stuck near the top of the slope. His partner rode to help him, observed the slide release, and saw his friend try to swim with the snow. The survivor turned his sled around and gave it full throttle, narrowly outrunning the slide. They had no beacons, shovels, or probes. The survivor searched for his partner using a tree limb for about 15 minutes before leaving the scene and contacting the Bear Lake County Sheriff's Office.

No rescue equipment

RESCUE SUMMARY

Confusion over the exact location of the accident site and difficulty getting rescuers there limited rescue efforts. The debris was randomly probed by about 30 people until the search was called off for the day, by which time they had found only the victim's helmet and jacket.

On Sunday morning, the rescue team returned to the site, this time with five rescue dogs. In less than an hour, searchers found the victim's body beneath six feet of snow near the toe of the debris. The report did not mention whether a probe or dog located the victim. The snowmobile was not located.

AVALANCHE DATA

The avalanche was classified as HS-AMu-R4-D3-O. It ran on a rain crust formed on January 19. The crown depth was two to four feet and was approximately 300 feet wide. The slide released on a 37-degree east-facing slope at 9,200 feet and ran to 8,600 feet. The avalanche path narrowed quickly into a gully and dog-legged to the left in the runout.

Persistent Slab avalanche

COMMENTS

All evidence points to two snowmobilers who gave no thought to avalanche danger. They were highmarking during a time of elevated avalanche danger. They were both on the slope together. They had no rescue gear.

After numerous accidents involving multiple riders, a cardinal rule of highmarking has become apparent: If a person gets stuck, do not send a second sledder to help. Doing so adds weight to the slope, which increases the chances of triggering an avalanche—one that involves two avalanche victims rather than one.

WRIGHT PEAK, SOUTH OF LAKE PLACID, NEW YORK

20000219b

February 19, 2000

Six backcountry skiers caught; five injured, one buried and killed

WEATHER AND SNOWPACK CONDITIONS

Few details are available on conditions before and at the time of the accident, other than that a storm had brought snowfall, wind, and blowing snow to the Lake Placid area.

ACCIDENT SUMMARY

This fatal accident occurred in the Adirondack Mountains of upstate New York, about five miles south of Lake Placid. At 4,580 feet elevation, Wright Peak stands adjacent to Algonquin Peak, which is taller and better known. But in September 1999, Hurricane

Floyd brought heavy rain to the Adirondacks, causing several major mudslides. A mudslide had removed a swath of dense vegetation on the north side of Wright Peak, creating an open slope—enticing for skiers.

On Saturday, February 19, six backcountry skiers, including Toma Jacob Vracarich (27), skinned up Wright Peak to ski the steep, open northeast-facing slope. They were described as experienced skiers, but they apparently had no rescue gear. On their approach, they passed several signs that warned of avalanche danger, and park rangers warned them of dangerous conditions verbally.

No rescue equipment

At about 13:00, all six were skiing together when they triggered the avalanche, and all six were caught. Vracarich was the only victim to be buried, but the other five sustained injuries. One of the survivors, Rohan Roy, later stated that he saw the fracture occur, and then heard a rumble as the avalanche swept the skiers down the slope.

More than one person on a slope

"It was like being strained through the woods, just like a little pinball being pushed through the trees by a 100 mph force,"[4] he recalled.

The slide was witnessed by others in the area, and they notified the park rangers.

RESCUE SUMMARY

It took an hour for park rangers to arrive at the scene and begin the rescue. After four hours of searching, a probe line found Vracarich. He had been buried almost 5 hours and had died. One other victim underwent surgery for serious injuries. The other four were briefly hospitalized and then released.

COMMENTS

This group was oblivious to the avalanche danger. They carried no rescue gear whatsoever and turned a deaf ear to the park rangers' warnings. They descended as a group, and all were caught. The standard safe travel protocols for the backcountry bear repeating: carry rescue gear and ski one at a time, so, in the event of an avalanche, the watchers can become rescuers.

Storm Slab avalanche

The storm conditions that led to a dangerous avalanche conditions in the Lake Placid area created a similar conditions 140 miles to the east on Mt. Washington, where a fatal avalanche occurred the following day.

20000220 GULF OF SLIDES, MOUNT WASHINGTON, NEW HAMPSHIRE

February 20, 2000

Two backcountry skiers caught; one partly buried, one buried and killed

WEATHER AND SNOWPACK CONDITIONS

Mt. Washington, at 6,288 feet elevation, is the highest peak in the northeastern United States. It is also the windiest. More than a foot of snow fell on the mountain February 18 and 19. On the afternoon of Sunday, February 20, winds from the west to northwest were blowing at 58 mph at the summit, with gusts to 64 mph. Visibility was 1/16 of a mile with blowing snow and freezing fog; the summit temperature was 3° F. US Forest Service snow rangers had rated the avalanche danger in Tuckerman Ravine as High.

High avalanche danger

ACCIDENT SUMMARY

David McPhedran (42) and his girlfriend Aimee Reiter (27) climbed a gully on the mountain adjacent to the Gulf of Slides, the first cirque south of Tuckerman Ravine. Both were familiar with the area, and in recent years they had skied in this area. They were equipped with beacons and shovels.[4]

Arriving at the top, they looked into the Gulf of Slides and saw a fresh avalanche fracture at the top. The crown convinced them not to ski that slope, so they headed back down the trail they had just climbed with an eye out for an alternative slope to ski. They decided to ski one of the chutes in The Fingers, located at the northernmost edge of the Gulf of Slides. McPhedran had skied this chute before; Reiter had not.

They dug a snow pit low in the chute and determined the snow to be safe to ski. They then put their skins back on their skis and began climbing up the edge of the chute. Eventually, they took off their skis and kicked steps higher up the chute. When they reached the point where they wanted to start skiing, they cut out a bench to sit and get organized.

They had stopped where two narrower chutes above them merged into a wider chute—the one they were about to ski. The weather was cloudy and very windy, with blowing snow. McPhedran helped Reiter put her skis and pack on, then began putting on his own gear. The time was about 12:30, and Reiter remembers being hit with a large gust of wind and snow. She put her head down, thinking it was just a gust, but then she was knocked off her feet by an avalanche. It swept both skiers down the gully.

RESCUE SUMMARY

When Reiter stopped sliding in the avalanche after about 200 vertical feet, she found herself buried to her chest. She looked uphill and saw McPhedran take a final tumble and stop, and then the avalanche snow buried him headfirst with his feet and skis out of the snow. He was about 40 to 50 feet above her.

It took Reiter, with her skis still attached, some time to dig herself out. She later described seeing McPhedran struggle with moving legs, and then the movement stopped. She had to cut her skis off, leaving them buried in the snow. She scrambled uphill and began digging McPhedran out. Once he was out, she laid him on his back, noticed a cut on his head, and checked for breathing and pulse. There was neither. She began CPR and continued for about 20 minutes, with no response. (Reiter was a National Ski Patrol member certified in first aid and CPR.) She knew she needed to find further medical assistance, so she headed back to the ski trail.

About a dozen rescuers responded and went to the site. They, too, were unable to revive McPhedran. The medical examiner later determined that death was caused by mechanical asphyxia.

AVALANCHE DATA

The Gulf of Slides has primarily an easterly aspect, and therefore was to the lee of the west-to-northwest winds that had arisen earlier in the day. Rangers had noted that within a couple of hours, blowing snow had created a two to three-foot-deep wind slab in nearby Tuckerman Ravine. Another observer had reported seeing natural avalanches running in the Gulf of Slides about the time McPhedran and Reiter were climbing up the gully.

Wind Slab avalanche

The fatal avalanche was a wind slab, and it most likely was a natural release, triggered by the loading from blowing snow several hundred feet higher on the mountain than where the victims were struck. The debris field in the runout was 350-400 feet long, 50 feet wide, with a depth of five to eight feet.

COMMENTS

"Red flag" indications of danger

On this day, dangerous avalanche conditions were widespread and obvious. Red flags that the party observed include the fresh crown, the amount of blowing snow, and the loading in the gullies. A snowpit dug far below the avalanche starting zone was guaranteed to give false information about conditions higher. More importantly, any data the party found in the snowpit should have had secondary importance to the obvious signs of avalanche danger they observed:

The storm conditions that led to high avalanche danger on Mt. Washington also created similar conditions 140 miles to the west near Lake Placid, where a fatal avalanche occurred the day before.

20000317 TONAR BOWL, SOUTHWEST OF ASPEN HIGHLANDS, COLORADO | March 17, 2000

Two sidecountry skiers caught, buried, and killed

WEATHER AND SNOWPACK CONDITIONS

In the winter of 1999-2000, Colorado experienced very low snowfall during November, December and early January. The lack of snow resulted in the development of a layer of large-grained faceted snow (depth hoar) near the ground. Storms that started the third week of January buried this layer. The storms also led to several fatal avalanches in Colorado in the last eight days of January (20000123, 20000125a, and 20000125b).

February brought slightly above-average snowfalls. By the end of February, the new snow had begun to settle into a stronger midpack, making it harder to trigger the weak layers beneath. The above-average snowfall continued into early March. Many skiers had begun to ski outside the boundary of Aspen Highlands ski area with no reported incidents in the three weeks prior to March 17.

Late afternoon and evening of March 15 brought about eight inches of snow to Aspen Highlands, with winds less than 12 mph. The 16th dawned clear and warm, and that stretch of clear weather lasted until the afternoon of the 17th, when a weak system brought snow showers to the area. Just after midnight on the 17th, the winds picked up to 15 to 20 mph for most of the night, blowing from the southwest. These winds were strong enough to cause blowing snow throughout the night.

ACCIDENT SUMMARY

Tonar Bowl sits southwest of the summit of Highland Peak (elevation 12,381 feet), the highpoint of Aspen Highlands. It lies on the windward side of the ridge running south from the peak, and most of the bowl lies above timberline and faces northwest. The name Tonar stems from a contraction of "totally gnarly." At the time of this accident, the backcountry access gate was below the summit of the peak, on the ridge between the peak and the ski area.

On Friday afternoon—St. Patrick's Day—a group of four skiers and two snowboarders left to ride Tonar through the gate on the ridge. They all had beacons, probes, and shovels. The skiers were Mike Hanrahan (49), Rick Wilder (46), Steve Parziale (40), and John Roberts (30). Rick, Steve, and John had been skiing the Highlands ridge backcountry for much of the season. They had tracked the snowpack stratigraphy with regular snowpits. Mike was a less frequent skier in that particular area. The two snowboarders were Justin Doty (32) and Brian Porter (30). They had planned their own trip to nearby Maroon Bowl but joined up with the four skiers.

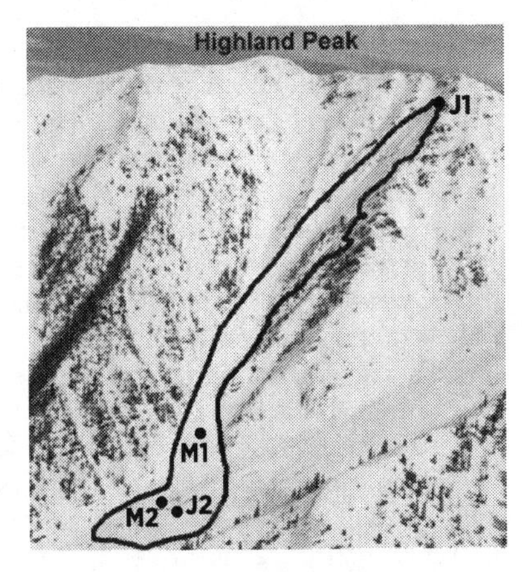

A view of the accident site in Tonar Bowl showing the locations of the two victims when the slide was triggered (J1 and M1) and the burial sites (J2 and M2). *Photo Kevin Heinecken, CAIC.*

Their plan this day was for each skier in turn to ski the entire length of Tonar down to the main basin, where several other paths join, and where the pitch mellows to about 15 degrees. Justin was first to descend. After arriving in the runout, he rode into some trees out of the way. Next to go was Mike, who skied straight down the gully but stopped before reaching the flats and stayed in the main track, visible to Justin but not visible to the men at the top.

Able to see only Justin from the top, Rick waited to see Mike. When he did not see him after some time, he assumed that Mike had found a safe area in some trees to skiers' left. Rick started his descent; partway down, he broke into the trees to look for Mike. Rick ended up crossing a slight ridge and skiing a south aspect into the basin, where he was out of sight of the rest of the group. Brian started down next and made about 10-15 turns, breaking out to boarders' right, where he could see the whole pitch better and take some photographs. He took cover below a large rock band. Fifth to go, Steve skied partway down and broke out left into the cover of another large rock outcrop.

The time was 12:15, and John was last to ski. About three turns into his run, the avalanche broke about one foot deep, and he yelled "Avalanche!" Several of the other men watched as John initially rode the debris and stayed upright, but after about 100 vertical feet, the slab released to the ground, about 4 feet deep. John was last seen tumbling in the flow.

In avalanche runout

Brian, standing on the side, later reported that as the avalanche went by, he could hear rocks rolling in the avalanche—similar to rocks being tumbled in the spring runoff of a river. In the runout, Justin saw the avalanche coming and yelled to Rick and Mike, who was standing low in the track. Both Rick and Justin began moving diagonally down in opposite directions to escape the flow. Rick later recalled that "the sky went dark, the wind picked up, and I thought it was over." Both Rick and Justin were able to outrun the debris flow.

Justin, from his position near the bottom of the slope, was the only one of the party who saw Mike disappear in the avalanche as it hit him from above. The debris rapidly decelerated and spread out after reaching the bottom of the track.

RESCUE SUMMARY

Brian and Steve had stopped partway down and on opposite sides of the slope. After the avalanche, they yelled for John and then began to move down the path, which the avalanche had polished smooth. They had several large rocky areas to contend with to get to the debris. Their beacons were on "receive" the whole trip down.

After the powder cloud cleared, Rick reported dead silence; he did not know where anyone was. He put his skins back on his skis and returned to the debris pile.

Justin's fast ride to escape the avalanche had taken him well below the debris. With no idea of who was left standing, and knowing that the trip back up in snowboard boots would be too long, he went for help. He reached the Maroon Creek Road and reported the avalanche to the T-Lazy-Seven guest ranch at about 12:45. They, in turn, notified the Aspen Highlands Ski Patrol and the sheriff's department.

The patrol responded for the county sheriff with a hasty team of three people. The only information they had was that a party of six was involved in a fairly large avalanche, and that the reporting party (Justin) was sure that the avalanche caught at least Mike.

Meanwhile, back at the avalanche site, the three searchers—Rick, Steve, and Brian—were certain only that John had been caught. But they all picked up two beacon signals, which confirmed that Mike was also involved. Though they initially had some trouble with the double signals, they were eventually able to pinpoint one of them. With some probing, they located the first body, which they dug up. Mike's lips were white and his face was completely blue. After clearing his airway, they found no signs of pulse or breathing, and, in the correct triage fashion, they turned his beacon off and began to search for John.

They quickly were able to pinpoint the second signal, and they probed and dug out John, who was at approximately the same elevation and within 100 horizontal feet of Mike. John had obvious signs of trauma. They could not detect any pulse and did not attempt CPR. After marking the bodies and re-activating the beacons, they skied towards Maroon Creek Road.

When they got to the road, they met up with a team of ski patrollers. It had gotten late in the day, and the weather was deteriorating. The patrol went in to confirm the identities of the two victims, mark their locations with probe poles, and take some coroners' photos.

Mountain Rescue Aspen recovered the bodies the next morning.

AVALANCHE DATA

Deep Persistent Slab avalanche

The avalanche released at an elevation of 12,200 feet on a northwest-facing slope, and it fell 1,900 vertical feet. The crown varied from one to five deep and was 500 feet wide. The avalanche was classified as HS-ASu-R3-G.

COMMENTS

Tonar Bowl is a high-risk, high-reward backcountry area. The group was very experienced and well-equipped, and they knew the terrain as well as anyone. Rick, Steve, and John had been digging snowpits regularly since they started their season on Thanksgiving day. They properly rode the slope one at a time and did a fair job of keeping eyes on each person as he descended. Most of the group picked safe locations away from the open slope to stop. Altogether, they did a good job of minimizing their exposure. And when their rescue skills were needed, their companion-rescue technique was flawless, and all kept their composure during adversity.

But one error was obvious: Mike's choice of a place to stop. He was directly in the path of the avalanche and could not escape before it hit him. That decision meant two fatalities instead of one.

It isn't clear if the group dug a snowpit on the day of the accident. If they had, it's not clear that they would they have found the fresh wind slab that had formed overnight or determined it to be unstable. After all, five skiers and snowboarders descended the slope without incident. It was the sixth man who triggered the wind slab, and once that released, it stepped down to the depth-hoar layer near the ground. This accident thus serves to underscore the inherent danger in backcountry skiing on steep avalanche terrain during a winter season when a thick layer of depth hoar lurks at the bottom of the snow cover.

ROMAN NOSE LAKES, WEST OF BONNERS FERRY, IDAHO

20000319

March 19, 2000

One snowmobiler caught, buried, and killed

WEATHER AND SNOWPACK CONDITIONS

On March 18, it snowed heavily, and southwesterly ridge-top winds gusted to 60 to 70 mph. On Sunday, March 19, it was still snowing, with moderate southwest winds. The Idaho Panhandle Avalanche Center had rated the avalanche danger for the Selkirk Mountains as Considerable above 5,000 feet, with the suggestion that backcountry travelers avoid steep and open north- and east-facing wind-loaded slopes.

ACCIDENT SUMMARY

The Selkirk Mountains are a north-south oriented range in the Idaho panhandle, with peaks rising above 7,000 feet. The Roman Nose Lakes lie just east of the crest and about 12 miles west of Bonners Ferry. The area is within the Snow Creek Winter Recreation Area.

On March 19, a group of snowmobilers was highmarking a steep, wind-loaded north-facing slope. At about 14:15, Robert Armbrust (39) was turning to come back down the slope when the avalanche released. The slope fractured above him and carried him through trees and to the bottom of the deposition area.

RESCUE SUMMARY

The party was equipped with transceivers and immediately began a beacon search for the victim. They found Armbrust 13 minutes after the avalanche occurred. He was buried in three feet of snow. One of the party members was a nurse. She began CPR, while another of the party members called the Boundary County Sheriff's Office by cell phone. The Sheriff's Office dispatched a deputy who arrived at the accident scene within an hour.

CPR efforts to revive the victim failed. Later, it was determined that Armbrust died of trauma to the head as a result of hitting a tree as he was swept down the slope.

AVALANCHE DATA

The avalanche was classified as HS-AMu-R3-D2. Fracture depth was two feet and width was 200 feet. The slope angle at the starting zone was estimated at 45 degrees. The slide fell 600 feet slope distance. The deposition was approximately five feet deep.

The avalanche occurred on a north-facing slope, which put it leeward of the prevailing southwest winds. It was determined that the recently-loaded wind slab released on two thin, dense unidentified layers, though some facets were visible. Also, depth hoar was found in the area of the fracture point near a rock outcrop, where the snowpack was shallower than the rest of the slide area.

Wind Slab avalanche

COMMENTS

Highmarking is an inherently dangerous niche of snowmobiling, since virtually every highmarking slope is a potential avalanche slope. Therefore, it's no surprise the avalanche-accident literature is filled with highmarking-related incidents, many involving riders who were unprepared for the dangers they were assuming.

This group of riders did several things to minimize their exposure and the consequences of triggering a slide. They were equipped with beacons and shovels, unlike many groups in previous accidents. (In more recent years, airbags are recommended.) They were going one at a time, with the observers in a safe zone out of the avalanche's reach. But despite preparedness, avalanches can still kill. A deep burial or—as in this case—a tree on the slope can be the fatal ingredient.

The black lines delineate the crown and toe of the avalanche. Rescuers uncovered the victim where the two men are standing. Handwritten annotatons on original image read (from left to right): "Snowmobile found here", "Debris Runout", and "Body Found here". *Photo Jess Sanders, courtesy Idaho Panhandle Avalanche Center.*

20000322 GILDART PEAK, SOUTHEAST OF BIGFORK, MONTANA

March 22, 2000

One snowmobiler caught and killed

WEATHER AND SNOWPACK CONDITIONS

From March 11 through 19, a sustained storm period brought significant snowfall to the Swan Range of northwest Montana. During this period, the Noisy Basin SNOTEL site—approximately 26 miles north of Gildart Peak —recorded 4.7 inches of snow water equivalent. This translated into perhaps two to three feet of snowfall in the higher elevations of the Swan Range. Also during this storm period, moderately strong winds had blown from the west and northwest.

The most recent avalanche advisory issued by Glacier Country Avalanche Center (March 21) rated the dry-snow avalanche danger at Moderate on recently wind-loaded slopes and the wet-snow danger as Considerable.

ACCIDENT SUMMARY

Gildart Peak is a 7,900-foot mountain in the Swan Range and is about 20 miles southwest of the town of Bigfork, Montana. The area is popular snowmobile terrain.

A party of seven riders had spent the day riding high on the crest of the Swan Range, at elevations of 7,000-7,500 feet. They had accessed the area via Soup Creek and Inspiration Pass to the west and south. All members of the party were carrying avalanche transceivers, probes, and shovels.

At approximately 14:00, the victim was highmarking an open slope on a southeast aspect on Gildart Peak when a slab avalanche released above him. He was carried by the flowing snow at a high rate of speed, smashed into a tree in the runout zone, and died of a massive head injury. The victim was not buried by the avalanche, was recovered on the surface of the snow, and, if it had not been for the tree, probably would have escaped the slide uninjured.

RESCUE SUMMARY

After the incident, one member of the party alerted authorities by cell phone while others attempted CPR on the victim. Kalispell Medical Center's ALERT helicopter arrived on scene approximately 45 minutes after the avalanche, and medical personnel pronounced the victim dead soon after.

AVALANCHE DATA

The avalanche was estimated to be 300 feet wide, ran 500 feet slope distance, and had a crown depth of three feet. The crown was just below the ridge crest. The slope where it released was estimated to be 32 to 40 degrees and faced southeast. The avalanche debris consisted of mixed dry and wet hard blocks. The slide was classified as HS-AMu-R3-D2-O.

Persistent Slab avalanche

COMMENTS

This fatal avalanche had much in common with another fatal avalanche that occurred three days earlier (20000319) west of Bonners Ferry in the Idaho panhandle. Both incidents involved snowmobilers, highmarking, and a fatal crash into a tree on the slope. As mentioned in the narrative for the earlier accident , highmarking is an inherently dangerous activity. The group involved in the avalanche on Gildart Peak was experienced and prepared for an avalanche incident, should it occur. Indeed, it did occur—with a big dose of bad luck.

Stan Bones of the Glacier Country Avalanche Center (now the Flathead Avalanche Center) investigated this fatal avalanche and wrote: "It is unfortunate that a tree stood in the way in the runout. If that had not been the case, the party would have undoubtedly only had a wild story to tell friends and family when they returned home. It's often only a fine line that separates existence from oblivion, happiness from despair and grief."

SUMMIT LAKE, NORTH OF PAXSON, ALASKA | April 8, 2000 20000408a

One snowmobiler caught, buried, and killed

WEATHER AND SNOWPACK CONDITIONS

During the 2000 Arctic Man Ski and Sno-Go Classic, spring conditions prevailed, but there were some wind and blowing snow episodes. On some slopes, blowing snow had settled on an ice crust or on near-surface facets. Away from the race corridor and the rolling hills crisscrossed with thousands of tracks, people had reported seeing several dozen avalanches on steep slopes as the sun baked the area. Event participants triggered—and were caught in—several avalanches on Friday, April 7. Alaska State Troopers and Arctic Man organizers urged the recreational snowmobilers to stay off steep slopes on Saturday, April 8.

ACCIDENT SUMMARY

The Arctic Man Ski and Sno-Go Classic is an annual spring event held in the Summit Lake area north of Paxson, Alaska. The site is about four hours northeast of Anchorage. The competition combines snowmobiling, skiing, and snowboarding. The event's website says, "Are there broken bones in this race? You bet." An estimated 15,000 people attended the four-day event in 2000.

Walter Coty (43) of Fairbanks was one of the thousands of attendees. He was an experienced snowmobiler who often rode in the area. On Saturday, April 8, Coty was riding in a bowl several miles from the groomed race course. While highmarking, he got caught in a small avalanche but got himself and his sled out of that without burial. A trooper asked him to carry an avalanche beacon if he was going to continue.

Coty continued riding, and at 13:00 he was highmarking another slope when he triggered an avalanche. This one buried him.

RESCUE SUMMARY

No rescue equipment

An initial search found Coty's helmet, but no sign of Coty. Without probes or dogs, the search could only cover the surface of the avalanche debris. After the surface search, troopers pulled the searchers out of the area because of the danger of other avalanches.

The next morning, the Alaska Search and Rescue Group arrived from Anchorage with probes and two avalanche dogs. Once on the debris, one of the dogs, Chili, quickly alerted. Probers confirmed the strike at 8:30.

Coty's body was found face-up under 4.5 feet of snow, about 40 feet downhill from where his helmet had been found.

AVALANCHE DATA

Persistent Slab avalanche

The avalanche was composed of a slab of wind-deposited snow—probably a hard slab—on an ice crust resting on a layer of faceted snow. Slab depth ranged from 10 inches near the flanks to a maximum of 5.5 feet. The slope angle was 35 degrees.

COMMENTS

Sgt. Paul Burke of the Alaska State Troopers helped coordinate the rescue. Following the body recovery, Burke showed some frustration, "Highmarking was the activity. It's pretty amazing where they go. How many of these [accidents] have we been on? It's the same conditions, the same thing. You'd think people would have more prudence."[5]

20000408b SNOWSHOE PEAK, SOUTHEAST OF TALKEETNA, ALASKA

April 8, 2000

One backcountry skier caught and killed; one snowboarder caught and injured

WEATHER AND SNOWPACK CONDITIONS

Newspaper accounts report the group was "enjoying late season snow," suggesting that snow had fallen in the days preceding the accident.

ACCIDENT SUMMARY

Snowshoe Peak (4559 feet) lies about 20 miles southeast of Talkeetna, Alaska. A broad, low-angled ridge rises from the west to the summit. The ridge is wide near its base but narrows near the summit. While it is possible to stay on low-angled terrain to the summit, steep slopes drop abruptly from either side of the ridge.

On Saturday, April 8, a group of eight skiers and snowboarders was taking a day off from a Wilderness First Responder class held in Talkeetna. Joe Kluberton (18) lived in Talkeetna and was showing the group the skiing on Snowshoe Peak. Michele Potkin (44), also from Talkeetna and an avid mountain climber and telemark skier, was one of the group.

Before riding a 37-degree slope, they dug a snow pit. They concluded that the snow was stable. Kluberton rode about 80 feet down on his snowboard, then hiked back up to do it again. At about that point, he and several others in the group noticed that "the snow was less stable farther down."[6]

Potkin, who was making tight turns as she skied down, stopped above Kluberton. "And everything just started to move," Kluberton said. An avalanche about two feet deep released; it moved slowly but then knocked Potkin down. One of her skis hit Kluberton in the head, and the two tumbled down the slope and over a 200-foot cliff.

More than one person on a slope

RESCUE SUMMARY

The rest of group reached Kluberton and Potkin; newspaper accounts suggest they were not buried. They provided emergency medical care and built a snow cave for shelter. Kluberton was eventually arlifted to an Anchorage hospital but later released. Potkin, however, suffered critical injuries; the force of the fall was enough to crush an aluminum coffee thermos in her backpack. Despite the group's care, Potkin's injuries took her life.

AVALANCHE DATA

It's not clear from the limited information available whether the avalanche involved a slab or loose snow, or whether it was wet or dry snow.

COMMENTS

Several members of this group of skiers and snowboarders had apparently gained a level of avalanche education, either through courses or their own backcountry experiences. The report mentions that they dug a snowpit before starting their first descent and concluded that the snow was stable. Their evaluation was wrong; either the data from the pit was not representative, or the group misinterpreted the data. And this error leads to a comment about relying on snowpits for determining slope stability.

Snowpit data can be definitive for determining slope stability, but only at that location. Because of spatial variation, snowpack properties such as layering, strength, and stability will almost certainly vary from one location to another on a slope or between slopes. And they will change over time. Therefore, any conclusions about stability should be based on more than one data point—one or more pits combined with other observations.

It's not clear where on the slope the group dug the snowpit. It may have been above the elevation where the avalanche released, in which case it might not have represented conditions below, where several group members identified a change in stability. It's also not clear how much time elapsed between when the group dug the pit and when they started riding the slope. It's possible that conditions changed, so the snowpit data and group's conclusions had, in effect, expired. In the Spring, avalanche danger can increase rapidly as temperatures rise, or be higher on steeper slopes that are more rapidly affected by solar radiation. Regardless, the accident illustrates the problems that can develop when relying on snowpits for conclusions about slope stability and avalanche danger.

One additional note. At least two people were on the slope at the time it avalanched. That may have increased the chances of triggering the slide, if it was a slab avalanche. It definitely meant more than one person tumbled over the cliff, increasing the complexity of the rescue. Expose one person at a time to avalanche danger, in order to minimize the likelihood and consequences of triggering a slide.

20000421 **MARJORIE BOWL, NORTHEAST OF ARAPAHOE BASIN, COLORADO** | April 21, 2000

Two sidecountry skiers caught, two injured, one later died

WEATHER AND SNOWPACK CONDITIONS

April weather in the Colorado Rockies seesawed between warm, sunny, spring-like days (when high pressure prevailed) and cold, snowy days (when fast-moving cold fronts blew in). This led to a spring snowpack with multiple layers, both strong and weak.

One of these cold fronts hit the Front Range on April 20 and dropped six inches of new snow overnight at Arapahoe Basin Ski Area and nearby Loveland Pass. Explosive control that morning in the ski area and along the highway produced minimal results. However, the backcountry snowpack surrounding the ski area was likely less stable because of the lack of ski compaction and explosive control throughout the winter season.

ACCIDENT SUMMARY

On Friday, April 21, a group of four men in their 20s and early 30s was skiing at Arapahoe Basin ski area when they decided to venture into the backcountry in pursuit of untracked powder. The group skied past a sign that read "Restricted Area" and ducked a boundary rope at the ski area—a violation of the Colorado Skier Safety Act—and entered a backcountry area known as Marjorie Bowl, just north-northeast of the ski area. They made one run in the area and then returned for a second run just before the lifts closed.

More than one person on a slope

Two men skied the slope without incident, and then the third man, Kip (31), began his descent. The fourth man, Jake, followed him a few seconds later. Jake triggered a shallow but wide soft slab avalanche that threw up a small powder cloud. Kip heard the moving snow and tried to ski away from it but the debris hit him from behind and swept him into a small tree and then into some rocks. It also swept Jake down into some rocks.

Neither victim was buried, but both sustained serious injuries. Jake suffered a broken wrist and a separated shoulder. Kip was suffering from internal injuries but said he could ski out on his own. By that point, the ski area had closed, so the group descended to the highway. One member of the group headed to the ski area parking lot to retrieve their truck.

The avalanche was not visible from the ski area. The group did not report the avalanche to the Arapahoe Basin Ski Patrol, nor did they take the victims in for treatment. Instead, they began the drive back to Denver. As they approached the city, Kip's condition worsened, and he said he needed to see a doctor. As one of his friends put it: "Kip's face was completely white, he was having trouble breathing, and he looked horrible."

They drove to a Denver-area hospital, where Kip was admitted for internal and head injuries, and Jake was treated for his injured shoulder and wrist. The group did not want to admit they had been caught in an avalanche after cutting through the closed boundary, so they told the emergency room doctor that Kip had been injured when he collided with a tree while playing "ski football". Before being admitted, Kip called his sister in Pennsylvania and told her to come immediately—also without telling her that he had been in an avalanche.

Kip's sister arrived in Denver on April 22; Kip died in the hospital the following day. Kip's friends then told his sister the truth about his injuries. It is unknown whether the doctors who treated Kip ever learned the truth.

AVALANCHE DATA

No dimensions or other significant data of the avalanche were reported. However, the slope faced mostly west, and the elevation of the crown was approximately 11,500 feet. The avalanche was likely classified as SS-ASu-R3. Additionally, sunshine and warming temperatures during the day may have contributed to a less-stable snowpack as the afternoon wore on.

All evidence of the avalanche had disappeared the following day when the next snow storm covered it up.

COMMENTS

This accident was eventually reported to the Colorado Avalanche Information Center in a semi-anonymous e-mail sent on May 27, five weeks after the event. When it came to light, the ethical—and legal—issues raised were apparent. The four skiers were concerned about getting busted for a violation of the Colorado Skier Safety Act, so they did not report the avalanche and did not seek medical help for Kip immediately at Arapahoe Basin. Hours later when Kip's condition became critical, they still lied to the emergency-room doctor on how the accident occurred.

We struggled, quite frankly, with how to present this fatal accident. Since one purpose of *The Snowy Torrents* is to learn from the mistakes of others, what can be learned from this report? Perhaps it's this: Paying a small fine for a misdemeanor is a small price if it saves your friend's life.

2000–2001 SEASON

20001127 HOODOO CREEK, NORTHWEST OF CODY, WYOMING

November 27, 2000

One hunter caught, buried, and killed

ACCIDENT SUMMARY

Traveling alone

The steep country of the North Absaroka Wilderness is located about 40 miles northwest of Cody, Wyoming. On Monday, November 27, Mark Nielsen (41) of West Linn, Oregon was hunting in the Crandall Creek drainage. He was crossing a steep snowfield above Hoodoo Creek when he triggered an avalanche that swept him down the slope and buried him.

RESCUE SUMMARY

Sometime later, outfitter Buck Porter went looking for Nielsen. Porter followed Nielsen's tracks in the snow, which led to the avalanche—with no tracks coming out the other side. Porter made a cell phone call to the Park County Sheriff at 14:50.

Later in the day, a rescue team arrived at the area. They found Nielsen's body at 17:00. He had died from severe neck, head, and chest injuries. Poor weather and darkness postponed the body recovery until the next morning, when Nielsen's body was evacuated by horseback.

COMMENTS

Persistent Slab avalanche

Over the years, there have been several fatal avalanches involving hunters. See 19981115 for another example. Because hunting season occurs during late fall and early winter, these avalanches are usually shallow, with depth hoar being the weak layer that fails at the ground. The shallow snowpack makes it easy to underestimate avalanche danger but increases the potential for trauma, as in this incident.

20001201 GLORY BOWL, EAST OF TETON PASS, WYOMING

December 1, 2000

One backcountry snowboarder caught, buried, and killed

WEATHER AND SNOWPACK CONDITIONS

November weather in the Teton Pass area of Wyoming had brought abnormally cold temperatures and periodic light snowfalls. From November 24 to 30, just under two feet of new snow was recorded at nearby Jackson Hole Mountain Resort. Persistent winds from the west and southwest were strong enough to produce blowing snow, which loaded the northeast-facing portion of Glory Bowl. December 1 was a clear day with moderate temperatures and calm winds.

ACCIDENT SUMMARY

Mt. Glory, at 10,080 feet elevation, looms above 8,431-foot Teton Pass. Glory Bowl is a large avalanche path on the east slope of Mt. Glory. When the path runs big, it buries Wyoming Highway 22, which crosses the avalanche path above the runout zone. The

Wyoming Department of Transportation frequently mitigates avalanche hazard to the highway with artillery and fixed installations. The slopes around the pass, including Glory Bowl, are popular with skiers and snowboarders.

On November 30, Sean Macauley drove to Teton Pass and hiked to the top of the Glory Bowl. When he got there, he didn't like what he considered to be sketchy snow conditions, so rather than ride down the bowl, he snowboarded a safer line along the trees near an area known as Twin Slides. But he planned to return the following day with a pair of snowboarding friends, Joel Roof (28) and Steve Westmoreland.

Traveling alone

A miscommunication among the three men led to Roof driving alone early on the morning of Friday, December 1. He parked at the pass and began a solo trek up the boot track toward the top of Mt. Glory with his snowboard strapped to his back. A short time later, Macauley and Westmoreland arrived at the pass and began their own hike up.

Roof got to the top ahead of his would-be companions. He started his descent into the bowl while they were still climbing and out of sight. He triggered a large avalanche that swept him down almost 2,000 feet and buried him. He was not wearing a beacon. A short time later, Macauley and Westmoreland got to the top, saw the fresh avalanche, and saw their friend's snowboard track end at the fracture line.

Inadequate rescue equipment

RESCUE SUMMARY

The avalanche roared across the highway at about 08:35, blocking the road with debris six to 10 feet deep but fortunately not hitting any vehicles. Motorists called the Teton County Sheriff's Office at 8:38 to report the avalanche. Meanwhile, Macauley and Westmoreland rode down Glory Bowl looking for Roof, to no avail. At the highway, they told the people on the road that they feared their friend had been caught in the avalanche. Macauley then called 911, which alerted Teton County SAR.

Macauley also told people on the road that he knew Roof owned an avalanche beacon but did not know if Roof was wearing it. Several motorists got their own beacons from their cars and began searching the debris for a signal. They got no signal, but someone found a glove on the snow.

Fairly soon after that, Teton County SAR arrived and coordinated a probe line. At 09:37, the probe line made a hit just above the highway. Shovelers dug Roof out from six feet of snow. He had been buried a little more than an hour and did not show obvious signs of trauma, though his snowboard was broken in two. Roof did not respond to resuscitation efforts, and the coroner later determined he had died of asphyxiation.

AVALANCHE DATA

The avalanche was classified as SS-ARu-R3. The fracture was only 1.5 to two feet deep but was 1,500 feet wide and pulled out almost half of the rider's right side of the bowl. The bowl narrows into a gully before hitting the road, concentrating the debris. The avalanche fell about 2,200 feet vertical. The slope aspect was east-northeast, putting it leeward of the prevailing southwest winds. The average slope angle across Glory Bowl is about 35 degrees. For this avalanche, the alpha angle was 29 degrees.

Persistent Slab avalanche

Snow depth in the upper starting zone varied from 32-52 inches. The avalanche bed surface was a crust layer from the early part of November. The failure plane was a layer of depth hoar with grains two to four mm in size. The depth hoar grains were well developed and striations were easily visible. Storm snow and wind-blown snow had buried this layer over the previous six days.

COMMENTS

An unanswered question is why Roof did not take his beacon with him this day. That decision (or oversight), coupled with his decision to go solo—did he even know his friends were fairly close behind him?—proved fatal. Riding in avalanche terrain without a transceiver and alone almost completely removes any chance of companion rescue.

20001209a DENALI NATIONAL PARK AND PRESERVE, SOUTHWEST OF CANTWELL, ALASKA | December 9, 2000

One snowmobiler caught, buried, and killed

ACCIDENT SUMMARY

On Saturday, December 9, a group of six snowmobilers unloaded their machines at Mile 196 on the Parks Highway, southwest of Cantwell, Alaska. They rode about 16 miles west, to just inside the Denali National Park boundary. This brought them to the steep end of a valley, where they began highmarking on a hill that tapered into a ravine.

More than one person on a slope

One rider became stuck on the hillside, and James Thompson (44) went to help. The first rider got himself unstuck and rode downhill. Thompson was just heading downslope went he was hit from behind by an avalanche. Witnesses said he probably didn't even see the slide coming and thus didn't accelerate to try to ride it out. Thompson was carried roughly 400 yards and buried.

RESCUE SUMMARY

Two or three people in the group witnessed Thompson get caught. There were other riders in the area in addition to the party of six, and some of those saw the avalanche and aided in the rescue effort.

Inadequate rescue equipment

They found Thompson's sled quickly. Apparently none of the searchers had beacons, or they knew Thompson was not wearing one. Some rescuers did have probes, so a group of five or six searchers began probing upslope from the sled. Within about 15 minutes, they struck the victim. He was buried face-down, four feet deep, roughly 20 feet upslope from his machine. He did not have a pulse. The rescuers began CPR while Thompson was still in the hole and continued it for 40 to 60 minutes without result.

The accident occurred around 13:30. A father and son who were in the area rode out for help. Another party of two also rode out to where they could make cell phone contact. The Alaska State Troopers received notification at 14:40. A Mast/EMS helicopter was launched from Fairbanks around 15:00. The Troopers staged a rescue response from the Parks Highway, but Thompson's partners brought his body out to the road by snowmobile.

AVALANCHE DATA

Persistent Slab avalanche

The fracture line of this avalanche was one to 1.5 feet deep, and it went to ground. The width was estimated at a quarter-mile, though visibility was poor, so that was a rough guess. The stratigraphy was new snow and windblown snow on depth hoar. Rescuers noted numerous other fractures in the area.

COMMENTS

Highmarking is challenging, fun, and dangerous—three reasons for many riders to do it. But these riders must prepare for the worst, and that means carrying avalanche rescue gear, especially probes, beacons, and/or airbags. Highmarking puts you in harm's way: be prepared when the avalanche happens.

This accident has a second lesson as well. A cardinal rule while highmarking is that if a person gets stuck, do not send a second rider up to help. Doing so could lead to two avalanche victims rather than one. In this case, it was the second rider that appeared to trigger the avalanche.

OLYMPIC BOWL, SOUTH OF TETON PASS, WYOMING

20001209b

December 9, 2000

One backcountry skier caught, buried, and killed

WEATHER AND SNOWPACK CONDITIONS

On Saturday, December 9, a storm moved into the Teton Pass area of western Wyoming and brought steady snowfall by afternoon. Forecasters at the Bridger-Teton National Forest Avalanche Center rated the backcountry avalanche danger as Moderate on Saturday morning, increasing to Considerable in the afternoon, and High by Sunday morning. The storm dropped 11 inches of new snow by Sunday morning.

The forecast stated that new soft slabs would form Saturday on a well-developed layer of surface hoar and that avalanches had the potential to step down to a weak layer of faceted snow at the ground surface.

ACCIDENT SUMMARY

Traveling alone

Terrain trap

On Saturday afternoon, Jonathan Beall (29) was on a solo ski tour in the Northwoods area south of Teton Pass. He apparently descended a gully which drains Olympic Bowl and which undercuts the steep last pitch of Titmouse Ridge. At some point, he released a very shallow slab avalanche that swept him into the gully and totally buried him.

RESCUE SUMMARY

When Beall had not returned by dark Saturday, he was reported missing. A Teton County Search and Rescue team responded that night and searched until 4:00 without finding any clues. On Sunday, several search teams returned to the area, and one team picked up a ski track. They followed the track until it came to a fresh avalanche, at which point they got a beacon signal at 14:45. The debris area was small but deep. They pinpointed the burial location and uncovered the victim's body at 15:00.

AVALANCHE DATA

Persistent Slab avalanche

The slide was 40 to 50 feet across, 150 feet in length, had only a six-inch crown, and ran on a buried layer of well-developed surface hoar. The teardrop-shaped debris pile was approximately 20 feet across, 25 feet long and five to six feet deep in the center. The slope faced southeast and was at an elevation of 7,920 feet. The slide was classed as SS-ASu-R2-D2-O.

COMMENTS

This small avalanche—a six-inch crown—had fatal consequences for two reasons. One was the gully where Beall was skiing. Gullies are always dangerous terrain traps because they force avalanche debris to pile up deeply rather than spread out over a large area. The second was the fact that Beall was alone. Had the victim not been skiing alone, he would have likely been uncovered quickly by a companion, even in the concentrated debris in the terrain trap. Riding in terrain traps alone leaves almost no margin for error.

20001214

WILLARD PEAK, NORTH OF OGDEN, UTAH

December 14, 2000

One snowmobiler caught, buried, and killed

WEATHER AND SNOWPACK CONDITIONS

Storms during the first half of November 2000 were generous to the Ogden-area mountains, depositing several feet of snow. But then winter's generosity stopped, with no additional snow for about three weeks. Instead, an arctic airmass brought clear skies and record-setting cold, which metamorphosed the snow cover on the shaded northerly aspects into about 18 inches of unsupportable depth hoar.

A storm cycle began on December 9 and deposited fresh snow on top of the very weak layer of depth hoar. By December 14, the Ogden Mountains had received approximately 30 to 40 inches of eight- to 10-percent density snow that formed a soft slab with four-fingers resistance. Additionally, there were west winds of 20 to 30 mph in the period leading up to and including the day of the accident. One survivor of this avalanche, Dave Hogan, commented later that the wind was moving a lot of snow around, limiting the visibility prior to and during the avalanche.

The Utah Avalanche Center rated the avalanche danger as Considerable the day of the avalanche.

ACCIDENT SUMMARY

On Thursday, December 14, four friends went for a nighttime snowmobile ride on Willard Peak Road. They left for the trip after work, arriving and unloading their machines at the snowmobile parking area at about 19:30. They rode about eight miles up the road and made it to the east side of the north ridge of Willard Peak.

Rob Allred (30) rode out in front of the other three and was on the road, which traversed several avalanche paths. The group was unaware of this danger. Allred unknowingly crossed one avalanche path and then got stuck in a drift part way into the track of another avalanche path. Dave Hogan and Don White stayed in place, shining their headlights in the direction of Allred so he could see while excavating his stuck sled. The fourth rider, Eric Wadman, headed forward on his machine to assist Allred. He triggered—apparently remotely—two avalanches, which released in both of the avalanche paths. Wadman had the good luck to be on the road between the two avalanches. Allred was not so lucky; he was hit and disappeared in the avalanche.

RESCUE SUMMARY

No rescue equipment

The group was not equipped with any rescue gear—no transceivers, shovels or probes. The party did have a cell phone that they used to dial 911 at 20:11. The Box Elder

County Sheriff's office activated their search and rescue plan at that time. Donald White left the scene by snowmobile to return to the parking lot to lead the search and rescue group to the avalanche site. The remaining two party members, Hogan and Wadman, began scuffing and digging with their hands near where they had last seen the snowmobile and Rob Allred.

The search and rescue team began arriving at the avalanche site at around 21:45. One of the rescue leaders organized a probe line that started at the toe of the avalanche and worked its way up until they found a ski from the buried snowmobile sticking slightly out of the snow. While some rescuers excavated and moved the snowmobile, others continued to probe in the area until one probe struck something. Rescuers shoveled down the shaft of the probe approximately four feet until they exposed Allred's helmet and head.

Allred was uncovered at about 23:10, about six feet uphill from his sled. He had been buried about three hours. He had no pulse and was not breathing. With no signs of trauma, he had apparently died of asphyxiation, which was later confirmed by an autopsy.

AVALANCHE DATA

This avalanche released in an east-northeast-facing bowl at an elevation of 8,760 feet and fell 340 vertical feet. The start zone slope angle was 35 degrees.

Persistent Slab avalanche

The avalanche was classified as SS-AMr-R3-D3-O. Crown depth was 2.5 to three feet and was 150 feet wide. The weak layer was depth hoar.

Investigators later determined that a third path located to the south had also run sympathetically.

COMMENTS

Experience counts for a lot. This party of four lacked avalanche experience in every way—no rescue gear at all, no awareness of avalanche terrain, no awareness of avalanche danger in the midst of a sustained storm, no knowledge that their local avalanche center was warning of a Considerable avalanche danger.

Lack of training

If this had been a group with avalanche experience, an avalanche death might not have occurred. First, an experienced group most probably would have not been in avalanche terrain in a storm at night. Second, this is the type of burial where companions can often save a life with a fast beacon search and shovel excavation.

PUZZLE CREEK, SOUTH OF MARIAS PASS, MONTANA

20001217

December 17, 2000

Two snowmobilers caught, buried, and killed

WEATHER AND SNOWPACK CONDITIONS

In northwest Montana, U.S. Highway 2 and the BNSF Railway split Glacier National Park to the north and the Flathead National Forest to the south. The highway and railroad both cross Marias Pass, at 5,213 feet elevation on the Continental Divide. The national forest south of the pass is a popular recreation area for snowmobilers.

The first half of November saw several storms that put down a base snowpack of several feet. Then the weather cleared for the latter half of November and into December. Cold temperatures created a steep temperature gradient in the snowpack, and this, in turn, led to faceting and weakening. In the second week of December, additional but unmeasured snowfall occurred, which put a soft-slab layer over the weak, basal depth hoar. It was snowing and windy the day of the avalanche, and snowmobilers in the area said it was difficult sledding because there was no base.

High avalanche danger

The Glacier County Avalanche Center (now the Flathead Avalanche Center) rated the avalanche danger in that area as High.

ACCIDENT SUMMARY

On Sunday morning, December 17, a party of eight snowmobilers was riding in the Puzzle Creek area southwest of Marias Pass. They rode about 15 miles on the Skyland Road, and a little before 11:00, they approached a deep ravine called the Puzzle Slide or the Chute. If riders can negotiate the Chute, they can ride all the way to Marias Pass and complete a loop

More than one person on a slope

One rider went ahead and got stuck. Two other men, Joseph Wipf (27) and Jacob Kleinsasser (27) went in on foot to help dig out the snowmobile. The three men freed the machine and turned it around. The rider rode back out, changed to another machine, and reentered the draw. Returning to the location where he had last seen Wipf and Kleinsasser, he found nothing but a mound of avalanche debris up to 20 feet deep and not a sign of his companions.

Terrain trap

RESCUE SUMMARY

No rescue equipment

The avalanche occurred a little after 11:00. No one in the group had avalanche rescue gear—no beacons, no probes, no shovels. As snowfall and blowing snow continued, the men conducted a surface search, with random digging and probing with tree stems cut on-site. They found nothing. At 13:00, they got a cell phone call to connect. The call notified the Glacier and Flathead County Sheriff offices, who dispatched a search and rescue team from North Valley Search and Rescue. They eventually found the victims by probing—the first at 17:23 and the second at 18:04. They were buried seven to 10 feet deep in very dense avalanche debris. Both had died of suffocation.

AVALANCHE DATA

Persistent Slab avalanche

The avalanche occurred in a snowpack which consisted of sugary depth hoar as the base layer and soft slab on top. The crown was two feet at its deepest and was 150 feet wide. The avalanche ran 125 feet slope distance. Slope angle was not recorded. The avalanche was classed as SS-AFu-R2-O.

COMMENTS

The key to this accident was the confinement of the draw. It was the perfect terrain trap. Backcountry travelers must recognize the danger of entering a terrain trap such as this; they should be avoided at all costs.

Equally important, though, this group had not thought of avalanche danger, or if they had, they had badly misjudged it. Avalanche education teaches us to look at terrain, snowpack, and weather to help determine the danger, and to possess (and practice with) rescue gear. The group did not demonstrate any of those practices.

SOUTH BADGER CREEK, NORTHEAST OF ALTA, WYOMING | December 25, 2000

20001225

One backcountry skier caught, buried, and killed

WEATHER AND SNOWPACK CONDITIONS

The Jedediah Smith Wilderness Area lies on the west slope of the Teton Range in western Wyoming, above the Teton Valley. The snowpack in the Greater Yellowstone region had been dangerously unstable for all of the early winter of 2000. Three fatal avalanches had occurred from November 27 to December 9 in northwest Wyoming (20001127, 20001201, 20001209b). The common ingredient in these avalanches were weak layers of depth hoar or buried surface hoar. In some incidents, these sat on a hard crust formed in October. The snowpack in the Jedediah Smith Wilderness Area possessed similar weak layers.

ACCIDENT SUMMARY

A party of three backcountry skiers set off on a Christmas Day tour in the Jedediah Smith Wilderness Area. The group included Sarah Campbell (26), Joey Palumba (31), and Nicoles Balla (24). All were experienced backcountry skiers, and they carried beacons, probes, and shovels. They entered into the area on snowmobiles from the west and parked at the Rammell Mountain trailhead. This trailhead is located in the northwest part of the Teton Range, roughly 12 miles northeast of Tetonia, Idaho. Their plan was to ski to Dead Horse Pass, staying on the ridge above South Badger Creek because of the high avalanche danger, then return along the same route. They left the trailhead at 10:00.

They climbed to their planned route on the ridge, which turned out to be windswept and rocky. They dropped below the ridgeline and began traversing a south-facing slope. They traveled about a quarter mile along the slope, 100 to 200 feet below the crest. They then came to a 150-yard-wide bowl of 30- to 35-degree steepness (estimated) and decided to cross one at a time due to their concerns about the slope stability.

The time was a little after 13:00, and Palumba and Balla crossed safely. Campbell began her traverse. The slope fractured 20 to 40 feet above her and approximately 100 yards wide. Campbell was carried some distance on the hard slab before it broke up, at which point she vanished from sight.

Terrain trap

The path funneled into a shallow ravine, then fanned out 1,000 feet below. Palumba and Balla quickly began a transceiver search. One headed down to the greater deposition areas at the toe of the slide, the other working down, checking various debris traps higher on the slope. They picked up Campbell's beacon signal near the toe of the slide in a deep deposition area where the drainage curved, creating a terrain/debris trap. Forty minutes after the slide and after digging down six feet, they hit Campbell with a probe. Then they removed an additional four feet of snow before uncovering her. They tried to revive her with CPR, but were unsuccessful.

Campbell was buried for 55 minutes beneath 10 feet of avalanche debris.

RESCUE SUMMARY

The Teton County Search and Rescue Team made the body recovery the following day.

AVALANCHE DATA

The avalanche was classified as HS-ASu-R3-D3-O. The avalanche released at an elevation of 9,200 feet and fell 1,400 feet vertical to an elevation of 7,800 feet. Fracture depth was 18 to 24 inches. The aspect was south.

Persistent Slab avalanche

The bed surface was the crust that still remained from a mid-October snowfall, though the avalanche slid to ground in some areas down the path. The weak layer was faceted snow, probably both depth hoar and buried surface hoar.

COMMENTS

This was an experienced party who carried full rescue gear, knew of the avalanche danger, and tried to pick a route to minimize the danger. But it didn't work. They recognized the danger presented by the bowl with slope angles of 30 to 35 degrees and chose to lower their risk by crossing one at a time. It was a choice that cost a life.

20001229 DIAMOND PEAKS, WEST OF CAMERON PASS, COLORADO

December 29, 2000

One backcountry snowboarder caught, buried, and killed

ACCIDENT SUMMARY

Cameron Pass is a popular recreation area about 55 miles west of Fort Collins. At the summit of the pass, a parking lot just off Colorado Highway 14 gives easy access to the Diamond Peaks, whose summits are about one mile west and 1500 vertical feet from the pass. The area offers good skiing in steep terrain, but it has been the site of several avalanche accidents over the years (19991214).

On Friday, December 29, Robert Christiansen (40) hiked up from the parking lot.

Traveling alone

He was alone, on snowshoes, and had his snowboard strapped to his backpack. He apparently intended to ride the steep east face of South Diamond Peak. A little before noon, he was seen climbing up the center gully on the face. Two snowshoers standing far below were filming the lone climber with their camcorder but stopped filming when Christiansen went out of their sight.

At 11:55, Christiansen triggered a large slab avalanche that released above him. The avalanche came down with a powder cloud, swallowed up the victim, and continued down the face. It flowed about 400 feet across a gentle bench and continued into a gully that extends toward the parking lot before coming to a stop. The two snowshoers witnessed and were narrowly missed by the avalanche. They then headed for the parking lot to get help.

RESCUE SUMMARY

No rescue equipment

Dan Myer of Fort Collins happened to be driving the highway and saw the powder cloud of the avalanche. He parked and put on his gear. It took him 35 minutes to climb to the debris field, and once there, he conducted a beacon search for 45 minutes, finding nothing.

Members of the Larimer County SAR team arrived at the scene and began a widening search of the debris area. At 15:15, one of the searchers saw the tip of a snowboard sticking from the snow. It was still strapped on Christiansen's back. The victim had been buried for about two hours and 20 minutes and was little more than a foot deep. Death may have been caused by trauma.

AVALANCHE DATA

This avalanche was classified as HS-AFu-R3-D3-O. The hard slab avalanche was about 750 feet wide, averaged two to three feet deep, and was five feet at the deepest part of the crown.

Persistent Slab avalanche

The slope faced east, and the avalanche released at an elevation of 11,500 feet and fell about 700 vertical feet.

COMMENTS

This fatal avalanche occurred on the same slope as another fatal accident the previous winter (19991214). Both were similar in that the victims showed almost total lack of avalanche awareness; they traveled solo, carried no avalanche rescue gear, and climbed an obvious avalanche slope.

EMIGRANT PEAK, SOUTH OF PRAY, MONTANA

20001231

December 31, 2000

Four hikers caught; one injured, two buried and killed

WEATHER AND SNOWPACK CONDITIONS

Emigrant Peak (10,195 feet) lies in the Absaroka Range on the east side of the Paradise Valley about 40 miles east of Bozeman. These mountains had gotten an early and lasting snow cover in November; several weeks of cold and dry weather followed. This caused the snowpack to turn to depth hoar, which would provide a very weak base for subsequent snow storms. This same weather pattern created a weak and very avalanche-prone snowpack in Montana, Idaho, Wyoming, and Utah that lead to numerous fatal accidents (20001127, 20001201, 20001209b, 20001214, 20001217, and 20001225). Additionally, on December 25 and 26, snowmobilers near Yellowstone National Park survived full burials in avalanches they triggered.

On December 29 and 30, the Absaroka Range received about eight to 12 inches of snowfall accompanied by west winds of 20 to 40 mph. This storm effectively doubled the snowpack depth. The new snow fell on depth hoar, creating a weak, collapsible snowpack. Sunday, December 31, was clear and sunny.

ACCIDENT SUMMARY

On Sunday, December 31, a party of four started an overnight trip to ring in the New Year on the top of the peak. The group consisted of Donald Cory (50), his sons Kasey (18) and Samuel (14), and a friend, Kevin Franke (18). They carried overnight gear but no avalanche rescue equipment. They intended to make a snow cave high on the peak and stay the night.

No rescue equipment

The Cory family owned a cabin in the area, and they were familiar with the terrain. The previous New Year's Eve, Kasey Cory and Kevin Franke had done this trip and had camped out.

"Red flag" indications of danger

Kasey subscribed to daily emails from the Gallatin National Forest Avalanche Center and was aware the avalanche danger this day was rated Considerable. He also later recounted that he was leading the group up a route in the trees to avoid a more open avalanche path. While in the trees, they got collapsing and whumpfing sounds coming from the snowpack. Kasey knew these were signs of unstable snow but felt that by being in the trees, they were safe.

On this day, the going was slow, as they were carrying heavy packs and breaking trail the whole way. Nightfall was just a few hours away, and they were still about 1,500 feet short of the summit but only a short walk to a ridge that would provide safety and a location to make their snow cave.

More than one person on a slope

In the trees the snow depth was one to two feet, but as they emerged from the denser trees, the snowpack deepened. Kasey was in the lead and breaking trail in waist-deep snow; the others followed single file and spaced 25 to 30 feet apart. Kasey was 20 feet from the ridge when the avalanche broke. The avalanche swept Kasey downhill and slammed him into a tree, injuring his knee. He then spun off the tree and was carried several hundred feet more before coming to a stop unburied. Kevin was immediately pinned against a tree that held him as the slide passed. The avalanche carried Don and Samuel Cory 1,600 vertical feet down the narrow, rock-ridden slide path and buried them near the toe of the debris.

RESCUE SUMMARY

Kevin and Kasey regrouped and started down the path to look for the other two. Going was slow, so Kevin dropped his pack and ran down the slope, looking for clues but also with the intention of getting to a nearby ranch to make a call for help. At the toe of the debris, Kevin saw a hand sticking from the snow. It was Samuel. Kevin began digging him out as Kasey came down the path. They performed CPR for about half an hour but to no avail.

Kevin then left to go to the ranch house while Kasey—tired, dehydrated, and with an injured knee—stayed at the scene. He randomly probed with a ski pole looking for his father, rested, and melted snow for something to drink. About an hour later, a call came in over his Motorola radio. It was Park County Search and Rescue saying they were on the way. Park County Search and Rescue arrived at the avalanche site later that night, and sometime after 21:30, they located Donald Cory. He had been buried under two feet of snow and was deceased. Both victims had died from trauma.

AVALANCHE DATA

Persistent Slab avalanche

The avalanche was classified as SS-AFu-R4-D3-O. It was two to three feet deep and 200 feet wide, releasing on a northwest-facing slope at an elevation of approximately 9,400 feet and falling 1,600 feet vertical. The snowpack in the start zone consisted of a layer of wind-drifted, soft-slab snow on top of depth hoar. Slope angle was 34 degrees. The avalanche scoured the snowpack to the ground in some areas. The toe area of the debris was about three feet deep and 60 feet wide.

COMMENTS

Several facts point to a failure to fully consider avalanches. First, they lacked rescue gear. Kasey was aware of the avalanche forecast and the group showed good judgment by climbing in a forested area. However, they failed to consider that once they left the denser trees, they lost their protection and entered into an avalanche starting zone. And finally, because they were not thinking about avalanche danger, they were close together, resulting in the entire group getting caught. This was a winter climb; it was not done safely, and it led to two deaths.

ROCK CREEK, NORTHWEST OF JACKSON, MONTANA

20010117

January 17, 2001

One snowmobiler caught, buried, and killed

ACCIDENT SUMMARY

On Wednesday, January 17, a group of seven very experienced snowmobilers was riding in the Beaverhead Mountains, northwest of the town of Jackson, Montana. This mountain range lies along the Continental Divide, which is also the state line that separates Montana and Idaho in this area.

Among the riders was David Shepherd (36), a highly-accomplished semi-pro snowmobiler known for his hill-climbing skills. Hill-climbing is an organized snowmobile event in which riders race to the top of a marked course and is not to be confused with highmarking.

This group of strong riders all carried avalanche beacons, shovels, and probes. Their route took them into Rock Creek drainage. They gathered below a steep, east-facing slope on Peak 9681 along the Continental Divide—a slope they wanted to highmark. The first rider made it a little more than halfway up and returned to the bottom. The second rider went two-thirds the way up before returning to the bottom. Shepherd was third to go, and had made it almost to the top when the slope avalanched. The slide carried Shepherd and his sled back down the mountainside. The time was 14:40.

The other riders kept track of Shepherd as long as possible, then quickly switched their beacons to receive and started a search. Within a minute or so, they found the signal from Shepherd's beacon. Several minutes later, they located the snowmobile with probe poles. Twenty minutes later, they found Shepherd buried under about six feet of snow.

While one man tried to resuscitate Shepherd, the others worked to enlarge the hole that would allow them to pull him from under the snow. Another man rode up a nearby ridge and used his cell phone to call for help.

RESCUE SUMMARY

Shepherd's companions were unable resuscitate him, despite a textbook-fast rescue effort. The depth of burial was too great, and 25 minutes was too long a burial to survive. A rescue team arrived several hours later for the recovery effort.

AVALANCHE DATA

Persistent Slab avalanche

The avalanche ran on an open, east-facing slope with a start-zone angle of 35 degrees, releasing at an elevation of 9,580 feet. The slab was 600 to 700 feet wide, and the fracture depth varied from two to four feet. The stratigraphy was described as five inches of new snow on top of 39 inches of firm snow (probably one-finger-hard) on top of five inches of depth hoar. The classification was probably HS-AMu-R3-D2-O.

COMMENTS

This group of riders had ridden this area and this slope numerous times. But the snowpack in the winter of 2000-01 was different from previous winters and had already proven itself to be a killer. This was the seventh fatal avalanche since November 27 in Montana, Idaho, Wyoming, and Utah, all occurring because of the base layer of depth hoar in the snowpack.

In the words of Deputy Sheriff Heinecke, who aided in the rescue, "It was a picture-perfect avalanche search and rescue. If David had been buried under two or three feet of snow, he might be alive today. But this year, the snowpack is the worst I've ever seen."

20010129 TWIN LAKES, NORTHEAST OF STEVENS PASS, WASHINGTON | January 29, 2001

Two snowshoers caught; one partly buried, one buried and killed. Three dogs caught; one buried and killed

WEATHER AND SNOWPACK CONDITIONS

For several days prior to this avalanche accident, the eastern slope of the Washington Cascades had been under the influence of light east winds and an arctic airmass, which had maintained cold temperatures. This likely caused surface hoar to form on slopes east of the Cascade crest.

On the morning of the accident, a storm system was moving into the Cascades from the west. In the passes, including Stevens Pass, winds shifted from light easterly to strong westerly. With the front, snowfall increased and temperatures warmed up with the change in airmasses. The effect on the snowpack was a rise in the avalanche danger because of warming temperatures and loading from falling and blowing snow. Stevens Pass, about 15 miles southwest of the accident site and higher in elevation, got about 10 inches of snow during the day.

ACCIDENT SUMMARY

Twin Lakes are two small lakes on the east side of Stevens Pass, Washington. From US Highway 2, summer hikers and winter snowshoers can access the lakes by driving past the much larger Lake Wenatchee and arrive at the trailhead near the Tall Timber Ranch. From there, the trail follows the Napeequa River, until the trail enters a steep-sided ravine with Twin Lakes Creek at the bottom.

On Monday, January 29, two snowshoers, Seneca Mott (29) and Jay Bowen (33), walked in three miles and arrived at the upper Twin Lake at about 14:45. They had three dogs with them. Two of the dogs, named Katie and Collier, belonged to Bowen, and the other was Mott's. It snowed lightly on their approach to the lake. They stayed for just a few minutes because of fading daylight, then turned around and started out at approximately 15:15. As they left the upper lake, their route once more took them into the ravine above the creek. Above them was a west-facing cliff band.

Terrain trap

No rescue equipment

In the ravine, they triggered a small slide that caught both snowshoers and all three dogs, sweeping them down toward the creek. Bowen was about 20 feet in front of Mott. She described the slide as being 75 to 100 feet wide and splitting and flowing around brush. Mott was carried a short distance downslope and was ultimately buried up to her waist. Two of the dogs—Mott's dog and Katie, who belonged to Bowen—were on top the snow and "freaked out". As Mott dug herself out, she yelled for Bowen but got no answer. There was no sign of him or his other dog, Collier. Mott probed with her ski pole for about 10 minutes, and during this time she heard whumpfing sounds.

As a result, Mott decided to leave for her own safety and try to get help. She and her dog crossed over to the other side of the creek and traversed out to the Napeequa

River trail. Bowen's dog Katie refused to leave the site of the avalanche and Mott left her behind.

Mott reported the accident to Stan Fishburn at the Tall Timbers Ranch, and they called 911 at 18:30. The sheriff had to make a decision: Because it was dark and the avalanche danger was still perceived as high, he decided to wait until morning to search. At this time, there were stars visible. Sometime that night, Bowen's dog Katie showed up at the Tall Timbers Ranch.

RESCUE SUMMARY

Coincidentally, Fishburn was teaching a backcountry awareness course at the Tall Timbers Ranch. On January 30, the course was scheduled to have an avalanche dog handler from the Stevens Pass Ski Patrol do a presentation on dog rescue and beacon searches, so this group merged with the sheriff's rescue team that morning.

Initially, a group of four went in. Fishburn led the group because of his familiarity with the area. When they arrived at the site, they reported that most of the snow had slid off the slope. The group felt fairly confident that it was safe for more searchers to come and assist. In the meantime, the initial party began probing what they presumed was the slide debris below the cliff band. Later, searchers brought in the rescue dog, but after an hour, the dog had not alerted and the probers had made no strikes.

Then the dog handler remembered Mott's statement about the avalanche running through brush. She noticed that there was no brush in the area where the search had been concentrated but that brush was showing at the other end of the slide. She took her dog to that area, and the dog quickly alerted. Digging at that spot revealed a ski pole, which searchers soon identified as Mott's. The search dog made no further finds, nor did the probers, and the search was terminated because of oncoming darkness.

The following morning, a rescue party returned to the site with a different dog and handler. This one did no better than the first. Searchers set up a fine probe line at the foot of the debris, which had covered the creek, and downhill from where the ski pole had been found the previous day. The probe line quickly struck Bowen's body and recovered him from beneath four feet of snow. He was dug out directly over running water. Bowen's dog Collier was not found.

AVALANCHE DATA

Persistent Slab avalanche

The slide was described as a small soft slab that released on a west-facing slope at about 3,000 feet elevation. It dropped about 60 to 80 vertical feet. The slope was steep—nearly 40 degrees. The fracture was about 18 inches deep and about 100 feet wide. The weak layer was facets on top of an ice crust at the ground. The classification was probably SS-AIu-R2-O.

COMMENTS

This accident is yet another example of a gully as a terrain trap. The avalanche was small, yet the victim was carried a short distance and buried deeply in the creek bed. The two snowshoers did not recognize the avalanche danger presented by the short, steep slope.

The two rescue dog handlers later discussed why their dogs did not alert on the victim's body. Both dogs did, however, alert on an alder tree that was over the creek bed and downstream from where the victim was later found by a probe. They surmised that the scent had traveled down the creek and come up next to the alder.

20010203 PEAK 7075, SOUTHEAST OF EUREKA, ALASKA

February 3, 2001

Six snowmobilers caught; two partly buried, two buried and killed

The following accident was investigated by Doug Fesler and Jill Fredston of the Alaska Mountain Safety Center, Inc.[1] *The results of their investigation appear here with minimal editing.*

WEATHER AND SNOWPACK CONDITIONS

The site of this fatal avalanche was on Peak 7075, just north of the headwaters pass at the source of the East Fork of the Matanuska River, on the northern side of the Chugach Mountain Range. The peak sits approximately 12 miles south-southeast of Eureka Lodge on the Glenn Highway.

The early winter was uncharacteristically mild for Eureka (warmer than the typical -10 to 20° F highs) with few storms. This resulted in a shallow snowpack (around two feet deep) consisting mostly of weak, well-developed, faceted snow. In early January, a major storm hit the area, adding 3.5 to four feet of new snow. Subsequent winds created widespread wind slab over depth hoar conditions. On the day of the accident, the weather was mostly clear, temperatures near -10° F, and windless.

ACCIDENT SUMMARY

The accident site was on the south side of Peak 7075 and consisted of a long, narrow, slightly S-shaped chute bordered by steeper side walls. This main chute faces generally south, with slope angles around 23 degrees at the base to 38 degrees at the top, but with steeper sidewalls ranging from 40 to 50 degrees. A second chute originating from a large bowl to the east intersects the main chute along a northeast-southwest axis near the midway point of the main path. A prominent rock pinnacle is on the opposite (west) side of the main path immediately across from the second chute.

More than one person on a slope

At approximately 12:10 on Saturday, February 3, a party of seven snowmobilers was ascending the main chute that leads to the top of Peak 7075 on the south side. They were traveling more or less in a line and were spread over a distance of approximately 400 feet. The riders in the lead, Dan and Clark, were approximately two-thirds the distance up the slope. David was about 30 feet behind them, followed at 60 feet by Rick, followed at another 60 feet by Scott, followed at another 60 feet by Mike, and finally, 200 feet below Mike, by Shane. The slope above and to their right (east) broke loose, and each snowmobiler immediately attempted to escape to the west side.

Dan, who was already in the process of turning his machine, was instantly flipped, tumbled, and carried with his machine 1,500 vertical feet downslope, where he was buried under eight feet of debris and killed.

Clark managed to point his machine toward the west flank of the path, gun his engine, and momentarily escape onto stable snow adjoining the slide, until the curve of the terrain forced him back into the main path, where the entire snow surface was in motion. Unable to stop, he was carried about 150 feet downslope. Finally, he was able to wedge his machine into some debris that had come to a stop. Most of the slide had passed in front of him, but some snow was still sliding when he came to rest.

David, who was attempting an escape to the west side, was hit and flipped end-over and upside down almost immediately. Trapped under his machine, his face pressed under the windshield, he was carried nearly 1,500 vertical feet downslope before stopping. He estimated he was carried that way for 95% of his ride, until, at the last moment, he popped to the surface next to his machine (which also flipped over) about 50 feet below where Dan was found. Later, it was discovered that his machine had been severely damaged by blunt impact.

Rick was roughly 40 feet above the rock pinnacle when he saw the snow coming and tried to get to the west side of the path. At the last moment, he leapt off his machine and ran upslope as the machine was swept away behind him. The machine was carried approximately 1,500 feet downslope and ended up five feet below David and his machine.

Scott never had a chance. He saw the wall of churning debris, pointed his machine to the west, and tried to reach safety. But the rock pinnacle blocked his escape. Hit from behind by the force of the snow, he and his machine were lifted upward against the face of the rock. In a desperate attempt to escape, he repeatedly grabbed for a handhold as his machine was swept away beneath him. Unable to hold on, Scott was pulled from the face and swept into the blocks of moving debris. His machine was last seen flipping end over end down the gully.

Mike, 60 feet below the rock, saw the slope on his right begin to buckle and move. Figuring he only had seconds to reach safety, he pointed his machine toward the west side and tried to escape. Seeing Scott's predicament and being farther downslope than Scott, he figured he had slightly more time in his favor and no rock face to obstruct his escape. When almost to the edge, he felt his machine starting to lift on the right side. He stood, leaning to the right. As it lifted on end, he leapt for the edge of the path and scrambled to safety.

Shane was the luckiest of all. Two hundred feet below Mike, he saw the avalanche breaking away from the face above, turned his sled downhill, and rocketed out toward the southwest. Because his back was to the avalanche, he was unable to note the positions of his partners.

RESCUE SUMMARY

When the snow came to rest, the runout zone looked something like a battlefield, with slab blocks ranging in size from office desks to trucks. The debris was piled 35 to 40 feet deep in the center of an area measuring roughly nine city blocks. Mike and Rick were within sight of each other midway along the western side of the path. Clark was out of view above the S-curve, farther upslope near the top. Shane was out of view, below the lower S-curve on the west side. David was now standing by his machine on the surface of the rubble. Mike made the first head count using the CB radios each of them carried. David and Shane moved toward each other on the lower portion of the path, while Mike, Rick, and Clark grouped above. Two other groups of snowmobilers, comprised of two people each, responded to the site from the valley below.

Inadequate rescue equipment

By 12:25, the group gathered together and hatched a plan. One team of two snowmobilers departed for help. Their plan was to get within cell phone range and call the Alaska State Troopers. Those with beacons spread out across the surface and conducted a beacon search. (Clark, Mike, Rick, and David carried beacons. Scott's beacon was found at his home later. Shane and Dan, who were new to the group, did not own beacons.) With the only two probes the group had, two people started probing for Dan and Scott, hoping to get lucky (all other probes had been stored with the machines, which were buried). Others started digging out Scott's machine, which was partially visible.

By 13:00, Scott's machine was out and Dan's machine was located directly under Scott's. By 13:15, Dan's machine was half out, and probers had struck Dan, two to three feet under his machine. By 13:30 his head and chest were uncovered, but it wasn't until 13:50 that he was completely excavated, pulled free, and examined. His airway was open. CPR was started at 13:55 and terminated at 14:30 without success. Meanwhile, probing continued for Scott.

By 14:30, prospects for finding Scott looked slim in light of the size of the slide, the limited rescue gear and personnel on site, and the fact that the survivors were getting cold. As the sun went behind the ridge, thoughts turned toward evacuation. Getting the group back to Eureka Lodge (roughly 15 miles by snowmobile) would not be easy. Five machines were seriously damaged (the damaged ranged from an estimated $800 to $4,500), and one was stranded high in the path. After an hour of patching together the more repairable machines, the group headed toward Eureka. Rick was becoming severely hypothermic, nodding off and acting sluggish. The group soon encountered the two snowmobilers who had gone for help earlier. They had contacted the Troopers and been told to make a signal fire at their location to guide the rescuers to the site. The group warmed Rick by the fire, and gave him food and liquid.

Formal rescue response (Alaska Mountain Rescue Group, Alaska Search and Rescue Dogs, and Alaska Mountain Safety Center personnel) arrived on scene by approximately 17:00. A Trooper, along with the two snowmobilers who'd gone for help earlier, greeted the rescuers. They pieced together the sequence of events at the accident scene, assessed the site as safe from further avalanches, conducted a thorough beacon search of the runout zone and an initial dog search, and transported Dan's body in the Army National Guard Blackhawk helicopter. Fuel vapors from the helicopter sickened several of the rescuers, and probably disabled the dogs as well. Searchers departed the site by 19:30, with a plan to return the next day with more searchers and the witnesses. They spent the night at Eureka Lodge, where they were able to interview the witnesses.

The next day's plan entailed searching the area with SAR dogs and probe lines. The bad news was that the first helicopter to arrive (an Alaska Fish and Wildlife Protection Robinson 44) crashed in flat light and was totaled. The good news was that pilot and two passengers were uninjured. A Blackhawk helicopter delivered additional rescuers to the site within 30 minutes. By 10:30, two SAR dogs alerted in a high probability area and probers confirmed the find. Scott was uncovered from beneath 10 feet of snow and the mission was terminated. Rescuers included members of the National Ski Patrol, Nordic Patrol, the Alaska Mountain Rescue Group, Alaska SAR Dogs, the Alaska Mountain Safety Center, the Alaska Snowmachine SAR Recovery Team, the Mat-Su Motor Mushers, and the Backcountry Avalanche Awareness Rescue & Recovery Team.

AVALANCHE DATA

Deep Persistent Slab avalanche

This was a very large avalanche (classified as HS-AM-R5-D4) with big blocks of broken hard slab debris measuring the size of office desks to automobiles. A few were larger than dump trucks. The fracture line ran more than 3,000 feet, crossed two ridges, and cleaned out three separate bowls. It had two runout zones a quarter-mile apart from one another. The fracture depth varied from 1.5 to 15 feet with the average around six feet. The avalanche in the main path traveled more than a half-mile and fell 1,800 vertical feet, from an elevation of 7,000 feet to 5,200 feet. Snow was piled 35 to 40 feet deep in both runout zones and was about one-third of a mile wide. The other path was about 30% smaller, but no less impressive. The fact that five people managed to survive this slide is amazing.

COMMENTS

For the most part, the victims did not have the training, knowledge, or skills to evaluate the hazard or the risks of avalanche terrain and snow conditions they could access with their powerful machines. Their riding skills were considerably greater than their hazard evaluation skills, as evidenced by their choice to travel through exposed terrain as a group, rather than one at a time, which significantly increased the risk of an incident like this. Only one member had any previous avalanche training, and his experiences had involved mountaineering and skiing, where the process of hazard evaluation occurs at a slower rate, with more input, and greater participation. He felt his ability to assess conditions was limited by tunnel vision (through a helmet's visor), speed, and the inability to hear and feel subtle sounds of the snow underfoot.

Conclusions: This instability is of the type that persists for a long time, yet is easily detectable. In essence, the group seems to have been lured into the den of the dragons by capable machines, favorable weather, spectacular scenery, and the idea of having a good time with friends. This group was not knowingly reckless, but they underestimated the strength of a thin snowpack and the amount of wind loaded snow in the starting zones and did not factor in the consequences of traveling closely together into a terrain trap. Note that even if the victims had been wearing avalanche beacons, the outcome of two fatalities would not have changed because of the deep burial.

ROCK SPRINGS BOWL, SOUTH OF JACKSON HOLE MOUNTAIN RESORT, WYOMING | February 6, 2001

20010206

One sidecountry skier caught, buried, and killed

ACCIDENT SUMMARY

Sometime on the afternoon of Tuesday, February 6, Ralph Toscano (43), visiting from Oregon, left the Jackson Hole Ski Area boundary and headed into the Rock Springs Bowl backcountry area alone. He was skiing above a cliff band that is broken by the Zero G, Spacewalk, and M&M couloirs. He triggered a soft slab avalanche 18 inches deep that swept him over a 100-foot cliff and onto a snow apron below the cliff. This triggered a four-foot slab on the apron that buried him.

Traveling alone

RESCUE SUMMARY

When Toscano did not show up at his motel that night, friends notified authorities. During the night, ski area groomers kept an eye out for Toscano. The next morning, searchers in a helicopter discovered the slide in Rock Springs Bowl. Members of the Jackson Hole Ski Patrol then skied into the bowl to the debris pile near the bottom of M&M couloir. There they saw a ski boot protruding from the snow. Rescuers dug Toscano's body free, and the helicopter flew it from the scene.

AVALANCHE DATA

The initial slide was classified as SS-ASu-R2-D2, with an 18-inch fracture depth. But after going over the cliff, it triggered a deeper slab avalanche on the slope below. Overall, the avalanche fell about 500 vertical feet. The avalanche released on a south-facing slope at an elevation of 9,800 feet.

COMMENTS

Two points: Skiing alone removes the safety net provided by companions. And cliffs are unforgiving terrain features that turn small events into killers.

20010217

LAKE ANN, NORTH OF CLE ELUM, WASHINGTON

February 17, 2001

One snowmobiler caught, buried, and killed

WEATHER AND SNOWPACK CONDITIONS

Lake Ann sits about 25 miles due east of Snoqualmie Pass, which is the route of highway I-90 over the crest of the Cascade Range, and about 15 miles north of the town of Cle Elum, also on I-90. The Cascade crest separates a warmer, wetter winter climate to the west from a colder, drier winter climate to the east. Therefore, winter conditions at this area are a transition between a wet crest and dry east. Moderate snowfall and cold, clear nights are common, as are the corresponding snow problems of a colder, drier climate—specifically, faceting and surface hoar.

Between February 15 and 17, Snoqualmie Pass received 17 inches of snow, which contained 1.35 inches of water, while Mission Ridge, 20 miles to the east, got only five inches of snow containing 0.27 inches of water. The Lake Ann area would have received something in the middle of these amounts. Prevailing east winds at 5,000 feet elevation averaged 20 to 30 mph on the day of the accident and would have loaded west-facing slopes.

ACCIDENT SUMMARY

Lake Ann is in a basin at an elevation of 6,160 feet, with a steep west-facing slope on its eastern side rising to 7,200 feet. A shallow gully, about 200 feet wide, cuts down that slope.

Around mid-afternoon on Saturday, February 17, a group of 12 snowmobilers were traversing the slope. The first two riders went through the gully, followed by the third, who was on a track 15 feet higher than the first two. He triggered an avalanche, which swept him and his machine down the slope.

The next few riders were far enough back that they did not see the avalanche occur, but they noticed it when they came to the area. At the time, they didn't think it was caused by one of their own party, so they kept riding and caught up with the first two riders at the lake. After a few minutes of discussion about where the missing man could have gone—which led to a few of the riders remembering seeing the windshield of a snowmobile in the debris—they realized that he may have triggered the avalanche in the gully.

RESCUE SUMMARY

Inadequate rescue equipment

The group returned to the avalanche site and quickly found the windshield of their friend's snowmobile sticking out of the debris. They began a search of the debris field, but unfortunately, they had only two shovels and two probes among them. No one had beacons. One member left with two cell phones to find a reception spot to report the avalanche. The Kittitas Sheriff and SAR were notified at 16:20.

Several hours passed before the victim was found (and the report does not specify how he was located). He was located 250 yards below the fracture line. He was buried 18 inches deep and 60 feet from his machine. The slope was open where he triggered the slide, but then the snow flowed into trees below. The victim struck the first tree, and the impact knocked off his helmet. It is likely that he died on impact.

AVALANCHE DATA

The avalanche released on a northwest-facing slope that was 42 degrees at the start zone. It released the new snow layer with a fracture that was 18 inches deep. The avalanche fell 350 to 400 feet vertical. It would probably be classified as SS-AMu-R3-D2-I.

Storm Slab avalanche

COMMENTS

This group was riding in avalanche terrain but—having no beacons and only two probes and shovels among them—was not prepared for an avalanche event. In this instance, rescue gear would not have saved the victim, but that is almost beside the point. The level of avalanche awareness for some riders in this group was very low.

WEST GULLY CHUTE, SOUTH OF SQUAW VALLEY, CALIFORNIA | February 21, 2001

20010221

Two sidecountry skiers caught, buried, and killed

WEATHER AND SNOWPACK CONDITIONS

In mid-February, the Sierra Nevada Range of California had seen a period of mild weather that produced a sun crust on southerly aspects. Then a storm system moved in from February 19 to 21 and dropped about 20 inches of snow, accompanied by south-southwest winds of 40 to 50 mph and gusts to 60 to 70 mph.

ACCIDENT SUMMARY

Sometime between noon and 14:00 on Wednesday, February 21, Brendan Allen (17) and Bryan Richmond (17) left the ski area boundary at Squaw Valley to ski a steep chute called the West Gully that drops down to the access road to Alpine Meadows Ski Area. The two young men were members of the Squaw Valley Ski Team. Both teens were familiar with the terrain and had skied it often. Neither carried avalanche rescue equipment. The West Gully is a prominent slide path that regularly hits the Alpine Meadows Road.

No rescue equipment

Apparently skiing close together, they triggered a slab avalanche that caught both of them. The slide swept them down the chute and totally buried both.

RESCUE SUMMARY

The Tahoe Nordic Search and Rescue Team began a search for the missing teens that night at 22:00. Heavy snow and winds covered up some of the clues, but rescuers found the slide debris at midnight and scuff searched. The search team found no evidence in the debris and moved into different areas.

Early the next morning, February 22, with the help of the Alpine Meadows Ski Patrol, avalanche dogs worked the debris in the West Gully but with no results. Later that morning, Tahoe Nordic SAR returned to the West Gully and began probing. The debris in the gully reached depths of eight feet. Searchers found the bodies at 11:30. Both boys were buried five to six feet deep and 40 feet above the toe of the debris. The bodies were within three feet of each other. Evidence suggests the boys skied into the gully together and the avalanche carried them into the enclosed terrain trap.

Terrain trap

Tahoe Nordic Search and Rescue, Alpine Meadows Ski Patrol, Squaw Valley Ski Patrol and Placer County Sheriffs Department were all involved in the search effort.

AVALANCHE DATA

Storm Slab avalanche

The West Gully path faces southeast with the starting zone angle about 35 degrees. This avalanche was classified as SS-ASu-R2-I, and it released the recent layer of storm snow, which slid on a sun crust. It fell 300 vertical feet. No crown was visible the following day because it had filled in with blowing snow.

COMMENTS

These young men were not thinking "avalanche" when they left the ski area and went into the backcountry, where the storm snow had produced an unstable slab on top of a sun crust. Skiing close together, they triggered the slide. Finally, the gully formed a terrain trap that caused the debris to pile up on top of itself, resulting in a deep burial.

20010223

GRANITE CANYON, NORTH OF JACKSON HOLE MOUNTAIN RESORT, WYOMING | February 23, 2001

One sidecountry skier caught, buried, and killed

WEATHER AND SNOWPACK CONDITIONS

The Jackson Hole Mountain Resort recorded three inches of snow on the morning of February 23, which brought the three-day total to 15 inches. The Bridger-Teton National Forest Avalanche Center was rating the avalanche danger as Considerable, meaning that human-triggered avalanches were likely.

ACCIDENT SUMMARY

On Friday, February 23 at 16:00, a party of four skiers left the boundary of the ski resort for an out-of-area tour to wrap up their ski day. One of the group members was Allen Wagner (24), a ski instructor. After crossing the ski-area boundary, they entered the Granite Canyon area of Grand Teton National Park. The group intended to ski a steep 200-foot chute near Caledonia Couloir. At 16:15, Wagner approached the chute a different way than his friends and triggered a small, shallow avalanche. This, in turn, released a two-foot slab that carried Wagner down the side of the canyon. The slide carried him over a 40-foot cliff and some 500 feet down the slope, where he was buried three feet deep.

RESCUE SUMMARY

The slide stopped at Granite Creek, close to Jeff Giffin, who had skied down first. He turned his avalanche transceiver to "search" and quickly got a strong signal from Wagner's transceiver. Zach Giffin arrived at the scene and hit Wagner with his first probe, under three feet of snow. They freed Wagner's face of snow in five minutes, but it took another 15 minutes to free his body to the point they could begin rescue breathing.

One of the party skied out to notify the ski patrol, who learned of the incident at 17:00. Grand Teton National Park launched a helicopter, and the resort dispatched four ski patrollers to the scene. The helicopter had to retreat in the face of darkness, but ski patrollers reached the scene at 18:30. Patrollers continued resuscitation efforts with an electronic defibrillator and oxygen, without success.

The skiers left the canyon that evening and Wagner's body was flown out Saturday morning.

AVALANCHE DATA

The avalanche released on a north-facing chute at about 8,000 feet elevation. It fell about 500 feet vertical, and though not a large slide, it went through steep, high consequence terrain. It was classified as SS-ASu-R2-O.

Persistent Slab avalanche

COMMENTS

It is always better to ski with friends who are good at rescue, and Wagner's friends executed a speedy rescue. But even that wasn't enough. Wagner had likely sustained serious trauma down the rocky chute. This group had chosen a risky day—with 15 inches of fresh snow and the danger rated Considerable—to ski this chute. And looking at the avalanche conditions more broadly, this probably was not even the winter to be skiing here. This was the sixth fatal avalanche in northwest Wyoming that winter—all due to a persistent weak layer near the bottom of the snowpack.

OHIO PASS, SOUTHWEST OF CRESTED BUTTE, COLORADO 20010225

February 25, 2001

One backcountry skier caught, buried, and killed

WEATHER AND SNOWPACK CONDITIONS

Total snowfall in the Crested Butte and Irwin Lodge area of the central Colorado mountains had been very close to normal from November to mid-February, and in the first two weeks of February, the avalanche danger hovered around Moderate in the mountains around Crested Butte. The next weather system, on February 14 and 15, brought about a foot of snow to the region, causing an increase in the avalanche danger, which contributed to two avalanche incidents near Crested Butte. First, on February 15, a backcountry skier was partly buried, and the next day, a backcountry snowboarder was buried and saved by his companion.

On February 18, the next weather system brought more snowfall, which contributed to a serious avalanche event on Mt. Emmons just west of Crested Butte. Robert Casper (39) was skiing alone when he triggered an avalanche, which slammed him into a tree and broke his femur. Casper, an EMT, was able to splint his leg with the handle of his shovel, and with no hope for rescue that evening, he dug a snow cave for the night. The following morning, he crawled to a point where his shouts for help were heard by another skier, which led to his rescue.

Following this incident, snowfall continued in the Crested Butte area between February 19 and 22, with 14 inches recorded at both Irwin Lodge and Crested Butte Mountain Resort. Then, on February 23 and 24 another 15 inches fell in the Kebler Pass and Ohio Pass area, along with west-southwest winds estimated at 20 to 25 mph.

The avalanche danger was rated Considerable on February 25 in the Ruby and Anthracite Ranges west of Crested Butte.

ACCIDENT SUMMARY

Ohio Pass lies at 10,000 feet elevation and is located six miles west-southwest of Crested Butte and three miles south of Irwin Lodge. The road over the pass is a summer road, but with a tow-in by snowmobile, it's a popular backcountry skiing site.

On the afternoon of Sunday, February 25, several groups of skiers were in the vicinity of Ohio Pass. One party of five skiers included Mitch and Susan Hoffman (both 40), Kris (48) and Bobby (40) Pogoloff, and Lynn McDermand (44). This group was well equipped and very knowledgeable about avalanches, and they knew the area well. They had made their first run in what the locals call 7 Bowl and had skinned back up for a second run, this time in East Bowl above the summit of Ohio Pass.

Kris went first, heading slightly left of the fall line, until he came to a stop in a small group of trees on a bench above the final steep pitch. Bobby went second and stopped next to Kris, where both could spot the other skiers as they came down. Mitch went third, heading on a line down the right side of the slope and went over the bench, coming to a stop below and out of sight of the other skiers.

The time was about 14:15 when Susan went down and stopped in the safe area by Kris and Bobby. They gave the sign for Lynn, skiing last, to come down. While Lynn was skiing, Susan asked the two men, Kris and Bobby, where Mitch had gone. They told her that Mitch was below and on the other side of the slope. Susan called out, Mitch answered, and Susan said she was going to join him and skied over the bench out of sight.

A few seconds later, Lynn arrived at the bench, and a few seconds after that, the three skiers there heard Mitch's voice from below shout out "Avalanche!" Kris, Bobby, and Lynn did not hear the avalanche, and it was only until they moved forward that they saw the fracture line on the steep face below them.

RESCUE SUMMARY

The three skiers on the bench yelled down to Mitch, asking if Susan was with him. He shouted back, "No!" The three skiers above switched their beacons to receive and dropped over the fracture line onto the bed surface. From below, Mitch told the searchers where he had last seen Susan. Within a minute or two, the searchers picked up a beacon signal and followed it to a tree, where they found Susan very shallowly buried and wrapped around a tree.

They were able to uncover her head and shoulders within four to five minutes of the avalanche, but it took shovels to dig out her legs. She had suffered a severe head trauma; there was no pulse, no breathing. Her rescuers—her friends and husband—knew Susan was dead.

Word of the avalanche quickly got to nearby Irwin Lodge, which has a snowcat skiing operation. Several of the guides and a doctor who had been snowcat skiing responded to the call for help. The doctor confirmed that, with the extent of her head injuries, the victim had likely died upon impact.

AVALANCHE DATA

This avalanche released on an east-facing slope at 10,540 feet elevation, just above the Ohio Pass road. It was 500 feet across and fell 400 vertical feet. The fracture line was generally three to four feet in depth but ranged up to five feet in places. The trigger point for the avalanche was a steep convex roll where the slope angle steepened from

30 to 50 degrees. Where the victim's ski tracks entered the fracture line, the slope angle was 35 degrees. The slab layer comprised one-finger and four-finger-hard snow, and it was classified as SS-ASu-R3-D2-O.

Persistent Slab avalanche

COMMENTS

This was an experienced group who knew the terrain well. They were knowledgeable about the avalanche potential, carried full rescue gear in case of emergency, and were skiing cautiously, given the known avalanche conditions. But the danger increases when trees dot an avalanche slope. As in this case, an otherwise survivable avalanche becomes deadly.

The victim's route—cutting across the steepest part of the convex roll—was perhaps the only bad decision the group made this day.

The victim was a well-respected teacher in Crested Butte. Her death was a terrible loss for her husband, friends, and the community.

RED ROCK CLIFFS, NORTHWEST OF CANYONS VILLAGE AT PARK CITY, UTAH | February 27, 2001

20010227

Four sidecountry skiers caught; two partly buried, two buried, one killed

WEATHER AND SNOWPACK CONDITIONS

The winter of 2000-01 was characterized in the Wasatch by a thin and unusually weak snowpack. An initial stormy period in early November produced several feet of snow cover that faceted into depth hoar during clear spells in late November and December. This weakening process was coupled with a lack of major storms that might have eliminated the weak layers by natural avalanching. Throughout the second half of January and all of February people triggered numerous avalanches in the Wasatch backcountry. Several small storms loaded extra weight on the weak layers, keeping the avalanche danger at Moderate and Considerable from mid-January to February 23. During the weekend preceding the accident—February 24 and 25—the east side of the Wasatch received about 16 inches of new snow, fitting the seasonal profile of a small storm increasing the danger. On February 24, the danger bumped to High, and then returned to Considerable for February 25 through 27.

ACCIDENT SUMMARY

On Tuesday, February 27, a party of seven skiers and snowboarders planned a backcountry tour from what was then known as Canyons Ski Resort. They rode to the top of the Ninety-Nine 90 ski lift and exited the ski area through a backcountry access point at about 11:30. The party traveled northwest along the ridgeline, passing over a high point known as Square Top, to the Red Rock Cliffs area. Red Rock Cliffs is a steep slope that funnels into a narrow, winding gully. It is an avalanche area, with starting-zone slope angles of 35 to 45 degrees. Locals rarely ski the area because of the nature of the slope—a steep starting zone above and a terrain trap below.

Upon reaching the Red Rock Cliffs, Andy Reinfurt, one of the group members, was concerned about the cornice that hung above the slope they wished to descend. He continued to travel to the northwest along the ridge, attempting to get a full view of the cornice. Before Andy returned, Sharon Reinfurt (43) decided she wanted to return

More than one person on a slope

to the ski resort. She skied down off of the ridgeline and began traversing diagonally across the slope. She then fell, losing a ski in the snow. Chris Rand, Conner Reinfurt, and Keith Latalliere skied down to Sharon to help find the lost ski.

The time was 12:45, and as Cassie Reinfurt and J.D. Lamb stood near the top of the slope, the avalanche released directly below Cassie's snowboard. (From the witness accounts, it is unclear if Cassie was moving at the time the avalanche released.) Lower on the slope, Sharon, Chris, Conner, and Keith were all caught in the avalanche. Keith was carried about 50 feet downhill and was buried to his waist. Conner was completely covered in the moving snow and was carried downhill until he struck a tree. He was then pushed to the top of the snow and was on the surface when the avalanche stopped moving. Chris and Sharon were both carried downhill and into the gully and out of sight. They were both completely buried in the avalanche debris.

Terrain trap

RESCUE SUMMARY

Cassie and J.D. waited above the crown line until Andy returned, and then the three of them traveled down the bed surface to assist in the rescue. Keith was able to dig himself out of the avalanche debris, and he and Conner began descending the debris pile looking for Chris and Sharon. About 60 feet below where Conner had hit the tree, they heard Chris yelling from beneath the snow surface. They began digging and uncovered Chris from under about 2.5 feet of snow.

No rescue equipment

At this point Andy, Cassie, and J.D. arrived. Some of the party continued to extricate Chris from the debris (taking 30 to 45 minutes), and the remainder began probing the snow with their equipment in an attempt to find Sharon. Sharon had been to the skier's left of Chris when the avalanche released; therefore, they concentrated their search in that area.

Shortly after Chris was uncovered, Keith left the scene to alert the ski patrol. Several people from other backcountry parties joined in the search, adding four or five rescuers to the initial searchers.

Sometime later, members of The Canyons Ski Patrol arrived at the Red Rock Cliffs area and determined that the accident site was still threatened by potential avalanches. They evacuated the searchers and conducted avalanche mitigation. The initial searchers had located Sharon's skis and left them near a tree, next to where they were recovered. Control work produced additional avalanching along both flanks of the original slide.

Once the accident site was deemed safe, a ski patrol search team, including two search dogs, was allowed onto the debris pile. After working the site for approximately five minutes, one of the search dogs alerted on a deep portion of the debris. A probe confirmed Sharon's location, and her body was recovered a short time later from under four feet of snow.

Sharon Reinfurt was recovered at 15:57. She was located approximately 60 feet downhill and to the left of where Chris had been buried. At the time of recovery, she was lying face down with her head pointing downhill. Rescuers reported that no ice mask had formed during the burial. She had been buried for approximately three hours and 12 minutes. Later, the medical examiner's report stated that the cause of death was asphyxia.

AVALANCHE DATA

Persistent Slab avalanche

The avalanche was classified as HS-ASu-R2-O. The crown depth varied from 1.5 to 3.5 feet and was 200 feet wide. The slope angle at the crown was 41 degrees. The slide fell 400 feet vertical. The slope faced east and was at an elevation of 9,600 feet.

COMMENTS

This family group was seeking powder and an alternative to a ski-area setting, but they lacked backcountry experience and avalanche skills. Therefore, they didn't even consider that there could be avalanche danger beyond the ropes. And when they came to the slope they wanted to ski, they showed more concern with the cornice than the stability of the slope below. Finally, without beacons, probes, and shovels, they were helpless when a member of their group was buried four feet deep.

PRATER MOUNTAIN, SOUTHEAST OF ALPINE JUNCTION, WYOMING | March 3, 2001

20010303

Two snowmobilers caught; one partly buried, one buried and killed

ACCIDENT SUMMARY

Prater Mountain, 10,078 feet elevation, is located in the Salt River Range, which lies very near the Idaho state line and southeast of Alpine Junction, Wyoming. Very little is known about this avalanche death—for example, the precise location, which may be known as Lee Bowl, is unclear. On March 3, a party of three snowmobilers was riding in the area. Two members of the group were caught in an avalanche. One member was partially buried and was dug out by the third person. The second rider, Jay Almos (39) was buried.

Other riders in the area aided in the search and used tree limbs to probe the area. After about 90 minutes, the searchers found Almos under two to three feet of snow. CPR efforts were administered on the victim without success.

COMMENTS

The lack of information available on this accident precludes comment.

UPPER CHALK CREEK, EAST OF OAKLEY, UTAH

20010310

March 10, 2001

Three snowmobilers caught; one partly buried, two buried and killed

ACCIDENT SUMMARY

East of Oakley, Utah, the Chalk Creek region of the Uinta Mountains is a popular snowmobile area. Fresh snow had fallen Friday, and on Saturday, March 10, a number of riders were in the area. One group of three included Jason Wade (29), Steven Barlow (29), and Jason Peacock (25), and they were riding in an area known as the Chutes.

Suddenly, the slope broke all around them and avalanched. Peacock tried to outmaneuver the slide on his snowmobile, but was caught, carried downhill, and partly buried. Wade and Barlow disappeared in the avalanche. The father of one of the missing men had been riding further downhill when the avalanche broke and was able to avoid getting caught.

More than one person on a slope

RESCUE SUMMARY

No one in the group had beacons or other rescue gear. Peacock was able to get out of the debris and rushed to the aid of his buried friends. Other riders in the area came to help

No rescue equipment

as well. Initially, searchers focused their efforts near the sleds. It took them some time to locate visible clues. Both victims were buried about 75 feet laterally away from their sleds. They were about three feet deep near the toe of the debris, one with a hand and the other with a foot sticking out. Rescuers gave CPR, but the buried men did not respond.

AVALANCHE DATA

Persistent Slab avalanche

This avalanche broke on a northwest-facing slope and released near an elevation of 10,000 feet. The main part of the slide was an hourglass-shaped path about 150 feet wide at the top, then choking down to 50 to 75 feet before opening back up to about 150 feet wide in the deposition area, where the debris was up to 12 feet deep.

The fracture also jumped out of the main slope and took out the next two gullies. Thus, the total width was about 500 feet. It ran 400 feet vertical. Although a couple of areas in the starting zone were about 40 degrees steep, most of the start zone was less than 35 degrees. Fracture depth was two to five feet. Alpha angle was 27 degrees.

Most of the bed surface was down to ground level, but in places the sliding surface was a faceted layer formed during a December-January clear spell. A pit on the flank of the start zone showed a two-foot-thick hard slab over very weak facets and depth hoar.

The slide was classified as HS-AMu-R3-G.

COMMENTS

None of the riders in this group carried avalanche rescue gear. If all party members had been equipped with beacons, it would have shortened the burial time. This may have saved the men's lives.

20010318a FARWELL MOUNTAIN, NORTH OF STEAMBOAT SPRINGS, COLORADO | March 18, 2001

One backcountry skier caught, buried, and killed

WEATHER AND SNOWPACK CONDITIONS

A storm moved into the northern mountains of Colorado on March 10 and brought daily snowfall through March 18. During this time, Steamboat Ski Area got 28 inches of snow, and snow was still falling on the day of the avalanche.

ACCIDENT SUMMARY

Inadequate rescue equipment

On Sunday, March 18, a group of five experienced backcountry skiers used snowmobiles to reach the slopes they planned to ski. Though they were all good backcountry skiers, they were not fully prepared for avalanche rescue. Among the five, they had only three beacons. They distributed the beacons to the "weaker" skiers. The group also lacked collapsible probe poles.

The group was on Farwell Mountain, a 10,840-foot peak about 27 miles north of Steamboat Springs and five miles east of Steamboat Lake. They skied a slope on the east side of the mountain and then returned for a second run. Three skiers skied down, one at a time, and moved out of the area at the bottom of the slope.

The time was 13:30 when Sean Patrick Clancy (34) headed down. He was one of the two skiers without a beacon. After several turns, the avalanche broke above Clancy and then overtook him. He disappeared in the flowing snow, and when it stopped, he was totally buried.

RESCUE SUMMARY

The three other men and one woman searched the debris for Clancy, but they found no surface clues. While three stayed to search the debris, one man left the area on his snowmobile and reached a phone to call Routt County Search and Rescue, who received the call about an hour and a half after the avalanche. Rescuers arrived a little more than an hour later with two avalanche dogs. One of the two—Pepper Dog—alerted within minutes, and the rescue team dug Clancy out from three feet of snow. He had been buried for three hours and had died.

AVALANCHE DATA

The avalanche was a small soft slab triggered by the victim and classified as SS-ASu-R2-O. The crown was 1.5 feet deep and 80 to 100 feet wide. The slope faced due north, the slope angle was 35 degrees in the starting zone, and the slide released at an elevation of 10,600 feet and fell 150 feet vertical. Toward the bottom, the slope narrowed into a gully, and this caused the debris field to be confined and therefore deeper, which resulted in the three-foot burial.

Terrain trap

The following day, observers went to the site to gather data. They dug a snow pit adjacent to the avalanche, which showed that the slab layer that released was the entire storm-snow layer that had accumulated in the previous eight days. There was a poor bond between the old and new snow surfaces, though investigators could not identify the grains in the weak layer. Shovel shear tests at that interface repeatedly produced easy, clean shears.

Storm Slab avalanche

COMMENTS

Most of these skiers (some lived in the vicinity) knew the terrain "like the back of their hand" and knew its avalanche potential. They were traveling safely, skiing one at a time while the others spotted from safe locations. Yet the avalanche rescue gear they carried was inadequate. Minimum rescue gear of beacons, shovels, and probes—for all—is required for group avalanche safety. The debris area of this avalanche was small, such that rescuers could have picked up a beacon signal from anywhere near the avalanche. In this case, choosing to ski when not everyone carried rescue gear proved to be fatal for the group member who triggered a slide.

SUMMIT LAKE, NORTH OF PAXSON, ALASKA | March 18, 2001 20010318b

Two snowmobilers caught and buried; one killed

ACCIDENT SUMMARY

Summit Lake is located northwest of Paxson, a small town on the Richardson Highway, about 175 miles south of Fairbanks. This area is the site of the annual Arctic Man Ski and Sno-Go Classic, and is near the site of a fatal avalanche on April 8, 2000 (20000408a).

On Sunday, March 18, a group of snowmobilers was riding in the Summit Lake area and had stopped low on Courage Mountain. The time was 15:00 when an avalanche released above them. Several of the riders were able to run to safety, but Gary Frederick (37) and Bambi Bender (25) were buried by the slide.

In avalanche runout

Inadequate rescue equipment

About 20 people began probing the area immediately after the avalanche, and they struck Bender and dug her out uninjured. Searchers probed another 15 minutes before they hit Frederick. The debris was hard packed, and it took another 30 minutes to dig him out. Attempts to revive him were unsuccessful.

COMMENTS

It appears that this group of riders did not have avalanche awareness in mind when they stopped in the runout of an avalanche path. Fortunately, some of the group was equipped with probes and shovels. This saved a life.

20010403

PEAK 9, SOUTHEAST OF COPPER MOUNTAIN, COLORADO

April 3, 2001

One snowmobiler caught, buried, and killed

WEATHER AND SNOWPACK CONDITIONS

In Summit County, west of Denver, a sustained storm system brought daily snowfall from March 25 to 31. During this time, Copper Mountain ski resort (one mile west of the avalanche site) recorded 32 inches of snowfall, and Breckenridge Ski Resort (one mile east of the site) recorded 37 inches. Strong winds caused blowing snow from March 28 to April 1. The combination of three feet of new snow followed by blowing snow produced widespread slab formation near and above timberline, and an extensive natural avalanche cycle occurred from March 29 to April 1. In Summit County, 97 avalanches were reported to the Colorado Avalanche Information Center, including a few on the west side of the Tenmile Range.

This unstable snowpack was further weakened when a rapid warm-up from April 1 through 3 brought thaw conditions below timberline. This was a snowpack with no safe zones: above timberline, the snowpack was unstable from recent loading, and below timberline, it was unstable because of thaw.

ACCIDENT SUMMARY

The Tenmile Range runs north-south through the center of Summit County, with Breckenridge on the east side and 10-Mile Creek on the west side. The small resort community of Copper Mountain sits at the base of the eponymous ski area. It's a steep range with ample avalanche terrain.

Traveling alone

Terrain trap

Chad Jones (22) was a guide for Timber Ridge Snowmobile Tours. On Tuesday, April 3, Jones was free-riding alone on the west side of the Tenmile Range. At approximately 9:00, he was riding in a narrow drainage below timberline on the west side of 13,195-foot Peak 9, about a mile from the highway. He may have been trying to scout a trail to the bowls above timberline on the west side of the Tenmile Range. Evidence later showed that he probably got stuck near the bottom of the gully, and he may have been trying to dig his machine out when the avalanche released. He was buried in the gully.

RESCUE SUMMARY

Several hours later, a group of snowmobilers went to look for Jones and followed his trail to the avalanche. They found a jacket on the snow and saw part of the snowmobile sticking from the avalanche debris. They probed uphill from the machine and located

Jones, who was four to five feet under. He had been buried about four hours and was not alive when uncovered.

AVALANCHE DATA

The avalanche released in a north-facing gully at an elevation of 10,900 feet, a little below timberline. Slope angle was 40 degrees. The avalanche was classified as SS-AMu-R2-O, with a fracture 1.5 feet deep and 80 feet wide, and a vertical fall of 100 feet.

Persistent Slab avalanche

A fracture line profile showed a total snow depth of 36 inches. This consisted of 16 inches of four-finger soft slab on top of 20 inches of depth hoar with a grain size of about 4mm. Stability tests caused easy column-collapses.

"Red flag" indications of danger

Investigators found the snowpack to be very weak, and they themselves caused several collapses. They also saw evidence of other collapses the last few days, plus several other small avalanches.

COMMENTS

This was a sad event, and one that avalanche awareness training would have prevented. Evidence of widespread avalanche danger was clear. It was a poor route on a poor day to be traveling alone. A companion—or companions—initially may have helped find a safer route altogether. If the avalanche had still occurred, a companion with safety gear may have uncovered Jones quickly enough to save his life.

LIONHEAD, NORTHWEST OF WEST YELLOWSTONE, MONTANA | April 4, 2001

20010404a

One snowmobiler caught, buried, and killed

WEATHER AND SNOWPACK CONDITIONS

About 17 miles northwest of West Yellowstone, Montana, the southern end of the Madison Range is a popular destination for snowmobiling. It offers a variety of terrain, including avalanche terrain. It is known as the Lionhead Mountains or Lionhead.

During the week prior to the avalanche, several small storms deposited eight to 12 inches of snow in the Lionhead area. These storms also brought strong west-to-southwest winds, which formed slabs on high-elevation, east-facing slopes. This slab formation was merely the most recent loading event of the 2000-01 winter season, a season that had been plagued by a layer of depth hoar that had formed in November and had been the underlying cause of numerous fatal avalanches all winter in several western states.

ACCIDENT SUMMARY

The avalanche occurred just after 12:00 on Wednesday, April 4. The ridge between Lionhead and Sheep Mountain lies at an elevation of about 10,000 feet. A group of riders was on the east side of the ridge, and one man headed up the steep east slope to make his highmark. He turned just beneath a cornice and was headed downhill when the avalanche released. He flipped over the front of his handlebars and became separated from his snowmobile. The avalanche carried his machine about 600 feet down the slope and it ended up partially buried near the toe of the debris.

No rescue equipment

Without beacons or other rescue gear, the other riders in the group were unable to locate the rider.

RESCUE SUMMARY

A call went out to the Gallatin County Sheriff, who dispatched a SAR team. A search dog found the buried snowmobiler at about 19:00. He was buried about two feet deep and was located about 75 feet upslope, diagonally, from his snowmobile. The victim had been buried for seven hours, giving him no chance of survival.

AVALANCHE DATA

Persistent Slab avalanche

The avalanche released at an elevation of approximately 10,000 feet and on a slope that faced east-northeast. The slope angle near the starting zone was estimated at 40 degrees. The crown was 200 feet wide, and the avalanche ran about 800 feet slope distance. The alpha angle was 28 degrees. The depth of the deepest debris was over 14 feet.

Crown depth varied greatly from two to eight feet, with the deep areas being hard wind slab and the shallow areas being soft slab. The avalanche ran to ground in places, exposing the depth hoar, which was the weak layer. The other party members were able to place where the victim was on the slope when he triggered the avalanche, and an investigator was able to determine that the trigger spot was one of the parts of the slope that had a thinner, soft-slab snowpack. From that point, the fracture propagated into the deeper hard-slab areas. The resulting fractures propagated up the slope and pulled out the hard wind slab and even sections of cornice. The classification was HS-AMu-R4-G.

COMMENTS

Without rescue gear and without any visible clues to where the victim was buried, the witnesses were helpless in their rescue effort. The victim was shallowly buried—about two feet. Therefore, rescuers with beacons, probes, and shovels would have had a good chance at saving a life.

On the same day, another fatal avalanche occurred about 90 miles to the north near Flathead Pass in the northern Bridger Range of Montana (20010404b).

20010404b FLATHEAD PASS, NORTH OF BOZEMAN, MONTANA

April 4, 2001

One backcountry skier caught, buried, and killed

WEATHER AND SNOWPACK CONDITIONS

The skiing terrain near Flathead Pass is located in the northern end of the Bridger Range, north of Bozeman. In the 10 days prior to the avalanche on April 4, snowfall containing approximately 4.3 inches of water fell in the Bridger Range, mostly in small daily amounts. But there was one exception: on the morning of April 3, 24-hour snowfall was nine inches; it was a dense snowfall containing 1.3 inches of water. Ridgetop winds averaged 20 mph with gusts to 40 from the southwest. Observers noted many natural avalanches—confined to the new snow layer—releasing on steep, wind-loaded slopes.

ACCIDENT SUMMARY

On Wednesday, April 4, a party of three skiers—Steve Copeland (38) and Lindsay and Mike (last names and ages unknown)—rode snowmobiles to Flathead Pass. They toured about 1.5 miles due south of the pass to the terrain they wanted to ski. They skied to a ridgetop, reaching it in early afternoon. There, they traversed north, kicking off cornices to test the stability of the snowpack. Nothing released.

The group reached the top of their line and skied off the ridge one at a time, down an open slope with an angle of 35 to 40 degrees. Lindsay skied down several hundred feet and came to a stop near some small trees. Mike went farther down, and also stopped by some trees. Above, Steve had been waiting about 150 feet below the ridge, and either while standing still or just beginning his run, the slope fractured 50 feet above him.

Both the lower two skiers, Lindsay and Mike, heard and felt a huge "boom" and saw a powder cloud approaching. They accomplished a high-speed traverse across the avalanche path, narrowly escaping the slide.

Inadequate rescue equipment

Once the avalanche stopped, Lindsay turned his transceiver to receive and yelled at Mike to turn his off so he could do a search. Mike responded that Steve wasn't wearing a transceiver. The two men made a quick decision that Mike would ski out to call for a rescue while Lindsay stayed on scene to search. (The accident report did not explain why Mike had to leave the avalanche site to make a cell phone call. It's unclear whether he needed to retrieve his phone from the snowmobile or to search for a spot that provided a cell signal.)

RESCUE SUMMARY

Lindsay began his search by entering the debris and post-holing uphill to Steve's last-seen point. He then began working his way downhill following Steve's probable trajectory. The avalanche had fallen 1,000 feet, and there was a lot of debris to search. Near the bottom of the debris on a bench, he found a ski tip exposed. He probed to locate the exact position and started digging. Steve had been buried an hour.

Steve's head was two feet under the snow surface, and he was slightly sitting up with no obvious signs of trauma. Lindsay performed CPR but was unsuccessful at reviving him.

Mike made a phone call and summoned rescue assistance fairly quickly. It wasn't too long after Lindsay had uncovered Steve and began CPR that a helicopter with two rescuers and an avalanche dog landed nearby. The dog was not needed, and further attempts at resuscitation were unsuccessful. The rescuers flew Steve's body, Mike and Lindsay from the scene.

AVALANCHE DATA

Persistent Slab avalanche

The avalanche released on a northeast-facing slope at an elevation of 8,525 feet. The slope angle at the crown varied from 36 to 38 degrees. Alpha angle was 31 degrees. The crown line was two to four feet deep and 1,000 feet wide, and the avalanche fell 1,000 feet vertical. The victim was standing 50 feet below the crown and was carried 600 vertical feet down the slope. The avalanche was classified as SS-ASu-R4-D3-O.

Investigators returned to the site the following day to get data on the snowpack. Importantly, they found that in the area where Steve had been standing, there was a pocket of surface hoar (five to eight mm size) that had been buried by falling and blowing snow. The investigators did not find buried surface hoar in the area where Lindsay and Mike had started their run from the top. Additionally, as the avalanche propagated across the top of the slope into adjacent gullies, it stepped down to a layer of depth hoar—a weak layer that had formed five months earlier in November.

On this same day, another fatal avalanche occurred about 90 miles to the south in Lionhead of the Madison Range of Montana (20010404a). Both avalanches were on northeast aspects, between 8,500 and 10,000 feet elevation, and had a basal layer of depth hoar.

COMMENTS

This group was avalanche savvy, at least in the way they traveled. They were stomping off cornice blocks to test stability, and when they skied, they went one at a time with everyone keeping an eye on the others. But what a surprise for Lindsay to learn that Steve did not have an avalanche beacon. That knowledge came too late in the game, and this failure to communicate probably cost a life.

Backcountry groups must be self-sufficient with beacons, probes, and shovels for everyone. It took an hour to locate this victim. Had this been a beacon search with two rescuers, the burial time could have been shaved down to a few minutes.

And there is one final point: if Mike had stayed instead of leaving to make a cell phone call, both men would have been searching for surface clues. An additional searcher may have cut the search time in half before one spied the exposed ski tip.

20010411 EASTON GLACIER, MT. BAKER, WASHINGTON | April 11, 2001

One snowmobiler caught, buried, and killed

WEATHER AND SNOWPACK CONDITIONS

The winter of 2000-01 had generally brought below-normal snowfall to the Pacific Northwest. The Mt. Baker area in northern Washington had been particularly dry, and by mid-March, the Governor declared a state of drought when the snowpack had reached only 30% of normal for the winter. On south-facing slopes on Mt. Baker, an ice crust formed because of daily thaw and freeze cycles.

Beginning on March 25, a series storms created a fresh layer of slabby snow that piled up on the ice layer. The last of these storm systems brought snowfall to most of the Cascade Range on April 9 and 10, along with winds that were loading, and building slabs on, southeast- to southwest-facing slopes. The storm had ended by the morning of April 11, but the avalanche danger remained Considerable above 6,000 feet.

ACCIDENT SUMMARY

On Wednesday, April 11, a group of snowmobilers was riding on the Easton Glacier on the south side of Mt. Baker in northern Washington. Strong northeast winds had blown overnight and into the morning, and this probably loaded south-facing slopes with blowing snow.

Inadequate rescue equipment

The time was about 10:00 and a 31-year-old rider was highmarking the slope when it avalanched and carried him and his machine down the mountainside. This was a medium to large avalanche, estimated to be 1,500 feet wide and 700 feet vertical, and other riders close by witnessed it. When the avalanche stopped, there were no visible clues of the man or his snowmobile. He was not wearing a beacon.

RESCUE SUMMARY

While a call went out to the Whatcom County Search and Rescue, other snowmobilers, some of whom had beacons and probes, responded right away. They found the victim's snowmobile and helmet fairly quickly, but not the victim himself. The debris was blocky, hard slab debris.

Search and rescue personnel arrived after 13:00. By this time, about 30 snowmobilers had gathered, about half of whom had probes, beacons or shovels, but an organized probe search had not been performed.

The search and rescue crew organized a probe line, which found the victim at about 17:30, buried about four to six feet below the surface. They found the body directly downhill of the last seen point, about 150 feet uphill from his snowmobile.

AVALANCHE DATA

The avalanche released on a south-facing slope at an elevation of 6,600 feet and fell about 700 feet vertical. The crown was two to 2.5 feet deep and 1,500 feet wide. The slide was classified as HS-AMu-R3.

COMMENTS

Everyone in the group must have avalanche rescue equipment. But even then, not all victims will survive. In this avalanche, the debris was heavy and dense, the victim was buried fairly deeply, breathing would have been almost impossible, and lifespan would be measured in minutes.

STAIRS GULCH, SOUTHEAST OF SALT LAKE CITY, UTAH

20010428

April 28, 2001

Two climbers caught, buried, and killed

The following report was written by Bruce Tremper of the Utah Avalanche Center[2] and appears here with minimal editing.

SYNOPSIS

Martin Gleich (38), a doctor from Salt Lake City, and Scott Dull (39), also a doctor from Eagle River, Alaska were killed Saturday, April 28 in Stairs Gulch, a tributary of Big Cottonwood Canyon near Salt Lake City. The pair left the trailhead about 03:30 to 04:00 to climb Stairs Gulch to Twin Peaks with ice axes and crampons, rope and snowshoes but no beacons (they did not own beacons). They did not return by their 11:00 am planned return time and the Sheriff was notified that afternoon.

Inadequate rescue equipment

That evening, a Salt Lake County Search and Rescue team walked up both Stairs Gulch and the nearby Broad's Fork looking for the missing climbers. They discovered fresh avalanche debris in Stairs Gulch and quickly found Martin Gleich's boot sticking out of the snow about 100 yards above the toe of the debris at an elevation of about 6,400 feet. His head was buried about four feet deep and he had a couple of lacerations on his head. Medical examiners later determined he died by asphyxia. After finding Gleich's body, Wasatch Backcountry Rescue was called, which is a volunteer group composed of avalanche professionals from northern Utah ski areas. They responded with personnel

More than one person on a slope

from Snowbird (the only ski area open at that late date) along with a rescue dog. The avalanche dog easily located the second victim, Scott Dull, about a 10-minute hike above the first victim at an elevation around 6,900 feet. Although he was buried eight to 10 feet deep, part of his fleece shirt was torn to shreds and it stretched out about 10 feet with part of it on the surface, which may be why the dog was able to locate him so quickly. Scott Dull had multiple fractures and the medical examiner reported that he was killed by trauma. The accident appears to have occurred as the pair ascended.

RECENT WEATHER

The first half of April was very snowy. From the 3rd through the 9th, 50 inches of snow fell in the Wasatch Range, which caused one large dry avalanche to release in Stairs Gulch on April 8th and descend 5,000 vertical feet, stopping only 400 feet short of the Big Cottonwood Canyon road. Another 16 inches fell by the 14th and finally, another two feet fell in a storm ending on the 23rd, only five days before the accident. Then the weather warmed dramatically. The last overnight freeze of the snow surface occurred on Wednesday night, three days before the accident and even that freeze was quite thin and short-lived. For the next three days, daytime highs at automated weather stations the same elevation as the accident were in the 50s, rising to a high of 61 on Thursday the 26th. Minimum temperatures were 35 to 45 degrees and the night of the accident the minimum air temperature was 47 degrees, combined with scattered clouds and strong southwest winds. This was the warmest overnight low since September. Daytime highs in Salt Lake City were near 80 degrees for the few days before the accident.

At the Utah Avalanche Center, we usually end our regular morning advisories in mid April, but because of continued storms and then the subsequent wet slide activity, I had been issuing sporadic afternoon or evening updates as time allowed until the wet cycle abated. According to national policy, I did not use any danger ratings because of the limited information coming in so late in the season, plus, I was the only staff left working and my time allowed only limited and sporadic fieldwork. (The Salt Lake County Sheriff incorrectly reported to the media that the avalanche danger was rated as "moderate", but I had not been issuing avalanche danger ratings for the previous two weeks.) The advisory did, however, warn people about the warm temperatures, the lack of an overnight freeze and the presence of wet sluffs, wet slabs and other glide avalanches in the area. I suggested that if people still wanted to get out into the mountains that they get an early start and return early. No one knows whether Martin or Scott called the advisory before heading out, although Martin was a regular caller during the winter.

TERRAIN

Stairs Gulch is the steepest and longest avalanche path in the Wasatch Range near Salt Lake City. It has a vertical fall of about 5,000 feet and the upper section is composed almost entirely of 45 to 55 degree sloping rock slabs. Because it is such steep and large terrain, very few skiers or boarders ever enter Stairs Gulch in winter but climbers sometimes practice their alpine skills there in spring after the snow stabilizes. The route usually requires crampons and ice axes.

AVALANCHE CONDITIONS

On Sunday morning, the day after the accident, I ascended the ridge to the east of Stairs Gulch to look at the avalanche, since the route up the bottom of Stairs Gulch

Glide avalanche adjacent to the larger fatal glide avalanche. *Photo Bruce Tremper, UAC.*

was not safe because of continued very warm spring weather. I noticed that the steep rock slabs on the west side of the drainage had recently produced what appeared to be two large glide avalanches with several other smaller avalanches, and the snow that had not yet released had numerous glide cracks and appeared to be on the verge of releasing. While I was on the ridge I saw one smaller glide avalanche release and descend onto the debris and stop just above where the upper victim was recovered the previous night.

Glide avalanche

The avalanche that most likely caused the accident was a glide avalanche about 700 feet wide with a fracture depth averaging about five feet. These glide avalanches occurred on northeast-facing rock slabs of about 45 to 55 degrees. The crown was around 10,000 feet in elevation and the avalanche descended 3700 vertical feet to an elevation of 6,300 feet, running about a mile in length.

(The media, including local news, CNN and the Weather Channel, incorrectly reported the avalanche to be 30 feet deep and two miles wide—obviously hyperbolic numbers since 30 feet of snow has probably not existed in Utah since the Pleistocene and Stairs Gulch is less than a mile wide.)

On Thursday, two days before the accident, I skied up Broad's Fork, the next drainage to the east, and noticed three recent, large, glide avalanches off the steep rock slabs with one more on the steep rock slabs in Mill B South, the next drainage to the east.

Glide avalanches are relatively unusual for Utah, but they do occur regularly each spring on the steep rock slabs in radical terrain such as Stairs Gulch and Broad's Fork, usually in a time window of about two weeks after the dry snow turns wet for the first time of the season. They occur when percolating water lubricates the interface between the snow and ground causing the entire snowpack to slowly slide like a glacier on the underlying ground, often over the course of days, until it suddenly releases. They occur mostly in very steep rock slabs during very warm weather. You can easily

Debris from the Stairs Gulch avalanche of April 28, 2001. *Photo Bruce Tremper, Utah Avalanche Center.*

recognize them by gaping crevasses on their upper boundaries and a rumpled-up look on their lower boundaries. Glide avalanches are very difficult to trigger even with explosives—and like a stubborn mule, they tend to release only when they are ready, more or less randomly in time, kind of like a calving iceberg or icefall. Paradoxically, they show a slight preference to release during the coldest part of the day, or during a freeze following a protracted period of melting, which would fit the pattern of this avalanche. These were average sized avalanches for Stairs Gulch and are a regular occurrence each spring.

Statistically, glide avalanches kill very few people because 1) they are difficult to trigger, 2) the warm and soggy conditions that produce glide avalanches often discourage people from traveling on snow, and 3) most people instinctively avoid crossing beneath them, as they look quite dangerous even to people who don't know much about avalanches. This is the first known fatality from a glide avalanche in Utah and possibly the first in the United States.

HOW IT MAY HAVE HAPPENED

I doubt if the pair triggered the avalanche. First, glide avalanches are notoriously difficult to trigger. Second, the avalanche had a large amount of volume, much more than the volume produced by a wet, loose avalanche they may have triggered on their likely route. Plus, there was no obvious avalanche on their planned climbing route that could account for the volume of debris. Third, all of the glide avalanches I noticed the following morning were on rock slabs to the west side of their most likely route. The climbing route usually follows the gully the whole way since all other routes are quite steep and difficult, especially the routes that would have crossed the glide avalanches. Fourth, Martin's body was found near the toe of the debris, indicating that it may have come down on them from above.

The evidence indicates that the accident occurred early in the morning when the pair was on their way up. The evidence includes the following:

Richard Green, a local climber, ascended Broad's Fork the same day as the accident and climbed to the ridgeline separating Stairs Gulch from Broad's Fork. He then followed the same route the victims planned to use, following the ridge to Twin Peaks and returned along the same route, returning around noon. He said that he did not see any tracks other than his own, indicating that the victims did not make it to the top of Stairs Gulch. Richard Green used an ice axe but no crampons. Alan Irdahl, one of the rescuers, flew in the helicopter the evening of the accident to look for the overdue victims. He saw these same tracks and assumed that they belonged to the victims.

On Friday, May 4th, the first day after the accident I felt was safe enough, I repeated their climb using crampons and an ice axe. After debriefing with their family members and friends at the burial site, I ascended Stairs Gulch alone to the summit ridgeline to take a closer look at their tracks. I did find what were probably Green's tracks at the top of Stairs Gulch that ascended to the ridgeline and also some nearby tracks that descended into Stairs Gulch. The tracks were in a place where a climber would naturally travel. The tracks were difficult to see since they had undergone several days of melting, then frozen by much colder weather, then buried by several inches new snow that had subsequently blown away. Only the top 200 feet remained visible since new snow and old wet sluffs covered up everything below that elevation. Complicating factors included one set of tracks that came from Broad's Fork and traversed into Stairs Gulch for awhile and returned again to the ridge, plus some mountain goat tracks that switch-backed up Stairs to the ridge. I spent about a half hour wandering around trying to sort it all out. As it turns out, Richard Green made the tracks along the ridgeline but did not make the tracks that ascended and descended into Stairs Gulch, so another party must have made them at another time. I believe that Gleich and Dull did not make it to the summit ridge but instead were caught as they ascended, mostly because of the following information:

Martin Gleich's sunglasses melted out of the debris nearly a month after the accident and they were still in their case, indicating that the accident occurred on the ascent, while it was still too dark to wear sunglasses.

Scott Dull's pack melted out of the debris a month after the accident and it appeared to contain an uneaten lunch. Martin's pack, recovered during the rescue, contained a couple of energy bars.

Martin Gleich carried a camera but he did not take any photographs; however, all his friends did not think this was conclusive since he almost never carried a camera nor took photographs. Plus, it was a rather cloudy day with very strong winds.

They did not use Martin's cell phone to call from the Summit, but there was no plan to do so. Scott's widow indicated that he often would call her on a cell phone when he got to the top of a ridge or mountain (he was an avid mountain runner), and she thought it was unusual for them not to call.

They were wearing crampons at the time of the accident and Martin had his ice axe strapped to his pack, indicating that they were not yet on steep terrain. They both were using their ski poles at the time of the accident. When they ascended they were walking on old avalanche debris from an avalanche on April 8th, and it probably would have been hard enough to warrant wearing crampons.

HUMAN FACTORS

Studies show that human factors are at least partially responsible for nearly 90 percent of avalanche accidents involving people with at least some avalanche experience and knowledge, and this accident also fits this pattern.

The time constraints on Scott Dull represent a large red flag. Scott and Martin were old friends. They had gone to medical school together and had climbed several mountains together including Mt. Orizaba in Mexico (18,491 feet), Mt. Rainier several times, and Mt. Baker. They had taken a climbing school on Mt. Baker as well as an avalanche course. The pair was on a constrained time schedule as Scott and his wife flew into Salt Lake City just for the weekend specifically to visit Martin and his wife. The victims' widows were also close friends. They had first made the plans a couple weeks previous to the accident. Scott and his wife had flown in from Alaska the previous evening, and Scott and Martin had stayed up late catching up and had woken up at 3:00 am for their climb. Therefore, Scott had no recent experience with the local snow conditions and we do not know if he checked the recent weather. He was probably following Martin's lead as Martin had climbed Stairs Gulch before and Scott had not.

On the Wednesday previous to the accident, Martin and two other friends attempted to climb Tanners Gulch (another nearby large and steep avalanche path in Little Cottonwood Canyon), but they turned around because of wet snow conditions as they were sinking in deeply. (The temperatures Wednesday morning were about 15 degrees cooler than Saturday, the day of the accident.) When Scott and Martin ascended Stairs Gulch on Saturday, they may have been fooled by the supportable snow conditions as they walked on old avalanche debris, which tends to be quite hard even in warm temperatures.

Both were extremely intelligent people who were very attentive of their day-to-day life decisions as well as their own personal safety. Although they took an avalanche course at one time, most of their friends reported that they were still relative avalanche novices. Also, although they both kept very fit and liked to hike in the mountains (Scott was an avid mountain runner and marathoner) they were still considered to be intermediate climbers.

THIS WAS AN UNUSUAL ACCIDENT FOR A NUMBER OF REASONS:

Most fatalities involve dry slab avalanches, yet this was most likely a glide avalanche and, as far as we know, no one has ever been killed in Utah by a glide avalanche.

The vast majority of avalanche fatalities in Utah trigger the avalanche that catches them, yet these two almost certainly did not trigger the avalanche.

Most avalanche fatalities in Utah do not call the avalanche advisory before heading out, yet Martin Gleich regularly called the avalanche advisory (although his wife did not know if he called it in the days before the accident).

2001–2002 SEASON

20011111 SUMMIT LAKE, HATCHER PASS, NORTH OF PALMER, ALASKA | November 11, 2001

Two snowshoers caught; one partly buried, one buried and killed

WEATHER AND SNOWPACK CONDITIONS

Hatcher Pass, elevation 3,886 feet, is situated in the Talkeetna Mountains, about 50 miles north of Anchorage and 13 miles northwest of Palmer. In the winter, the road through the pass is closed, but the area is popular for motorized and non-motorized recreation. The first measurable snow of the winter came on October 22. This covered the ground and then day-by-day metamorphosed into depth hoar as the days were short and the skies mostly clear. Local skiers recorded and observed two significant wind events, one on October 31 and another on November 3. During these events, isolated wind slabs formed over faceted snow. The weather on the day of the incident was calm, clear, and sunny with temperatures in the mid 20s F.

ACCIDENT SUMMARY

On Sunday afternoon, November 11, Travis and Becky Patton (30) left their car at the Hatcher Pass Lodge for a day of snowshoeing. Traveling with two dogs, a husky and blue heeler, they climbed the two miles up the snow-covered Fishhook Road toward Hatcher Pass. They explored the area around Summit Lake, then turned around to begin their return trip back to the parking lot. At 14:50, they traversed across a steep slope, 200 feet above the Summit Lake access road.

More than one person on a slope

Travis was in the lead, with Becky following five feet behind. (It's unknown where the dogs were at the time of the slide.) Travis proceeded out onto the slope for 10 to 12 steps—with Becky close behind—and "started to feel like he didn't belong there." As he turned around to go back, the slope started to move. Both he and Becky were caught in the avalanche. For the first 150 feet, Becky was sliding on the surface on her stomach with head uphill and feet downhill. As she reached the runout zone, the debris apparently spun or flipped her onto her back with her head downhill, and the snow flowed over her. Travis was able to stay on top of the moving debris and was only buried up to his thighs. He dug himself out, only to see that Becky was nowhere to be found.

No rescue equipment

Travis searched for five to 10 minutes using only his MSR snowshoe as a probe. At 15:00, he ran 200 yards to the pass and started yelling for help.

RESCUE SUMMARY

At 15:02, Kip Melling, an avalanche instructor with the Alaska Mountain Safety Center/Anchorage Nordic Ski Patrol, and ski partner Terri Pauls, a trained patroller also with the Anchorage Nordic Ski Patrol, were climbing Fishhook Road just below Hatcher Pass. Both were out for a day of skiing. They spotted a man, who was yelling, "Avalanche! Help, avalanche!"

As soon as the man explained the situation, Melling yelled down to two young snowboarders, also hiking the road below him, to go to the lodge and notify the park ranger. Pauls and Melling then proceeded to climb the remaining grade to the pass and met up with Travis and his two dogs. They gathered as much witness information as possible, then skied and hiked the short remaining distance to the site, where they arrived at 15:10. Travis stated that neither he nor Becky was wearing an avalanche transceiver.

Rather, the only avalanche rescue equipment they had was a probe, which Becky had in her pack and which was now buried.

Melling and Pauls had probes in their packs. With no surface clues, the witness, Travis, pointed out where he last saw Becky, and the three searchers began probing the debris below the Area Last Seen (ALS) using probes, ski poles, and skis. The debris had come to rest in a trough, 210 feet below the fracture line. The blue heeler dog (Barley) was sitting on the debris. Melling asked Travis, "Who owned the dog?" When Travis said it was Becky's, the searchers immediately started to probe that area. But after a few minutes of unsuccessful spot probing, the searchers tried to get a better trajectory of where Becky might have ended up.

Shifting over several steps, they began probing again. Lined up, they made five probe-line advances when Melling hit a snowshoe with his probe. They started digging with shovels and had excavated about three feet of wind slab and faceted snow when park ranger Pat Murphy arrived with a snowmobile and sled, and four to six other skiers and snowboarders. The digging went faster, but it still took several more minutes to get Becky out of the snow and gain an airway.

Becky was found lying on her back, head downslope, face-up, with snowshoes and pack still attached. She had been buried under four feet of snow for 40 minutes.

The victim was driven by ambulance to a hospital in Palmer, 25 miles away, and later transferred to Providence Hospital in Anchorage. She was taken off life support Tuesday morning at the request of family members.

AVALANCHE DATA

The avalanche was 84 feet wide with a crown of only eight to 12 inches; it was classified as HS-AIu-R2-O. Though it was a small slide, the debris flowed 210 feet slope distance and piled up deeply in a trough—a classic terrain trap. Debris depth in the deposition zone ranged from three to six feet deep and consisted of pencil-hard slab blocks intermingled with unconsolidated faceted snow. The slope angle was 38 degrees. The aspect was north, which put it leeward to the prevailing winds.

Terrain trap

Persistent Slab avalanche

COMMENTS

An avalanche was the last thing this couple expected. After all, they had planned a short snowshoe hike with their two dogs. But neither Travis nor Becky had any avalanche training, knowledge, or skills to evaluate avalanche terrain or hazard, so they did not recognize the clues that were present. The most obvious signs of the hazard were several other small avalanches visible along their route, and in fact, the couple had passed by a similar avalanche 100 feet away from where they were caught. It was a sad, harsh example of how fragile life can be.

YANKEE DOODLE LAKE, WEST OF ELDORA MOUNTAIN RESORT, COLORADO | November 28, 2001

20011128

Two backcountry skiers caught; one killed

WEATHER AND SNOWPACK CONDITIONS

The early winter of 2001-02 was depressingly dry in the Colorado mountains with little or no snow cover by mid-November. What snowpack there was had turned to sugary

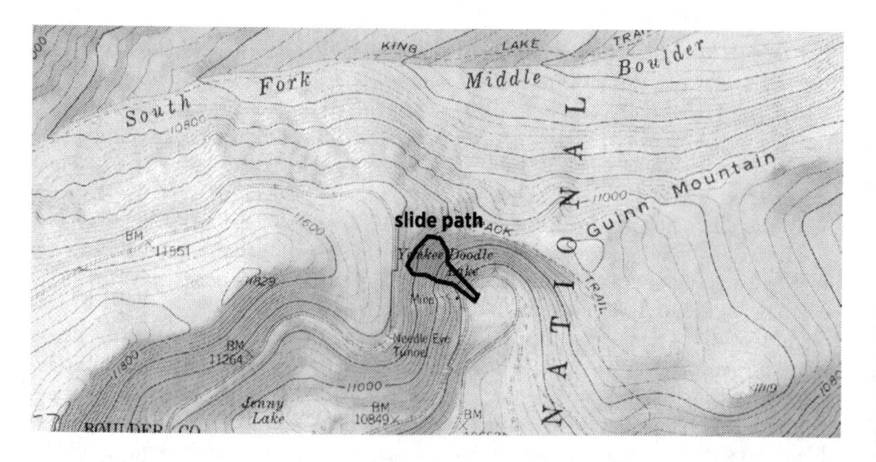

A map of the area around Yankee Doodle Lake. The black shape outlines the approximate path of the November 28, 2001, avalanche.

depth hoar. Then, on Thanksgiving Day, November 22, a sustained storm system moved in. When it ended on the 27th, the storm had dropped two to 4.5 feet of snow on Colorado's northern mountains. This storm initiated a major cycle of natural avalanche releases, with about 180 avalanches being reported to the Colorado Avalanche Information Center.

Eldora Mountain Resort is on the east slope of Colorado's Front Range and is 15 miles west of Boulder. Eldora saw a little more than a foot of snow from the recent storm system, but the higher peaks a few miles west of Eldora received considerably more. Persistent winds formed slabs near and above timberline, and on November 26 and 27, Eldora reported heavy blowing snow. The morning of the 28th dawned sunny.

ACCIDENT SUMMARY

On Wednesday, November 28, two backcountry skiers left the Eldora Mountain Resort and trekked five miles west up the Jenny Creek trail to Yankee Doodle Lake, on the east side of Rollins Pass. The two men were Joe Despres (29) and Peter Vaughn (47). This was the men's third day in a row to ski into this area and then ski a slope above Yankee Doodle Lake.

On the previous two days, they enjoyed terrific powder. They were experienced skiers, had solid avalanche awareness skills, carried full avalanche rescue gear, and were aware of the avalanche potential in this terrain.

More than one person on a slope

Before starting their descent, the pair dug a snow pit. Apparently satisfied with what they found, they agreed to ski short distances one at a time, taking turns watching each other while the other would wait at a safe spot. The time was 13:00, and Vaughn went first and skied on a diagonal line from left to right and stopped just below some rocks on a semi-bench. He watched as Despres began his run.

Despres had made three or four turns when Vaughn felt that something wasn't right. Vaughn realized the snow had moved under his skis. In the next second, the entire slope was moving. Vaughn's safe spot wasn't safe.

The avalanche was large, about 400 feet across, and it swept both men down the slope. The avalanche fell about 600 feet, crossed the summer road, hit the frozen lake with great

Top: A view of Yankee Doodle Lake after the November 28, 2001, accident. The three figures standing under 1 mark the edge of the debris. The figure under 2 stands where rescuers found Despres, 91 feet from shore. The figure under 3 stands where the avalanche deposited Vaughn in the lake, roughly 190 feet from shore. *Photo Dale Atkins, Colorado Avalanche Information Center.*

Bottom: Looking northwest across Yankee Doodle Lake and up at the avalanche path. *Photo Dale Atkins, Colorado Avalanche Information Center.*

force, broke through 10 inches of ice, and created a soupy slush. The impact was so great that it created a tidal wave that threw ice 20 feet up the bank on the far side.

Despres disappeared in the snow, ice, and water of the lake. Amazingly, Vaughn survived, and later described his ordeal: "I'm on the slope, and the next thing I know, I'm in the slide, being rubbed along the ground, being suffocated for 600 feet. It's as if someone was blowing up an air suit, pushing against you. The farther you go, the tighter it packs around you. You know what's happening; you just can't do anything about it."

Then Vaughn hit the lake. The water washed away the snow that was hardpacked around Vaughn, and then, "Just as I was about to suffocate, I could move my arm. I saw light and I punched through."

Vaughn was about 190 feet from shore. His skis and backpack were gone. Getting out of the lake proved to be an ordeal. He tried using ice chunks to keep him afloat and occasionally could touch bottom with his boots. After what he estimated to be half an hour, he fought his way to shore. He saw no sign of Despres. His yells brought no response. His beacon worked, but he got no signal. His cell phone was waterlogged and dead. He had lost his gloves, he was soaking wet, the temperature was far below freezing, and he was five miles from help. The time was 13:30. Vaughn set out for help and began hiking the five miles to the ski area.

RESCUE SUMMARY

At about 16:00, an employee at Eldora Mountain Resort saw someone stumbling toward the lodge. Peter Vaughn had made the endurance trek of his life and reported his friend, Joe Despres, had been lost in an avalanche.

That evening, Vaughn was taken to a hospital in Boulder to be treated for severe hypothermia and frostbitten hands and feet, while a rescue team including Eldora patrollers and a Boulder County Sheriff's SAR team rode in on snowmobiles to the avalanche site. It was cold and there was blowing snow, but a full moon helped visibility.

Initially, all the searchers plus two rescue dogs (flown in with their handlers by helicopter) worked only the avalanche debris around the lake. They found no clues nor picked up any beacon signal. Everyone was concerned about a second avalanche from a portion of the slope that had not avalanched.

At about 21:00, a county plow finished scraping the snow from the summer road, which allowed a dive team to get to the site. The lake had refrozen so that a few searchers could walk on the ice, only occasionally breaking through. They found Vaughn's backpack frozen in the ice about 90 feet from shore.

Later, as the lake had frozen hard once more, a searcher with a beacon began working the jumbled ice surface—and got a signal. Rescuers then punched through the ice where the beacon signal was strongest, and found Joe Despres' body under three feet of ice and water, 90 feet from shore. The time was almost midnight.

AVALANCHE DATA

Deep Persistent Slab avalanche

The avalanche released at an elevation of 11,300 feet on a southeast-facing slope above Yankee Doodle Lake. The slope angle was 34 to 36 degrees, and the avalanche fell 600 feet vertical and crashed into the lake. The crown was 400 feet wide and was about two feet deep at the edges and five feet deep in the middle. The avalanche ran to ground in places and was classified as HS-ASu-R4-D3-O/G.

The snowpack at the crown consisted of three layers: a hard, icy melt-freeze crust at the ground, a two-inch-thick layer of facets (developing depth hoar), and a uniform pencil-hard layer of wind slab.

About halfway down the slope, the avalanche path narrowed to about half its width. This would make it more difficult for a skier, if caught in a slide, to either escape to the side or ride it out.

COMMENTS

In *The Snowy Torrents* accident reports, the Comments section is the part where we critique the avalanche accident and, when warranted, point out mistakes made by the victims, such as lack of awareness, overlooking obvious danger signs, no rescue gear, poor route selection or travel procedures, overconfidence, etc.

But not this time. They were prepared in every way for the risk they knew they were taking. They dug a pit, and certainly saw the depth hoar (which by itself is not a flashing danger sign). Their observations told them it was a risk worth taking. They carried rescue gear and knew how to use it, and they tried to ski the slope—a slope they had skied without incident the previous two days—cautiously.

Avalanches are mean and powerful adversaries. We have no problem with high risk tolerance, so long as the risk-takers understand the stakes. It was a tragic outcome, but these men understood that possibility.

Joe Despres was a well-known and well-liked man in the Eldora-Nederland-Boulder area. As a tribute to him, Eldora Mountain Resort sponsored the DoJoe Memorial Uphill-Downhill Telemark Race at the ski resort. This annual event began in February, 2002, and serves as a fund-raiser for avalanche awareness. It has since been renamed the "DoJoe on the DownLow."

Lastly, all avalanche transceivers are built to meet a specification of transmitting for one hour at a water depth of 15 cm (six inches)—just in case you, the reader, were curious.

HENEY PEAK, SOUTH OF CORDOVA, ALASKA

20011212

December 12, 2001

Three snowmobilers caught; one partly buried, two buried, and one killed

WEATHER AND SNOWPACK CONDITIONS

Dangerous avalanche conditions had set up throughout southcentral Alaska, initially because of a widespread snowfall in late October. The snow from this first storm turned to depth hoar in the following weeks, and therefore formed a deep persistent weak layer that was buried by snowfalls in November and December. In the two days before December 12, an estimated 16 to 18 inches of new snow fell in the Heney Mountains south of Cordova, Alaska. This snow buried a layer of either surface hoar or depth hoar—either way, a very weak substratum.

ACCIDENT SUMMARY

More than one person on a slope

On Wednesday afternoon, December 12, a group of five snowmobilers went for a night ride on Heney Peak, at 3,126 feet, the highest peak in the Heney Mountains. The temptation was riding in the fresh snow and being able to see the lights of Cordova in the distance. It is not clear whether the group was highmarking, but James Dundas (30) got his sled stuck while climbing a slope. Mark Lobe (24) went up to help dig out Dundas. Lobe later said, "When we were digging our machines out, we thought, 'This is not a very good idea.' Two seconds later it all came down. It was kind of like a muffled gunshot going off, and then it was silent."[1] Lobe and Dundas turned and ran. They did not get far.

"I looked back to see it coming," Lobe said. He was swept off his feet and tumbled downhill. He remembers being rolled to the surface of the snow once and then disappearing beneath it—until the world stopped turning. "I ended up with my head about two feet down in a hole," he said. "But I had an airspace. The rest of my body was almost completely buried. I had an arm out."

RESCUE SUMMARY

Lobe couldn't move. "It's like you're just cast in concrete," he said. "Everything around you is solid."

Inadequate rescue equipment

Dundas was only partly buried and was able to dig himself out. Friends Jason Flatt (27) and Tracy Whitcomb (27) also escaped the slide, and they joined Dundas to come to the rescue of Lobe. Twenty to 30 minutes later, they had managed to dig Lobe free using only their hands. Lobe had been lucky.

Donovan J. Lee (37) was not so fortunate. The last Lobe saw of him was the flash of a headlight. "I could see his light on the wall of snow coming down on me," Lobe said. Then Lee and his machine disappeared into the mountain and the night. Lee was the only one not wearing an avalanche beacon.

An estimated 50 volunteers responded to a rescue call. They worked probe lines through Wednesday night in search of Lee. Early Thursday morning, rescuers finally found Lee's body beneath almost three feet of snow.

COMMENTS

Avalanche awareness was in short supply with this group, just as their rescue gear was in short supply. Only four of the five riders had transceivers. Why not all five? Beyond that, the group carried no shovels or probes. Lee had been lower on the slope, which may (or may not) have had something to do with him being the only person to be completely buried. In any case, Lee was the only person in the group without a beacon, which prevented his companions from locating him.

20011223

SWETMANN MINE AREA, SOUTH OF HOPE, ALASKA

December 23, 2001

One snowmobiler caught, buried, and killed

WEATHER AND SNOWPACK CONDITIONS

High avalanche danger

Dangerous avalanche conditions had set up throughout southcentral Alaska, initially because of a widespread snowfall in late October, which put down the first snow cover of the season. The snow from this first storm turned to depth hoar in the following weeks, and therefore formed a deep persistent weak layer that was buried by snowfalls in November and December. The Alaska Mountain Safety Center had issued several alerts about this persisting avalanche danger, the most recent warning coming on Thursday, December 20.

ACCIDENT SUMMARY

On Sunday, December 23, numerous snowmobilers were riding in the mountains off the Palmer Creek Road, about 12 miles south of Hope, on the Kenai Peninsula of Alaska. Several groups of riders were staying in gentle terrain because of the avalanche potential. The area surrounding the historic Swetmann Mine, which dates back 100 years, contained steeper terrain.

One group of seven riders included Russel Foster (35), from Anchorage, and a friend, Bobby Frankson. This group of seven then merged with a second group of five local riders from Hope. Many of the riders in this group of 12 had beacons, probes, and shovels, including Foster and Frankson.

At about 13:00, Foster and Frankson separated from the other ten and rode off about two miles toward the Swetmann Mine area. They came to a steep slope, and Foster headed up while Frankson stayed below. Frankson then watched as the snowpack on the mountainside broke above Foster. Frankson turned and outran the avalanche; Foster did not, and the debris buried him.

RESCUE SUMMARY

Frankson immediately rode his machine back to the larger group and told of them of the avalanche. Several of this group took off for the avalanche site, and as one of them recounted later, they crossed the debris of several small slides on the way. Arriving at the site of the burial slide, several searchers began a beacon search and fairly quickly picked up a signal. They used probes to pinpoint the victim and then dug him out with their shovels.

Foster had been buried under 3.5 feet of snow for 30 minutes. One rescuer described the snow as being as hard as concrete. For the next two hours, the group took turns performing CPR but couldn't revive Foster.

COMMENTS

Several facts about this accident require comment. First, the two riders had crossed the same debris from several small slides that the rescuers noticed on their way to the accident site. This was a clue to instability that apparently did not register with the first two men.

Second, it was a mistake for the witness to leave the avalanche scene to summon more help. Given the density of the debris, survival time was short—perhaps as little as 10 minutes. If you are on site with a beacon, search!

ALASKA RANGE, SOUTHWEST OF CANTWELL, ALASKA

20011224

December 24, 2001

One snowmobiler caught, buried, and killed

ACCIDENT SUMMARY

Cantwell is a small town at the junction of the Parks Highway and Denali Highway, about 75 miles south of Fairbanks. In the winter, the motels fill with snowmobilers who come for the riding in the nearby mountains.

On Monday, December 24—Christmas Eve—Dwayne Dufford (30), from Fairbanks, was snowmobiling with a group of friends in the Alaska Range, about 20 miles southwest of Cantwell. Dufford was known as an expert rider and mechanic. The group of eight was highmarking, and all were equipped with beacons and shovels. Dufford's sons, ages 11 and 13, were part of the group.

Dufford was on the slope when he triggered an avalanche estimated to be 400 feet wide. The avalanche fell about 400 feet vertical and buried Dufford.

RESCUE SUMMARY

When the avalanche stopped, the other party members started the rescue immediately by turning their beacons to receive. They quickly picked up the beeps from Dufford's beacon, zeroed in, and started digging with their shovels. They dug down six feet and realized they had missed him. Then they dug to the side and located Dufford four feet down. He had been buried only 18 minutes and had died from injuries sustained in the avalanche.

COMMENTS

This group of riders was experienced, knew the potential for avalanche, and was equipped for rescue. Despite a fast rescue, the victim died.

It's worth noting, too, that this rescue could have been faster—if the group had carried probes, in addition to beacons and shovels. Digging past the victim cost valuable minutes. Each of the three tools has its purpose—a beacon to locate, a probe to pinpoint, and a shovel to dig—to achieve minimal burial time.

Inadequate rescue equipment

The snowpack in central and southeast Alaska during the early winter of 2001-02 was especially dangerous, as shown by four fatal avalanches in 44 days, including one in January (20020112).

20011231 **GOAT MOUNTAIN LAKES, WEST OF DEER LODGE, MONTANA** | December 31, 2001

One snowmobiler caught, buried, and killed

ACCIDENT SUMMARY

The Flint Creek Range lies between Deer Lodge on I-15 to the east and Phillipsburg on Montana Hwy 1 to the west. Mt. Powell, at 10,168 feet, is the highest peak in the range and is a popular snowmobiling area.

Traveling alone

On Monday, December 31, Randy Ring and his son Kory (21)—possibly spelled Cory—and two other companions were riding snowmobiles in the Flint Creek Range. Specifically, they were in the Goat Mountain Lakes basin, which lies 4.5 miles northwest of Mt. Powell. At about 13:45, Kory separated from the others. A short time later, Randy and his two companions went looking for Kory. The track led to an east-facing bowl on the south side of Goat Mountain—and to a fresh avalanche in the bowl.

The three men went to the avalanche and soon saw Kory's partially buried snowmobile and helmet near the toe of the debris. There was no sign of Kory.

RESCUE SUMMARY

No rescue equipment

None of the three men had beacons, probes, or shovels. At 14:25, one of the men called the Granite County Sheriff on his cell phone, while another rode for help. He found another group of snowmobilers, and two of them had probe poles and shovels. They returned to the site and after about an hour of probing, one of them struck Kory about 100 feet above his snowmobile.

The snowmobilers uncovered Kory at about 15:40 from under 4.5 feet of snow. He had been buried for approximately an hour and 40 minutes. He had not survived. The County SAR team arrived about an hour later and transported the body out.

AVALANCHE DATA

Persistent Slab avalanche

The avalanche released on an east-facing slope at an elevation of 8,800 feet. Slope angle varied from 35-40 degrees. The crown was about 500 feet wide and 12 inches deep. The avalanche fell about 300 feet vertical. The classification was probably SS-AMu-R3-D2-O.

An investigative team did a fracture line profile several days later. There was a 10 to 12 inch thick layer of depth hoar at the ground. Above that was a layer of denser snow, capped by an ice layer. The ice layer probably formed on the snowpack surface during several warm, sunny days. It became the sliding surface for the avalanche when subsequent storms then buried it.

COMMENTS

Kory was traveling alone, and investigators were unable to tell where he was on the slope when the avalanche released, or whether he was climbing, traversing, or descending. None of the group had avalanche rescue gear, which perhaps meant that they had planned a mellow ride and would not need rescue gear, or that they were unaware of the avalanche risk in this terrain. Regardless, had all party members been equipped for, and competent in, rescue, it may have prevented a death.

CONY MOUNTAIN, NORTH OF PAXSON, ALASKA

20020112

January 12, 2002

Three snowmobilers caught; one partly buried and injured, two buried and killed

ACCIDENT SUMMARY

Cony Mountain is a peak in the eastern Alaska Range and sits about 15 miles north of Paxson. On Saturday, January 12, a party of five snowmobilers was riding on the Gulkana Glacier adjacent to Cony Mountain. The group included husband and wife Wesley (39) and Susan (38) Rice, Wesley's brother Donnie Rice (35), Donnie's daughter Jessica (13), and another relative, Tony Baca. They were on four snowmobiles, with Jessica riding double with her father Donnie.

Mid-afternoon, they were riding as a group and climbing up a gentle slope on the glacier when Wesley Rice and Tony Baca stopped to change a spark plug on Wesley's machine. The other three riders on two sleds continued on, wanting to reach a spot at higher elevation where they could make a cell phone call to Fairbanks.

Susan later recalled what happened over the next few minutes. Donnie and Jessica stopped on a cornice and got off their snowmobile. As Susan pulled alongside, she saw the snow crack between the two machines. Instantly she felt herself free-falling and saw only white. Susan, Donnie, Jessica and one snowmobile fell when the cornice collapsed. The snow from the cornice fall went down the mountainside and flowed into a ravine.

Susan briefly passed out and when she came to her senses, she was buried to her neck in snow. She was facing the steep, rocky slope she had just tumbled down. Her helmet had been knocked off, and her snowmobile lay close by. She called out for her brother-in-law, "Donnie, help me!"

RESCUE SUMMARY

About five minutes later, Wesley Rice, who had been following the snowmobile tracks, approached a breakover where he saw only one snowmobile and no people at all. He was confused at his companions' absence and called out for his wife and brother, then heard a shout coming from over the edge. That's when he noticed the broken cornice, and then he heard Susan's voice. He dropped to his knees and peered over the near-vertical drop. Susan was far below, and Wesley could see only her head sticking from the snow. She said she was in pain, that her head and legs hurt, and she didn't know where Donnie and Jessica were.

Without giving it much thought, Wesley jumped off the cornice. Tumbling at first, he then gained a little control and slid down several hundred feet. He was now bruised and bleeding himself, but he came to a stop near his wife. At about this time, Tony Baca had arrived at the top of the slope and peered over the edge of the broken cornice. Wesley yelled up to Baca, saying there had been an avalanche, and Baca raced off to get help.

In a few minutes, Wesley was able to uncover Susan by digging with his hands. She had a cell phone in her pocket, and Wesley used it to make a 911 call. The dispatcher said that Baca was on the other line and that State Troopers from the town of Delta and an Air National Guard helicopter had been dispatched.

Daylight was fading fast, and all Wesley could think of was how he could find his brother and niece. He scrambled over the steep slope but found no sign of them. He then built a shelter with the hood of the snowmobile to protect Susan from the wind and lay beside her to keep her warm. Wesley was also staying in contact with the emergency dispatcher with periodic cell phone calls.

It was an hour and a half after the avalanche and fully dark when a helicopter flew into the area. The terrain was too rough for the helicopter to land, so searchlights on the helicopter swept the area but rescuers were never able to light up the two victims on the snow. Wesley was talking to the dispatcher in Delta, who in turn was talking to the helicopter pilot to guide the ship to the right spot, but without success. Eventually Wesley's cell phone died, and the helicopter had to break off the search to refuel.

The rescuers then went to the ground, with two Alaska State Troopers coming in on snowmobiles to the top of the broken cornice. It took an hour for them to ride in. The temperature was near zero and the wind was howling when they shined lights down the slope and saw the reflective strips on Wesley's jacket. The troopers then signaled the helicopter back in. The pilot was able to find a precarious landing spot several hundred feet from the victims. They brought Susan Rice out on a stretcher and flew her and Wesley to Fairbanks Memorial Hospital, arriving at 23:30 Saturday night.

Susan and Wesley were both suffering from hypothermia, but additionally, and far more seriously, Susan's pelvis was broken in three places, and she spent a week in the hospital.

Rescuers could not find Donnie or Jessica Rice that night and delayed the search until the next morning. At that time, a rescue team, search dogs, and an Air National Guard helicopter crew descended on the scene. A pararescue specialist with the 210th Air Rescue was lowered by cable into the avalanche area and found the victims' bodies that morning. The specialist confirmed they were dead, but the rescue team determined the avalanche risk was too great to put a ground team in to retrieve the bodies.

The bodies of Donnie and Jessica Rice were finally recovered three weeks later, in early February, by the Alaska Alpine Rescue Group out of Fairbanks.

AVALANCHE DATA

Cornice fall

This avalanche was a Cornice Fall avalanche and classified as C-AMu-R3.

COMMENTS

Cornice Fall avalanches involving people are fairly rare when compared to slab avalanches. They are more common in major mountain ranges around the world—the Alps, Andes, Himalayas, and Alaska—where giant cornice falls can trigger giant slab avalanches on the slopes below. When people trigger cornice falls, it's often because they moved onto the unsupported cornice, instead of supported snow. It can be very difficult to predict where the terrain ends and the unsupported snow begins. Our advice: stay well back from the edge, and then back up even further.

20020126 SHEEP MOUNTAIN, NORTHEAST OF BONNER, MONTANA

January 26, 2002

Five snowmobilers caught; one partly buried, four buried and killed

WEATHER AND SNOWPACK CONDITIONS

Sheep Mountain is a 7,646-foot peak located about 15 miles northeast of Missoula, or five miles northeast of the small town of Bonner, Montana. Wisherd Ridge runs southeast from the peak; its southwest side is broad and low-angled, but the other side is cut by five narrow, northeast-facing bowls. It is a popular destination for both backcountry skiers and snowmobilers in the winter.

A series of weather events that began in late December contributed to high avalanche danger on the day of the accident, January 26.

The entire avalanche path viewed from the runout. *Photo Steve Karkanen, West Central Montana Avalanche Center.*

First, from December 25 to 27 with mostly clear skies, a significant layer of surface hoar formed on the snow surface. Over the next 10 days, 10-12 inches of snow fell, burying this layer intact on north and east aspects. This weak layer remained undisturbed in the upper parts of the bowls on Sheep Mountain because of poor climbing conditions for snowmobiles.

Next, by mid-January, the weather pattern shifted to a period of steady snowfall. From January 18 to 25, Montana Snowbowl, a ski area five miles west of Sheep Mountain, measured 54 inches of new snow. This snow contained three inches of snow water equivalent, as measured at the nearby Stuart Mountain SNOTEL site. The storm then continued with warmer temperatures on January 25 and 26, and the SNOTEL site recorded an additional 1.4 inches of snow water equivalent, which would convert to an additional 14 to 16 inches of snow.

Lastly, west winds averaging 30-35 mph scoured snow from the southwest west side of Wisherd Ridge. This snow went to two places—the growing cornice above the bowls and the starting zones of avalanche paths in the bowls.

High avalanche danger

The backcountry avalanche danger increased steadily during the sustained stormy period after mid-January, so that on Friday, January 25, the West Central Montana Avalanche Center, based in Missoula, issued a warning for a High avalanche danger through the weekend.

ACCIDENT SUMMARY

The five bowls on the northeast side of Wisherd Ridge are locally numbered from southeast to northwest, with Bowl 5 nearest Sheep Mountain. It is steep and mostly treeless, and is a popular area for snowmobiling, especially highmarking. A little more than halfway up the bowl is a prominent bench on the south side, where riders can idle and rest, away from the main climbing area.

On Saturday, January 26, three groups of snowmobilers were riding in Bowl 5 on Sheep Mountain. All were equipped with beacons, probes, and shovels.

Group 1 included Forest Rodgers, Darran Rodgers, and Dave Darrah. These men came in from the top via Wisherd Ridge at 11:15 and rode to the bottom of Bowl 5.

Group 2 included Kelly Stensrud, Mark Cheff (27), Lou Ployhar (17), and Garrett Grothen (29). They came in from the bottom and arrived at 11:30.

Group 3 included Jace Olson (26), Brad Popham (31), and Chris Novak (25), who also came in from the bottom and arrived at 11:40.

The men in Group 2 talked with those in Group 1, and then they rode to a small slope to the south of the main Bowl 5 slope. They used this small slope as a test slope, sidehilling several times to see if there were signs of instability. They saw none. However, as noted by the investigators who came in after the avalanche, this may have been an unrepresentative test slope because it had recently been tracked up, though the tracks were covered by recent snowfall.

Avalanche debris on the bench, mid-track on the avalanche path. The larger blocks of debris are cornice blocks. *Photo Steve Karkanen, West Central Montana Avalanche Center.*

By noon, the 10 riders in the three groups had made about 15 runs up and down the slide path, and they were spread out in the bowl. At the bottom were Forest Rodgers, Darran Rodgers, and Dave Darrah, all on their snowmobiles with their motors running. Alongside was Chris Novak, who was working on the engine of his machine.

Up on the big bench were Mark Cheff, Kelly Stensrud, and Brad Popham. And riding the upper bowl—and starting zone—were Jace Olson, Lou Ployhar, and Garrett Grothen.

That's when the avalanche released, and it was big. The crown broke from three to 15 feet deep and 830 feet wide. Some large blocks of the cornice broke off, apparently sympathetically.

More than one person on a slope

From the bottom, Forest Rodgers recalled seeing the slope fracture just below the highest highmark and then seeing the cornice start to break. Mark Cheff, on the bench, said he saw the cornice break first. Regardless, the riders scrambled to get out of the path. At the bottom, Forest Rodgers, Darren Rodgers, and Dave Darrah raced into the trees to the south and escaped being hit. Chris Novak, however, was working on his engine and had nowhere to go. The avalanche swallowed him up.

On the bench, Kelly Stensrud had been idling beyond the flank of the avalanche and was not hit. Mark Cheff raced toward the south flank but was hit and knocked off his sled. With luck on his side, he was thrown into undisturbed snow beyond the flank on the bench and was uninjured. Brad Popham was hit, swept to the bottom of the slope and buried.

Of the three riders in the upper bowl, only one survived. Jace Olson described his experience: "I had just come down the mountain, and I was turning around to go back. I didn't actually see it until it hit me—I had my back to it. It knocked me off my sled, and I started swimming with it. All I could see was light and dark and light and then it would go dark again. When it finally came to a stop, my body was under about a foot of snow, my head was up and out and one arm was out." While Olson had been only partly buried, the debris carried Lou Ployhar and Garrett Grothen the full length of the avalanche path, where they were completely buried.

RESCUE SUMMARY

All the men were carrying beacons, probes, and shovels. As soon as the six survivors found their footing, they began searching. Additionally, seven other riders came into the area to help search, and most, if not all, had beacons, probes, and shovels.

20020126 SHEEP MOUNTAIN, MONTANA

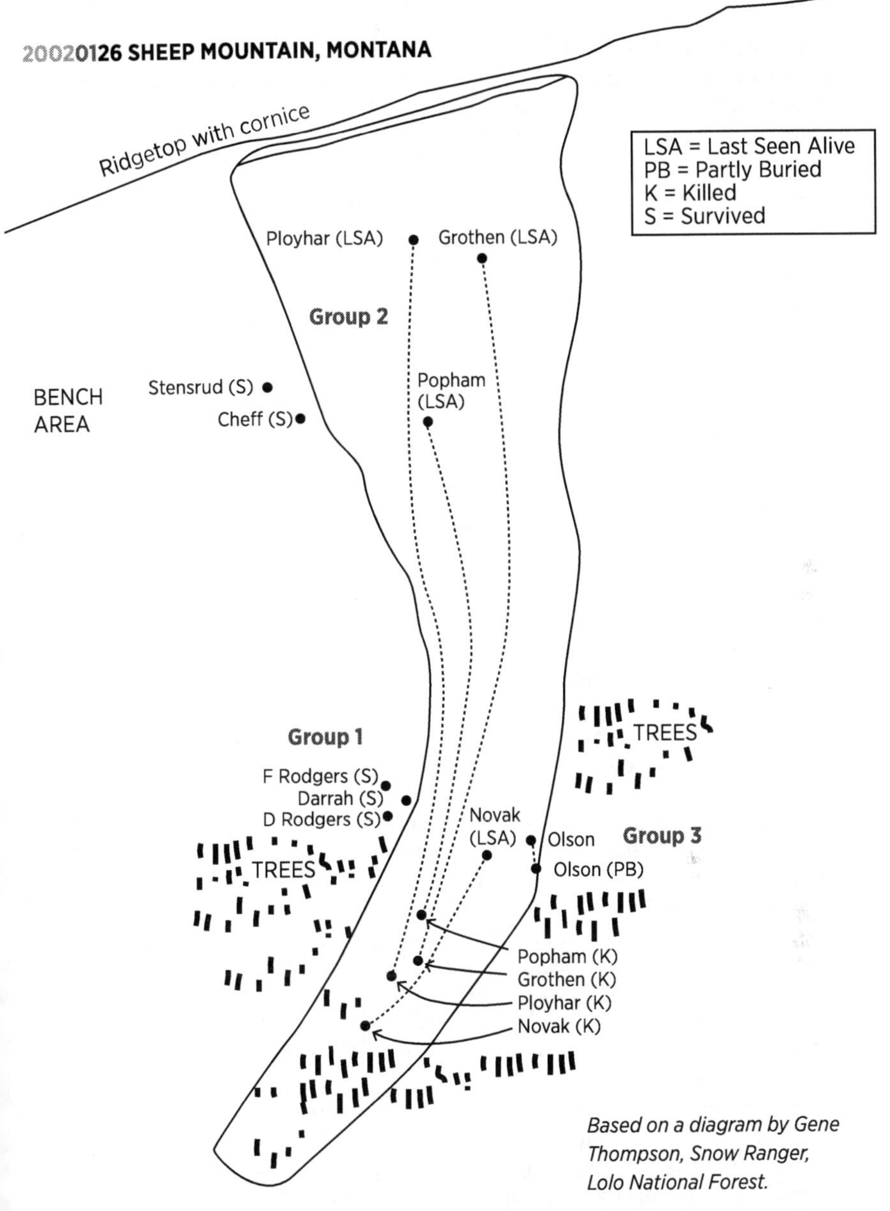

Based on a diagram by Gene Thompson, Snow Ranger, Lolo National Forest.

Kelly Stensrud and Mark Cheff, the remainder of Group 2, began a beacon search on the bench, thinking some of the missing riders may have stopped there. Getting no signals on the bench, they began carefully working down the path above the runout zone. As they got into the runout zone, they got a signal, which they closed in on. But they could not pinpoint the victim with probes. It turned out this victim, Brad Popham, was buried 12 feet deep, beyond the reach of their probes. While shovelers worked this spot, the survivors and seven other riders continued searching for other victims. The shovelers uncovered Popham's body two hours later.

Searchers got another signal about 70 feet downhill from the first. This was Garrett Grothen. He was buried under six feet of debris for 30 minutes and did not survive. Another beacon signal 25 feet downslope of Grothen led to Lou Ployhar, who was under eight feet of snow. He had been buried for 60 minutes when dug out. He did not survive either.

Searchers located Chris Novak last. They found him 100 feet from Ployhar under seven feet of snow. He had been buried 2.5 hours when uncovered, and he, too, had died.

The survivors had recovered all four victims by the time search and rescue teams arrived on the scene.

AVALANCHE DATA

Deep Persistent Slab avalanche

This avalanche was classified as HS-AMu-R5-D3-O. It released on an east-facing slope at an elevation of 7,280 feet and fell almost 600 feet vertical. The crown was 830 feet in length and varied from three to 15 feet deep, but averaged five to six feet deep. The peak slope angle at the crown was 44 degrees. In the runout, the debris was channeled into an area 135 feet wide, which caused it to pile up in an elongated mound 15 to 20 feet deep.

COMMENTS

The 10 riders in these three groups were very familiar with the Sheep Mountain terrain in general and Bowl 5 in particular. They all had been riding there for five to 12 years. All the people debriefed after the accident said they had seen avalanches in the bowl but had never seen one run past the "big bench." And they all knew snow conditions were unstable that morning.

They did a stability test on a small slope, which they said they normally do. But that slope had been disturbed by riders on previous days, so any confidence they gained from this test was misplaced.

When the avalanche released, nine of the 10 riders were in the slide path (with the tenth man off to the side on the bench). Regarding this, Gene Thompson, who prepared the original report on this avalanche, said it well: "Perhaps more than any other single fact gleaned from a review of this accident, this speaks to the group's disregard for existing high-hazard conditions and their confidence in being able to deal with any problem that might arise." Thompson also learned that five of the six survivors had triggered avalanches in the past, four of the six had been caught in slides, and one had been totally buried and dug out by his companions. Again in the words of Thompson in his report:

> The risk assessment this group made that morning was based only on past experience. Their assumptions about snow stability on that site that morning were unfounded. They had failed to judge the consequences of being caught in an avalanche that was larger than any they had previously experienced. Ultimately, this group was over-whelmed by a series of poor decisions based on observations and experiences that had nothing to do with snow conditions found in Bowl 5 that morning.

The mismatch between the expected and actual size of avalanches in not uncommon when dealing with persistent weak layers. Failures often propagate in surprising and unpredictable ways, and the avalanches can span multiple terrain features. See 20020314b for another example.

WINDY RIDGE, NORTHEAST OF KAMAS, UTAH

20020131a

January 31, 2002

One backcountry skier caught, buried, and killed; one dog killed

WEATHER AND SNOWPACK CONDITIONS

The Uintas are a west-to-east-oriented mountain range in northeast Utah. Windy Ridge is a small sub-range in the northwest portion of the Uintas, and this area lies about 18 miles northeast of the small town of Kamas. Weather data taken from the Smith & Morehouse SNOTEL site—at an elevation of 7,600 feet and within a few miles of the accident site—showed the following:

There was no snow before November 20, but then two inches of snow-water equivalent fell through December 1. This may have totaled two feet of snow. December brought a series of small storms, followed by a fairly dry January. A major storm hit late on January 26, and by the 28th, three inches of snow-water equivalent had fallen, which could have been three feet of snowfall. The Utah Avalanche Center rated the avalanche danger in the nearby Wasatch Range as Considerable.

ACCIDENT SUMMARY

On Thursday morning, January 31, Brian Roust (29) and a friend began skinning from the intersection of the Weber Canyon and Smith & Morehouse Roads. They were accompanied by their two dogs. They carried full avalanche rescue gear, plus their dogs were wearing beacons. Roust was a very experienced backcountry skier and had been a ski patroller at Park City. At the time, he worked in the snow safety department at the Canyons Resort.

Their plan this day was to ski on the Thousand Peaks Ranch, which is private land but is open to public use. They crossed the Weber River and headed east for about a quarter-mile, then they turned north, heading up a ridge that leads to the Windy Ridge area. They ascended the ridge to an area locally called Nor'easter Bowl at about 9,400 feet elevation. This bowl basically faces northeast (thus its name), with skier's right being more north-facing, and skier's left more east-facing.

Ahead of them, another group of four skiers had already made one run in the bowl and was climbing up. Their skin track made switchbacks up a treed ridge to the south of the bowl and then traversed across the starting zone of a small slide path before gaining the main ridgeline. On the previous day, some members of this party of four had skied the northern portion of the bowl, and that day, they had used a skin track to the north of the bowl to ascend. All members of this group were equipped with avalanche rescue gear.

Brian Roust, his companion, and the two dogs reached the top of Nor'easter Bowl. Then the men skied and the dogs ran down the south side of the bowl (skier's right) next to the trees. At the bottom they began skinning up the track set by the party of four. The skiers and the dogs traveled up the track at different speeds and quickly became spread out over the track.

The group of four reached the top and began their second run on the skier's left side of the bowl. The second skier in the group triggered an avalanche; one of his friends yelled "Go left!" and the skier made it out of the slide. It was a sizeable slide; the crown was two to four feet deep and 300 feet wide.

At this point, members of both groups made voice contact with each other and quickly determined that no one was caught in the avalanche. The group of four had two on the ridge and two at the bottom of the bowl. Roust's group of two was spread out along the skin track; Roust and his dog Ginger had climbed faster and were well up the track, while his companion and dog were near the bottom.

Traveling alone

Roust was out of sight from all the other skiers when he triggered an avalanche at about 13:00. The avalanche released when he was climbing near a stand of trees in the starting zone, and it carried Roust and Ginger down through several stands of trees before burying them both. None of the other skiers in the two groups saw the avalanche. The only witness was a skier in a third group, about a quarter mile away.

RESCUE SUMMARY

When Roust's companion neared the top of the skin track, he saw that the last switchback had been washed out by an avalanche. There were no ski tracks on the bed surface, and upon reaching the top of the ridge he realized that Brian had been caught in the slide. He called out to the other skiers in the area, and they all went into rescue mode.

Roust's partner turned his rescue beacon to receive and began searching from the top of the slide, while the two skiers below began searching lower portions of the debris. The rescuers lower in the slide path quickly picked up the signal from a transmitting rescue beacon and dug up a loose beacon about two feet below the snow surface. They turned the beacon off and continue searching. They picked up a second signal and began probing and digging. This was Roust's beacon, and they found him buried under four feet of snow, 400 vertical feet below the crown line. His skis and poles were not found. He had been buried 20 minutes, had suffered head and neck trauma, and did not respond to resuscitation. It was later affirmed that Roust had died from head and neck trauma, not suffocation.

The rescuers determined that the first beacon they found had been on Ginger, Roust's dog. They didn't find Ginger.

AVALANCHE DATA

Persistent Slab avalanche

The avalanche occurred on a northeast-facing slope, releasing at an elevation of 9,365 feet and falling about 665 feet vertical. Slope angle at the starting zone was 34 degrees. The alpha angle from toe to starting zone was 26 degrees. Vegetation on the slope was stands of mixed aspen and fir trees with openings running both vertically and horizontally through the path.

Investigators classified the fatal avalanche as HS-ASu-R3-O. The fracture line varied from two to four feet deep and was 150 feet wide. There were deep piles of debris on the uphill sides of the trees in the path. The debris near the toe had flowed into a gully about 75 feet wide. The first slide was similarly classified as HS-ASu-R3-O.

COMMENTS

Two avalanches were triggered by two groups in the same bowl a few minutes apart. The Utah Avalanche Center rated the danger as Considerable that day, meaning human-triggered avalanches were likely. It was every bit of that. The members of these two groups were experienced backcountry skiers, and they most likely knew the avalanche danger rating. And they knew they were exposed to avalanches not only on their descents but also near the top of their skin track. It was a risk that they apparently accepted.

Putting beacons on dogs has spurred a bit of debate. It's understandable that dog owners would like their dog to be found quickly if buried in an avalanche. But if a dog and person are both buried in an avalanche, the rescuers cannot distinguish between signals. If the dog is located and dug out first, the buried person has a lower chance of survival. This has raised a moral dilemma: should dogs be on an equal-rescue footing as humans? We'll let you, the reader, decide.

LIONHEAD, NORTHWEST OF WEST YELLOWSTONE, MONTANA | January 31, 2002

20020131b

One snowmobiler caught and buried

ACCIDENT SUMMARY

The southern end of the Madison Range is a popular destination for snowmobiling. It is about 17 miles northwest of West Yellowstone, Montana, and offers a variety of terrain, including avalanche terrain. The area is referred to as Lionhead, the Lionhead Mountains, and the Henrys Lake Mountains.

Inadequate rescue equipment

On the afternoon of Thursday, January 31, two snowmobilers were riding—and highmarking—on a slope of Lionhead. Both were experienced riders, knew the risks in highmarking, and carried beacons and shovels.

One rider got stuck trying to climb a steep, 600-foot hill. He got off his sled and while he was trying to free it, the slope fractured about 400 feet above him. His partner witnessed the avalanche from a safe spot—a small ridge—near the bottom of the avalanche path.

When the avalanche stopped, the rider who witnessed the avalanche rode onto the debris. He did not see any surface clues, so he began a beacon search. He acquired a signal almost right away. Within a few minutes, he decided he was close enough to start digging. About 10 minutes after the avalanche, he had dug through about five feet of debris and struck his partner's helmet. The buried man, though unconscious, was breathing.

The rescuer took several minutes to make a cell phone call to notify the authorities in West Yellowstone. He then spent another 10 to 15 minutes removing the remainder of the snow that covered his partner. The buried man regained consciousness after being buried for a total of about 20 minutes. He remembered being caught in the avalanche and heard his partner searching for him before he blacked out. He was buried lying on his side, perpendicular to the slope, and wasn't injured.

The next day, the men retrieved the snowmobile, which was buried under five feet of debris, at the same elevation and 20 feet from where the victim had been buried.

AVALANCHE DATA

Persistent Slab avalanche

The avalanche was about 500 feet across and ran about 600 feet vertical. The crown was at 8,400 feet in elevation and was two to four feet deep. The avalanche fractured on a buried weak layer of near-surface facets that had formed near the snow surface during a cold, dry spell around Christmas. The average slope angle of the bed surface was 37 degrees. The avalanche was classified as HS-AMu-R3-O.

COMMENTS

This was an avalanche incident with a feel-good outcome, and, quite frankly, we wish we could write up more events that focus on the positive. This pair took plenty of precautions. They carried rescue gear and practiced with it, so they would be fast when the real event happened. They rode the slope one at a time, with the other observing from a safe location. And lastly, when one man got stuck, he was left on his own to get himself out, thus ruling out both men getting buried. In an interview after the accident, they stated that they rarely rode together on the same slope.

Our only criticism is the lack of probes. Once the beacon search has reduced the burial site to a small area, a probe will pinpoint the exact burial spot. Shoveling can be the most exhaustive and time-consuming part of a rescue, and it can be a fatal error to dig a hole that's a few feet off.

This accident occurred very near the site of a fatal snowmobile highmarking avalanche on April 4, 2001 (20010404). That accident the previous spring led to a death partly—mostly?—because none of that group carried rescue gear.

20020201 **ASPEN HIGHLANDS, COLORADO** | February 1, 2002

One lift skier caught, buried, and killed

WEATHER AND SNOWPACK CONDITIONS

The snow conditions that contributed to this fatal avalanche began three months earlier, in November. In the Elk Mountains, Aspen Highlands got only 70% of its normal November snow, with most of that coming in a storm at Thanksgiving that dropped two to four feet of snow. In December and January, snowfall continued to be on the light side, with Highlands measuring 67% of normal. The shallow snowpack was thus prone to the faceting process, and indeed much of the natural snow cover had turned to depth hoar. Below treeline on shaded aspects, the snowpack was almost entirely sugar-like, faceted snow.

Note: The weather pattern described in this accident report was one of low snowfall in Colorado for November, December, and January. Extra cold temperatures were also the norm for much of the winter. The combination of low snow and cold temperatures would have a lasting effect on the mountain snowpack through March. This shallow snowpack succumbed to the process of faceting, which created a layer of depth hoar near the ground that seemed to be everywhere. This would be a major contributing factor to five other fatal avalanches in Colorado from February 24 to March 17. See reports 20020224, 20020314a, 20020314b, 20020315, and 20020317.

ACCIDENT SUMMARY

Traveling alone

On Friday, February 1, Robert Littlewood (67) was skiing with friends at Aspen Highlands when they became separated. His friends waited at the bottom of the lift, but when Littlewood failed to arrive, they rode the lift and retraced their route. Unable to find their friend, they reported him missing to the ski patrol at 14:15. Shortly afterwards, a patroller spotted Littlewood's ski in the snow a short distance below the area where Memory Lane and Troyer's Trail intersect with the Park Avenue run. The ski was just beyond the roped ski area boundary.

The victim had triggered a very small loose-snow avalanche that carried him down slope and buried him under 18 inches of snow. Littlewood was buried about one hour, and the coroner determined he had died from asphyxiation.

The accident was the result of several unintended mishaps. Littlewood did not duck under the boundary rope and leave the ski run on purpose. The coroner found internal injuries that would indicate he had suffered a high-impact fall that incapacitated him and caused him to slide off the trail. He narrowly missed trees and landed in a very small pocket of undisturbed, faceted sugar-snow. That loose snow avalanched, carried the victim down about 60 vertical feet and buried him.

AVALANCHE DATA

The avalanche occurred on a north-facing slope at about 9,000 feet elevation. The avalanche released just over two feet deep and to the ground, but was only a narrow ribbon of snow four to six feet wide and traveled only 60 to 70 feet vertical. This avalanche is classified as L-ASu-R1-G, and is likely one of the smallest fatal avalanches known.

Loose Dry avalanche

COMMENTS

What incredible bad luck. A series of minor circumstances led to a fatal event. First, the victim became separated from his friends and was skiing alone. Second, he fell hard on the ski run and was either unconscious or otherwise physically unable to help himself. Third, he slid off the ski run, under the rope line, and onto a steeper slope. Fourth, that slope had two feet of sugary depth hoar, which crumbled into a small avalanche, and lastly, he was totally buried.

CRYSTAL PEAK, EAST OF FRIENDS HUT, COLORADO

20020206

February 6, 2002

One backcountry skier caught, buried, and killed

ACCIDENT SUMMARY

The Friends Hut sits south of Pearl Pass and is an overnight stop for hut-to-hut skiers between Aspen and Crested Butte, Colorado. Crystal Peak is a 12,777-foot peak one mile east of the hut. The hut and peak lie in the Elk Mountains.

On Sunday, February 3, six men left Ashcroft, near Aspen, for what was intended to be a five-night hut trip. They spent the first night in the Green-Wilson Hut between Ashcroft and Pearl Pass. On Monday, February 4, the group toured across Pearl Pass to the Friends Hut.

On Tuesday, February 5, the group had a safe day of skiing in the trees on Hunters Hill, about two miles southeast of the hut. On Wednesday morning, February 6, under clear skies, the group practiced with their beacons near the hut before heading out on the day's tour. Then five of the six left the hut to ski near Crystal Peak, about a mile east of the hut. Everyone in the party carried beacons, shovels, and probes. One of the men was David Rooney (39).

According to ski partners Chris Webster and Myron McCallum, the group climbed up Crystal Peak and then took a route that led them over a ridge on the south side of the peak. However, Rooney, saying his clothes were wet and consequently wanting to stay off the exposed ridge, skied off by himself, traversing below the ridge on a southwest aspect.

Traveling alone

Webster followed but did not close the distance with Rooney in order to stay relatively close to the skier behind him. Eventually, Rooney skied out of sight of the rest of the group. It is not known what exactly happened, as no one witnessed the avalanche, but tracks indicate that Rooney was traversing across slopes with a generally thin snow cover, only about four inches deep. At about 14:45 Rooney encountered deeper snow

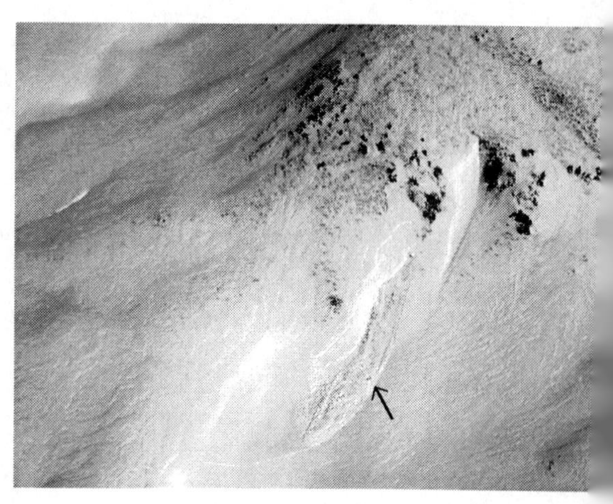

Left: Note the hard slab blocks. The skis (barely visible on the far side of the avalanche) mark Rooney's burial site. *Photo Alan Bernholtz, Crested Butte Avalanche Center.*

Right: The avalanche viewed from the air. Rooney's friends found him buried on the right side of the debris, roughly where the black arrow points. *Photo Rob Hunker, Colorado Avalanche Information Center.*

on a steep, 40-degree, convex roll, where he triggered an 18-inch-deep fracture. This fracture eventually stepped to the ground to be about three feet deep, and the avalanche ran approximately 300 vertical feet. Rooney was totally buried.

RESCUE SUMMARY

About 10 to 15 minutes later, Webster and the other skiers came upon the avalanche and saw tracks leading in and none coming out. The hard slab avalanche was about 150 feet wide, and there was no sign of Rooney. Immediately, the rescuers switched their beacons to receive and headed down the slide path. They got a signal within three minutes, pinpointed the burial position, and started digging.

They uncovered Rooney from four feet of snow. He had been buried 20 to 25 minutes. Another skier on the trip, Kirk Kritner, began resuscitation efforts immediately but found that until Rooney was completely uncovered his chest would not expand due to the surrounding snow. So the rescuers spent another few minutes digging the victim out and then restarted CPR. Eventually they knew their efforts were not to be rewarded and ceased.

The skiers made a 911 cell-phone call and then returned to the hut for the night. The following morning members of the Crested Butte Search and Rescue Team arrived for the body recovery.

AVALANCHE DATA

The avalanche released on a southwest-facing slope at an elevation of about 12,000 feet. It was a hard slab about 150 feet wide that fractured 1.5 to three feet deep and fell 300 feet vertical. It ran to ground and was classified as HS-ASu-R3-G. The slope angle at the crown was 40 degrees. The fracture line profile was typical of the winter's snowpack—depth hoar covered by wind slab.

Persistent Slab avalanche

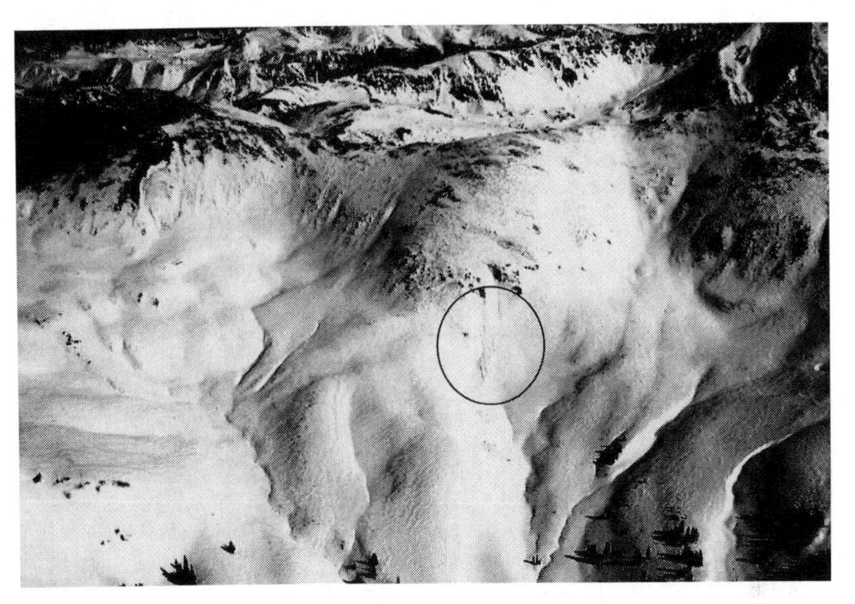

Crystal Peak is the high point in the left of the photograph. The avalanche is circled, in the gully visible in the center of the image. *Photo Rob Hunker, Colorado Avalanche Information Center.*

COMMENTS

A few small details ultimately led to this fatal avalanche. The group had originally agreed upon a ridge route that would avoid avalanche starting zones. But Rooney was getting chilled because of damp clothing, so he chose to take a low route—out of the wind—instead of the planned ridge route. Rooney's route took him across a very steep slope. Additionally, either because he was cold or simply because he may have been a stronger climber, he left the others behind and, therefore, was alone when he triggered the avalanche.

UPPER WHITEFISH LAKE, NORTHWEST OF WHITEFISH, MONTANA | February 10, 2002

20020210

One snowmobiler caught, buried, and killed

ACCIDENT SUMMARY

On Sunday, February 10, a party of four snowmobilers was riding north of Upper Whitefish Lake in the Whitefish Range in northwest Montana. Riders commonly access this area from the upper end of Whitefish Lake, north of the town of Whitefish, or the small town of Olney, to the southwest. The party worked ridges and bowls most of the day prior to dropping into a bowl above the east fork of Swift Creek and just south of the Flathead-Lincoln county line. All riders were carrying transceivers, probes, and shovels.

The bowl faced east through south. Recent snowfall and prevailing westerly winds had loaded the bowl with wind-blown snow, with heavier loading on the east aspect and lighter loading on the south.

More than one person on a slope

The time was 15:30 when one rider neared the ridge at the top of the bowl. Further down slope, a second rider, Joseph Anthony Garrisi (39) of Kalispell was heading up. Two other men were sitting on their idling sleds off to the side at the bottom. The upper rider triggered an avalanche, but he was able to power on up and gain the ridge. The avalanche hit Garrisi, carried him down the bowl, and buried him. The avalanche did not hit the other two men near the bottom, and they became the first searchers.

RESCUE SUMMARY

A transceiver search fairly quickly located the burial position, but Garrisi was buried beneath his snowmobile in compact snow. Digging was difficult and it took 30 to 45 minutes to uncover Garrisi from five feet of snow. The rescuers administered CPR without success. The body recovery was delayed until the following morning.

AVALANCHE DATA

Persistent Slab avalanche

The avalanche ran on a bowl-shaped slope that faced east through south. Recent storm snow and blowing snow had formed a slab that was deeper on the east aspect, so that the fracture was about 3.5 feet deep there yet only one to two feet deep on the south aspect. An estimate of the width of the avalanche was more than 1,000 feet, and it fell about 300 feet vertical. The classification probably was HS-AMu-R3-O.

The upper snowpack consisted of a slab of wind-blown snow lying on top of a melt-freeze layer. Additionally, it appeared that a thin layer of surface hoar had formed on top of the melt-freeze layer. That became the weak layer that failed beneath the wind slab.

COMMENTS

This group was prepared for avalanche rescue, and indeed pinpointed the burial spot fairly quickly. But the victim was buried deeply in very dense avalanche debris. Life span is very short in such circumstances, and the rescuers could not get through the debris fast enough to save a life.

20020216 MT. ABUNDANCE, NORTHWEST OF COOKE CITY, MONTANA | February 16, 2002

Three snowmobilers caught; one partly buried and injured, two buried and killed

WEATHER AND SNOWPACK CONDITIONS

In the Absaroka and Beartooth Ranges of south-central Montana, a period of thaw in early January created an ice crust on sunny, south-facing mountain slopes. The next storm put down several inches of snow that, in time, turned into a four-inch-thick layer of facets. Over the next few weeks going into mid-February, two to four feet of pencil-hardness wind slab built up on top of the weak faceted snow.

ACCIDENT SUMMARY

Mt. Abundance is a 10,098-foot peak about eight miles northwest of Cooke City, Montana. It's a popular area for snowmobilers, but it has its dangers. Mt. Abundance has been the site of several large avalanches triggered by snowmobilers.

On Saturday, February 16, a party of five snowmobilers was riding on the large, open slope on the mountain's south side. The time was about 10:30, the group was

The looker's right side of the crown of the February 16, 2002, avalanche. The fracture depth is about four feet. *Photo Gallatin National Forest Avalanche Center.*

highmarking, and all five were on the slope when it avalanched. Two were able to ride to safety, but three were caught. One was partly buried and able to dig himself out. He suffered only a broken nose. The avalanche completely buried the other two riders, Michael Martin (41) and Joey Pierce (37). None wore beacons nor did they have other rescue gear such as probes or shovels.

No rescue equipment

RESCUE SUMMARY

The two riders lower on the slope were able to turn their machines and outrun the avalanche, but therefore they did not have a good last-seen area for the missing riders. One of these men returned to the debris field to start a search while the other rode until he could make a 911 call, which was received at 10:48. The rider who returned and the injured rider who dug himself out began walking the debris field looking for signs of the two missing men.

Fairly quickly, other riders in the area either saw or heard of the avalanche and came to help. Two US Forest Service employees riding in the area were able to get to the scene within 15 minutes. They assisted in the scuff search, and as more people arrived, they helped organize probe lines.

Searchers located both snowmobiles, both mostly buried. One was 10 feet above the toe of the debris at the far left edge (as viewed from the bottom), and the other was well up the slope below a tree on the far right flank (again as viewed from below).

Probing did not locate either of the buried men by the time a rescue team with a dog and handler arrived sometime after 14:00. Fairly quickly, at 14:25, the dog alerted, and searchers dug out the first victim about 10 feet uphill from the toe of the debris. He was two feet under, and 75 feet away from where searchers found his snowmobile.

The dog found the second victim at 15:15, 230 feet vertical above the first victim, almost in the same fall line. This rider was near the right flank, pressed against a tree and three feet under. His feet were almost touching his partially buried snowmobile below him.

Rescuers attempted to resuscitate both victims, but their efforts failed. Both were pronounced dead at the scene and were evacuated by snowmobile.

AVALANCHE DATA

Persistent Slab avalanche

The avalanche released on a south-facing slope at a little below 10,000 feet elevation. The avalanche was a hard slab, about 300 feet wide and falling 600 feet vertical. The crown varied from two to four feet deep. The slope angle was 34 degrees for much of the slope, but was 38 degrees at the crown line. The alpha angle was 27 degrees. The avalanche classification was probably HS-AMu-R3-O.

The weak layer was a four-inch-thick layer of facets about 28 inches below the snow surface. The facets had formed on top of an ice crust, which itself had formed during a thaw-freeze cycle about five weeks earlier in January. Finally, the slab layer was two to four feet of pencil-hard wind slab.

COMMENTS

Most popular highmarking slopes are steeper than 30 degrees. While these slopes are the most fun to recreate on, they're also potential avalanche slopes. Given that reality, avalanche rescue gear is mandatory if riders hope to survive an avalanche or rescue their riding partners.

20020224 MINER BASIN, SOUTHWEST OF CARBONDALE, COLORADO

February 24, 2002

One snowmobiler caught, buried, and killed

WEATHER AND SNOWPACK CONDITIONS

Miner Basin is situated about 13 miles southwest of Carbondale in central Colorado. A layer of fresh snow had accumulated on top of a firm wind crust, making for good snowmobile riding. At the ground, though, was a layer of depth hoar. (See 20020201 for a description of the weather that had prevailed in Colorado for the winter of 2001-02.)

ACCIDENT SUMMARY

The Thompson Divide, southwest of Carbondale, is popular with snowmobilers for its mix of groomed trails and play areas. Miner Basin, just west of the divide, is a frequent play stop. Several unnamed peaks in the area of Miner Basin extend above 10,000 feet elevation, including Pt. 10250, on the north side of the basin. Bowls on the north and south sides of this peak comprise most of the avalanche terrain in the vicinity.

About 12 to 15 inches of snow had fallen in the week prior to the avalanche. On Sunday, February 24, a group of eight snowmobilers was riding in Miner Basin; some in this group had been riding in this area for the past six to seven winters and were familiar with the terrain.

"Red flag" indications of danger

Though the group knew the terrain, they apparently paid little attention to the threat of avalanches. Prior to the accident, they triggered two small avalanches earlier

Left: Looking up the path of the February 24, 2002, avalanche from the burial area. The two objects lying in the snow to the right of the ski poles are aspen branches used by companions to probe the snow. *Photo Rob Hunker, Colorado Avalanche Information Center.*

Right: A view across the start zone of the February 24, 2002, avalanche with a fracture line profile visible in the foreground. Fracture depth was 2 feet and is shown near the exposed shovel handle. *Photo Rob Hunker, Colorado Avalanche Information Center.*

on this day and had caused several audible collapses of the snowpack. They had no avalanche rescue gear at all among them.

No rescue equipment

At about 14:30, the riders were highmarking a bowl on the north side of Pt. 10250. A large cornice sat along the ridgeline above the slope. The first rider made it near the top and turned across the slope to exit while a second rider climbed. This man, Grant Walker (19), was halfway up when apparently the weight of two snowmobiles triggered the avalanche. The higher rider was able to escape to the side, but Walker was caught, carried downhill, and buried.

More than one person on a slope

RESCUE SUMMARY

Part of Walker's snowmobile was visible in the debris, and the other riders began searching for the young man. Without beacons or probes, they searched the last-seen area, using tree branches and sticks to probe the snow. One of the searchers was able to call a friend in the town of Silt, 20 miles away. This friend in turn notified the Sheriff's Office.

After 30 to 45 minutes, one of the searchers struck Walker under two to three feet of debris. The group then used the windshields from their machines to dig him free.

The snowmobilers were highmarking in this gully and bowl and triggered several slab avalanches low on the slope. The victim triggered the fatal avalanche on the slope to the right of the sunlit ridge; part of the crown is visible near the top. *Photo Rob Hunker, Colorado Avalanche Information Center.*

Walker did not respond to the group's resuscitation efforts. Later that evening, a SAR team retrieved the victim's body.

AVALANCHE DATA

Persistent Slab avalanche

This avalanche was classified as SS-AMu-R3-O. It released on a slope that faced roughly north and at an elevation of 9,800 feet. The crown was two feet deep and 300 feet wide. The slope angle was 37 degrees, and the avalanche fell 600 feet vertical.

There was a layer of depth hoar at the ground, but the avalanche did not break that deep. Rather, it released on a very thin layer of surface hoar or facets, which had formed on a hard wind crust in the middle of the snowpack. That weak layer had then been buried by snow that had fallen and blown in during the previous week or two.

COMMENTS

Lack of training

Unfortunately, this group had no avalanche awareness training. They failed to recognize the threat revealed by the two small slides that they had released earlier in the day, as well as the threat shown by a small natural slide on the slope where the men were riding. Additionally, they had no avalanche rescue gear whatsoever. This might not have been a fatal event for a better-educated and better-equipped group.

MOUNT JUDAH, EAST OF SUGAR BOWL RESORT, CALIFORNIA | March 8, 2002

20020308

Two sidecountry snowboarders caught and partly buried; one skier caught, buried, and killed

WEATHER AND SNOWPACK CONDITIONS

The summit of Mount Judah lies less than a mile and a half from Donner Pass in California's Sierra Mountains. Its western slopes are part of Sugar Bowl Resort, while its steep east face lies outside the resort boundary. Riders can reach the summit reached by hiking roughly 20 minutes from the resort's chairlifts.

In late February, a warm storm brought rain and snow to the Sierra Nevada of California. Under the spring-like conditions that followed, a four-inch-thick crust formed at the snow surface. This was followed by a clearing period with cold nights, causing surface hoar to grow on top of the crust.

On March 6, another warm storm moved into the Sierra. By the morning of March 8, the storm had left a total of 34 inches of snow at Sugar Bowl Resort. During this storm, automated stations recorded winds of 80 to 100 mph. The blowing snow that resulted did two things: one, it added to the already-large cornices along the ridgelines; and two, it added a layer of cohesive snow on top of the surface hoar.

ACCIDENT SUMMARY

Sometime around 13:00 on Friday, March 8, one skier and two snowboarders left the Sugar Bowl Ski Area boundary. The skier was Jonathan Clodfelter (30). They traveled a short distance and walked out onto the top of a giant cornice on the summit ridge of Mt. Judah. An enormous chunk of the cornice under the men broke off. Witnesses estimated it broke 15 to 20 feet back from the edge, 60 feet wide, and 20 feet deep. It fell on the slope below and triggered a slab avalanche about three to four feet deep and 150 feet wide. The avalanche ran about 400 feet vertical, and the entire length of the path was filled with debris. There were many cornice blocks still intact all the way to the toe. All three men disappeared into the avalanche.

RESCUE SUMMARY

Eight to 10 other riders witnessed the avalanche, some of whom called 911. The Sugar Bowl ski patrol got the call at 13:15 and responded immediately, dispatching a hasty search team equipped with beacons, shovels, probes, and oxygen. Three patrollers reached the top of Mt. Judah within 10 minutes. There they learned that several witnesses knew the victims and that none of the victims were wearing transceivers.

Inadequate rescue equipment

One patroller remained with the witnesses on the ridge to organize a probe line if needed, while the other two dropped in to evaluate the avalanche hazard for rescue teams. The two patrollers ski cut the right flank of the slide and concluded it would be a safe route in for rescuers.

But there was still the problem of the cornice, which was still overhanging along the entire length of the ridge. The patrol set up avalanche guards along the ridgeline to prevent rescuers from getting anywhere near the edge.

Another patroller traversed around the north shoulder of Mt. Judah and was nearing the toe of the slide when he came upon the two snowboarders, who were unharmed. One had been spit out to the flank of the slide, and the other had been mostly buried near the toe but had dug himself out using his helmet. There was also an onlooker who had made his way down from the top and was looking for the third victim.

The victim who had been buried up to his neck said that he had seen Clodfelter, the missing man, close by as they had been swept down the path. This information allowed rescuers to focus their search on the lower part of the debris. The patroller organized the three men into a probe line, and they began working upward from the toe of the debris. As other rescuers arrived, they joined the probe line. A rescue dog and handler began working the slide from the top down.

At 14:20, the probe line struck Clodfelter. He was uncovered from three feet of snow, had been buried for more than an hour, and showed no life signs. The patrol started CPR immediately and continued doing so until they transferred care to the flight crew of a Careflight helicopter which landed in a meadow below the slide path. Clodfelter had been buried too long and died in the avalanche.

AVALANCHE DATA

Cornice fall

The avalanche was a cornice fall that triggered a slab avalanche on the slope below. That slab was three to four feet deep and 150 feet wide. Slope angle was about 50 degrees immediately below the cornice and then shallowed out to 35 degrees in the track. The avalanche fell about 400 vertical feet and was classified as C-ASu-R3.

COMMENTS

Cornice falls are nothing to mess with. Certainly this group of three thought they were safe where they were standing, but… not so. Cornices seem to be solid and strong, yet they have complicated layering from building up one storm to the next. The best advice is to stand back—way back. A remarkable outcome of this avalanche is that two men actually survived. See 19980211 for a similar incident involving the same cornice and slope.

20020312 GROVE CREEK, WEST OF VICTOR, IDAHO | March 12, 2002

One snowmobiler caught, buried, and killed

WEATHER AND SNOWPACK CONDITIONS

The Big Hole Mountains are a small mountain range west of Victor and Driggs, Idaho. Jackson Hole Mountain Resort is about 20 miles to the east of the Big Holes, and from March 7 to 11, the resort recorded about three feet of snow containing nearly three inches of water. The Big Holes probably did not get this amount of snowfall because of lower elevations, but nonetheless, a significant amount of new snow fell in this smaller mountain range during the same period.

ACCIDENT SUMMARY

Traveling alone

On Tuesday, March 12, Chance Schiess (16) was snowmobiling alone in the Grove Creek drainage of the Big Hole Mountains just a few miles from his home. He stopped his snowmobile on top of a cornice, which collapsed, sending him and his machine into a ravine. Schiess was totally buried, while his sled was partially buried. When he did not return home that evening, his parents reported him overdue to the Teton County Sheriff.

Terrain trap

RESCUE SUMMARY

The following morning, a search team apparently followed Schiess's snowmobile track to the site of the avalanche. They saw the snowmobile in the debris. Knowing the victim did not have a beacon, the search team began probing. After a few hours, a search dog and handler arrived from the Targhee Ski Resort, and the dog located the victim quickly. He had been buried three feet deep and was deceased.

AVALANCHE DATA

The avalanche occurred on an east-facing slope at an elevation of 7,400 feet. It was a cornice fall and was classified as C-AMu-R2. The cornice blocks triggered a small loose-snow avalanche on the slope below, and all the debris flowed into a ravine. The slide fell about 180 feet vertical.

Cornice fall

COMMENTS

With so few details, we have just a few comments. This accident points out the danger of traveling alone—no companion to serve as a rescuer in case of an accident. It also underscores the danger of combining a cornice collapse and terrain trap: the debris of a small avalanche can pile up deeply.

STRAWBERRY GULCH, EAST OF ASPEN MOUNTAIN, COLORADO | March 14, 2002

20020314a

One sidecountry skier caught, buried, and killed

WEATHER AND SNOWPACK CONDITIONS

The first week of March was dry and very cold, which did nothing to settle and strengthen the mountain snowpack. The second week brought two small storms to the Aspen area, but, more importantly, strong winds caused blowing snow and widespread slab formation. Then, on March 13, a one-day storm brought 10 inches of new snow to Aspen Mountain ski area.

(For the weather history of the winter of 2001-02 in Colorado that contributed to this avalanche, the reader should refer to the discussion in 20020201.)

ACCIDENT SUMMARY

On Thursday, March 14, Dana Martino (39) and a friend spent the day skiing at Aspen Mountain. At about 14:30, they split up. Martino's companion stayed inbounds, and Martino went through a backcountry gate on the east boundary. Later, patrollers would follow her route as they searched for her.

Traveling alone

Martino skied down from the boundary and came to Loushine's Road, which is a snowmobile-packed road that traverses back to the ski area. Most skiers take this back to the ski area, but whether on purpose or because she was not familiar with this terrain, Martino crossed Loushine's Road and continued through the very rugged, wooded terrain of Strawberry Gulch and down toward the valley. Some locals refer to this area as Pandora's Box.

Terrain trap

Martino's route led to a very steep gully. As she attempted to traverse from one side to the other, she triggered a soft-slab avalanche that carried her to the bottom and buried her. The time would have been about 14:45.

RESCUE SUMMARY

No rescue equipment

At about 16:30, well after the lifts had closed, the Martino's father notified the ski patrol about the missing woman. A couple of ski patrollers exited the gate and skied down to Loushine's Road. From there, Martino's track was easy to follow, as it was the only track continuing below the road. The patrollers followed her track to the fresh avalanche. They called for a rescue team, and at about 19:15 a probe line located her and dug her body out from under five feet of snow.

AVALANCHE DATA

Persistent Slab avalanche

The avalanche released at an elevation of about 9,800 feet on a north-northeast-facing side of a gully. The slope angle was 45 degrees, and the slope was a classic terrain trap in which all the snow that slid piled up deeply at the bottom. The fracture was four feet deep, the avalanche fell 200 vertical feet, and it was classified as SS-ASu-R2-D2-O—a deep release on a small path. The bed surface was in a deep layer of depth hoar about a foot above the ground.

COMMENTS

We cannot know if Martino missed a turn that would have led her back to the ski area via the road, or if she intended to ski this difficult backcountry route to the valley floor. Nonetheless, it was a dangerous route. Knowledgeable backcountry skiers would have recognized the 45-degree slope as an avalanche starting zone and recognized the gully as a deadly terrain trap.

A second fatal accident occurred on the same day 10 miles to the south, near the Lindley Hut outside the historic town of Ashcroft (20020314b).

20020314b

LINDLEY HUT, SOUTH OF ASHCROFT, COLORADO

March 14, 2002

Five backcountry skiers caught; three partly buried, two injured, one buried and killed

WEATHER AND SNOWPACK CONDITIONS

The first week of March in the Colorado Rockies was dry and brutally cold. March 2 was the worst, with lows falling to -30°F and highs around -10. This late cold snap did nothing to strengthen an overall shallow snowpack throughout most mountain areas, and most likely it created a snowpack that would be a weaker base once the storms returned. The second week brought two small storms to the Ashcroft area, but more importantly, strong winds caused blowing snow and widespread slab formation. Then, on March 13, a one-day storm brought five to 10 inches of new snow.

(For the weather history of the winter of 2001-02 in Colorado that contributed to this avalanche, the reader should refer to the discussion in 20020201.)

ACCIDENT SUMMARY

The Lindley Hut is one of the Alfred A. Braun huts and is a 4.5-mile ski from the trailhead at Ashcroft, which is 10 miles south of Aspen. On Thursday, March 14, a group was staying at the hut and skiing in the area. The group included Jim Ellis (63), Jesse Logan (58), Jill Baron (47), Dennis Ojima, and a fifth skier. Everyone carried beacons, probes, and shovels, and they dug several snowpits earlier in the day to get information on layering and stability.

About a quarter-mile east of the Lindley Hut is a mellow slope with angles of 22 to 24 degrees. However, this slope is directly below a steeper slope. The group made several runs on the lower, mellow part of the slope. At about noon, Logan climbed a little higher on the slope to dig a snowpit. While digging the pit, a portion of the slope to the skier's right fractured, and seconds later the steeper slope above the group released. This avalanche came down on all five members of the group. One managed to escape the slide, but the other four were carried downhill.

More than one person on a slope

Ojima later recalled his experience: "It just knocked me over, and then I felt like I was in a washing machine, just tumbling around. I instinctively felt my way upward, and that happened to be in the right direction."[2] Ojima had been carried several hundred feet and ended up partly buried and uninjured.

Logan and Baron both suffered knee and ankle injuries, but had been only partially buried. The only missing person was Jim Ellis; there was no sign of him when the avalanche stopped.

RESCUE SUMMARY

The survivors collected themselves, scanned the snow for Ellis, and then began a beacon search. They soon got a signal and finally pinpointed the man against a tree and under three feet of debris. He had been buried 30 minutes and did not respond to CPR.

Meanwhile, a call had gone out for rescue assistance. Several people from the nearby Lindley Hut and others from the Pine Creek Cookhouse a few miles away responded, but the survivors had found the victim by the time the additional searchers reached the site. Later, a team from Mountain Rescue-Aspen arrived by snowmobile and recovered Ellis's body late that afternoon.

AVALANCHE DATA

The avalanche occurred on a west-facing slope at about 11,000 feet elevation. It was estimated to be 600 to 800 feet across, fell 300 to 400 feet vertical, and released to the ground, scouring out the layer of depth hoar. Fracture depth was estimated at three feet. It was remotely triggered from below and was classified as SS-ASr-R4-G.

Persistent Slab avalanche

It is important to note that rescuers responding to the accident reported significant instability—in their words, a "really scary snowpack." They remotely triggered a small bank slide that deposited four feet of snow onto the summer road, and they also caused shooting cracks under their skis.

COMMENTS

This group was experienced and was avalanche-smart—up to a point. They did three things right and one thing wrong. The right things were carrying rescue gear, digging pits to gain data (even though they did not discover the weak layer), and skiing on a low-angle slope. The thing they did wrong was skiing on a low-angle slope that was connected to a steep slope above.

People can trigger avalanches on persistent weak layers long distances. In this case, the group triggered the avalanche from below, and the avalanche released from steeper terrain above the group. In February 1987, a backcountry skier triggered and was caught in a similar avalanche on this slope. On March 13, 2010, a backcountry skier triggered another similar avalanche on the slope. That skier was caught, buried, and killed. The group in 2010 had planned to play on the low angled slopes, and had left their rescue equipment in the Lindley Hut.

On the same day as this fatal avalanche near the Lindley Hut, a second fatal accident occurred 10 miles to the north, beyond the boundary of Aspen Mountain Ski Area (20020314a).

20020315 TEMPTATION BOWL, EAST OF TELLURIDE SKI RESORT, COLORADO | March 15, 2002

Two sidecountry snowboarders caught, 1 injured, 1 buried and killed

WEATHER AND SNOWPACK CONDITIONS

In mid-March, the snowpack in the Telluride region of Colorado's San Juan Mountains was about 85% of normal and typically weak. December snowfall had been well above normal, providing a good base, but then snowfall in January and February was far below normal, which led to the snowpack weaknesses that carried into March. Light snow of a few inches per day had been the pattern leading up to March 15, with southwest winds strong enough to load north through east aspects. Temperatures had been cold, with lows near zero and highs near 15°F, so that there was no settlement or strengthening of the backcountry snowpack.

In the 24 hours leading up to this avalanche, Telluride measured 10 inches of new snow containing 0.6 inches of water. Winds had been from the southwest with a peak gust of 68 mph. The avalanche danger was rated Considerable.

(For the weather history of the winter of 2001-02 in Colorado that contributed to this avalanche, the reader should refer to the discussion in 20020201.)

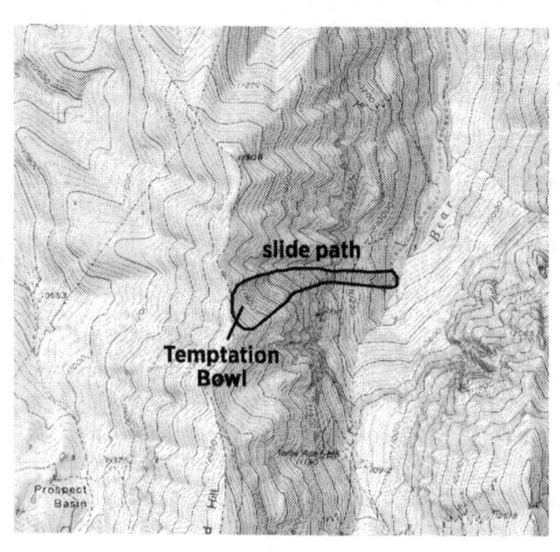

Topo map showing the avalanche path, from its starting zone just beyond the ski area boundary (which runs along the ridgeline to the left (west) of the avalanche, to its runout in Bear Creek.

ACCIDENT SUMMARY

Temptation Bowl is part of Bear Creek Canyon, which lies just beyond the eastern boundary of Telluride Ski Resort. The bowl is large and is essentially a complex group of avalanche paths. A continuous roped line with signage marks the ski

The two snowboarders ducked a rope along the groomed track at the upper right, triggered the avalanche, and were swept into a chute below, out of the picture at the lower left. *Photo Craig Sterbenz.*

area boundary along the top of Temptation Bowl. It is a permanently closed area, per an agreement with the US Forest Service—the steward of the land—along with San Miguel County and the Telluride Ski Corporation. This agreement came about after a number of fatalities—incidents that put the rescuers at high risk.

At about 13:00 on Friday, March 15, two snowboarders—Erica Ghini (31) and Marty Simpson—ducked the closure rope and dove into the bowl. Simpson was a local; Ghini was from San Diego and was described as a competitive snowboarder. A short way down Temptation Bowl, they triggered an avalanche that carried them both down the bowl and into a chute—a couloir also known as Tempter Tube. Partway down, the chute chokes down to a mere seven to eight feet wide. There, the avalanche spit Simpson out to the side, and he ended up on a cliff band. Ghini, however, was carried 2,200 feet to the bottom of the gully and buried deeply when the debris piled up 30 feet deep in Bear Creek. Neither victim was wearing an avalanche transceiver.

No rescue equipment

RESCUE SUMMARY

Whit Richardson and Brian O'Neil were also skiing in Bear Creek, and they saw the avalanche. Richardson skied toward it and saw Simpson on the cliff. They spoke a few words, and then Simpson lost consciousness. Richardson then made a 911 cell phone call at 13:19. A short time later, a party of three Telluride patrollers was dispatched.

The patrollers made contact with Marty Simpson and called in the Helitrax helicopter (the local heli-ski business). They managed to secure Simpson and airlifted him out using a long-line litter. He was hospitalized with a broken femur, collapsed lung, and head injuries.

Rescuers briefly searched the debris area at the bottom of the canyon and did not find any surface clues. It was far too dangerous to put more searchers at risk for what was sure to be a body recovery, so that waited until the next day, when full avalanche control measures cleared all hangfire from above.

On Saturday, March 16, explosives released several major avalanches, which cleared the way for ground teams to search the area. Five rescue dogs searched the debris, with no alerts. Searchers formed a probe line, but their probes were useless in many areas because they could not be pushed in deeper than a foot into the cement-like snow. Searching continued the following day, Sunday, but again without results.

Search teams periodically searched the area the next seven weeks. Finally, on May 7, a rescue team was able to retrieve the body of Erica Ghini.

AVALANCHE DATA

Persistent Slab avalanche

The avalanche was triggered in an east-facing gully by two snowboarders at an elevation of 11,800 feet. It fell 2,200 feet vertical to Bear Creek, at 9,600 feet elevation. Debris in the creek bottom was 30 feet deep. The crown was two to three feet deep and 300 feet wide, and the slope angle was 36 degrees. The slide was classified as SS-ARu-R3-O.

COMMENTS

By all appearances, the lure of powder and a challenging backcountry run led these two snowboarders to attempt a ride down Temptation Bowl. We can only wonder if they considered the avalanche risk. They knew they faced a fine if caught, but they were willing to take that risk. What they got was much worse—one lost her life and the other suffered critical injuries.

20020316a **SOUTH CANYON CREEK, NORTH OF COLUMBIA FALLS, MONTANA** | March 16, 2002

Two snowmobilers caught and buried; one killed

ACCIDENT SUMMARY

On Saturday, March 16, a group of four men was riding their snowmobiles in the mountains about six air miles north of Columbia Falls, Montana. The four men were Byron Cameron (60), brothers Rory (19) and Trey (17) Buckallew, and Mike Stickney. They all carried beacons, probes, and shovels.

More than one person on a slope

The group was in the South Canyon Creek drainage, and earlier in the day, they had left some spare gasoline on a packed road above the creek. They were at creek level, and Rory rode up the hill to retrieve the gasoline but got stuck partway up. Cameron then headed up the hill, and the two men were working together to free up the machine when they triggered an avalanche.

RESCUE SUMMARY

The avalanche released at about 16:40. Both men and their machines were carried down the hillside and buried. Mike Stickney and Trey Buckallew drove to the debris. A party of three who had witnessed the slide joined them at the site. These three—Art, Sherry, and Shawn Foster—were also equipped with beacons, probes, and shovels. The rescuers performed a beacon search, and within minutes they had pinpointed the burial site and started digging. They also called 911, and the sheriff dispatch logged the call at 16:48.

It took some time to dig down to the victims, who were buried five to six feet deep and almost touching each other. They had been buried about 15 to 20 minutes. Rory Buckallew was wearing a full-face helmet, and he was breathing when uncovered. Byron Cameron was not wearing his helmet at the time and was not breathing. The rescuers immediately began CPR on Cameron.

The ALERT helicopter arrived fairly quickly, at about 17:30. It could not land at the site on the steep terrain, but did drop off its paramedic to take over resuscitation efforts on Cameron. After an hour of resuscitation, the paramedic made contact with the ER via cell phone, and the doctor on duty advised him to cease efforts.

AVALANCHE DATA

The avalanche ran on a south-facing slope at an elevation of 5,200 feet. The crown was about 300 feet wide and was two to three feet deep. The avalanche fell 520 feet vertical, and was classified as SS-AFu-R3-O.

Persistent Slab avalanche

Sometime in the past, a hard ice crust had formed due to melt and re-freeze on this south-facing slope. Additional snow then fell and covered the crust, and this layer of snow, in time, metamorphosed into facets. Further storms put two to three feet of soft-slab snow on top of the faceted layer. Now, all the necessary ingredients for an avalanche were in place—slope, slab, and weak layer. The snowmobilers provided the trigger.

COMMENTS

A safety rule in highmarking is to not come to the aid of a stuck rider, because it increases the chance of triggering an avalanche and increases the number of potential victims. These men were not highmarking, but the scenario was the same—a second rider came up to help the first. This, coming to help a stuck rider, is a common scenario for snowmobile accidents. The snowpack couldn't handle it, and it cost a life.

On the positive side, the group was prepared for an avalanche rescue, and that paid off by saving one young man's life. Perhaps a full-face helmet would have provided the necessary air space for Cameron as well.

DOG LAKE, WEST OF BRIGHTON SKI RESORT, UTAH

20020316b

March 16, 2002

Two sidecountry snowboarders caught, buried, and killed

WEATHER AND SNOWPACK CONDITIONS

A major storm hit the Wasatch Mountains from March 12 to 15. Some of the resorts in the Cottonwood Canyons received over five feet of snow. The Utah Avalanche Center posted a High backcountry avalanche danger rating, and a fairly widespread cycle of deep, large avalanches occurred. By March 16, the cycle of natural avalanches had ended, and the avalanche danger was lowered a notch to Considerable. Weather on the day of the accident was foggy with light snow showers.

ACCIDENT SUMMARY

On Saturday, March 16, 12 young snowboarders rode the Crest Lift at Brighton Ski Resort and headed into the backcountry by hiking west along Pioneer Ridge. The group intended to build a jump in the Dog Lake area, so six members of the group were carrying shovels. They passed the signs at the resort boundary, which indicated that there was no avalanche control or ski patrol services beyond the sign and that the backcountry avalanche danger was rated Considerable by the Utah Avalanche Center.

After traveling along the ridge, they rode from the top of the peak marked as 10,354 feet down a steep north-facing chute to an elevation of around 10,000 feet and regrouped.

Two of the men, Richard Jones (19) and Allen Chatwin (18), said that they preferred to hike up higher so that they could more easily traverse to the jump site. After hiking up, they strapped on their boards again and began traversing a very steep slope, heading west, while the others either waited off to the side or descended the rider's right side of the slope. While the two men above were on a very steep part of the slope near a shallow rocky area (estimated at 50 degrees), they triggered the avalanche. It fractured above them, taking them quickly down the slope. No other party members were caught, and none had avalanche transceivers or probes.

Inadequate rescue equipment

RESCUE SUMMARY

The remaining 10 party members descended to try and find their friends, and at 12:36, one party member called 911 on his cell phone. There were no surface clues, so those with shovels dug some random holes, with no luck.

Patrollers from both Alta Ski Area and Brighton responded. The Alta patrollers arrived first, as they could easily traverse to the site from the top of Alta's Superior Lift. They arrived about an hour and a half after the accident. Eventually, avalanche search dogs from Alta located the victims. One victim was two to four feet deep, in a prone position, and had an ice mask around his face. The other was about two feet deep and was wrapped around a tree.

Neither of the victims responded to CPR and the coroner's report later indicated that they had died from asphyxiation.

AVALANCHE DATA

The avalanche ran in an open bowl that faced east-northeast at an elevation of about 10,000 feet. It fell 500 feet vertical. The starting zone was very steep—between 40 and 50 degrees. The crown was 300 feet wide and averaged 2.5 feet deep, but it was eight feet deep at one point. The avalanche was classified as HS-ARu-R4-D3-O.

Persistent Slab avalanche

COMMENTS

Ski resorts on public land in the United States have open boundary policies, as the public has a right to access public land. Signs at resort boundaries clearly inform the public that there is neither avalanche control nor ski patrol services outside of their boundaries. The vast majority of people who leave ski area boundaries to recreate in the backcountry do it safely and without incident. The wise and educated ones carry avalanche rescue beacons, shovels, probes and use safe travel techniques to minimize their risk.

This party of young snowboarders did not carry any rescue gear, and from interviews after the accident, they had little, if any, avalanche education. They were simply trying to have fun but were unprepared for the seriousness of the backcountry avalanche conditions. Lastly, it was clear from the victims' traverse of the avalanche starting zone that they did not know the dangerous path they were on.

PAGODA PEAK, SOUTHWEST OF STEAMBOAT SPRINGS, COLORADO | March 17, 2002

20020317

Three snowmobilers caught; one partly buried, one buried and killed

WEATHER AND SNOWPACK CONDITIONS

In March, the snowpack in the Colorado mountains remained shallow and weak—conditions more typical of mid-winter than spring.

(For the weather history of the winter of 2001-02 in Colorado that contributed to this avalanche, the reader should refer to the discussion in 20020201.)

ACCIDENT SUMMARY

Pagoda Peak, at 11,120 feet elevation, is a distinctive and solitary peak in the Flat Tops of northwest Colorado. It is located about 36 miles southwest of Steamboat Springs.

On Sunday, March 17, a group of seven riders was highmarking on a large, open slope on the east side of Pagoda Peak. At 13:30, three riders were on the slope, including Daniel James Ovenden (30). This group triggered an avalanche, which caught all three. One man was able to escape without being buried, another was partly buried, and Ovenden was carried down and completely buried. This party of seven had no avalanche rescue gear.

No rescue equipment

RESCUE SUMMARY

The rest of the party and the two survivors began a search for Ovenden but saw no clues. They made a 911 call, and both Routt County Search and Rescue and Rio Blanco County Search and Rescue responded. Because of the remoteness of the area, however, it took several hours for search-and-rescue teams to arrive on site. Darkness was falling when rescuers located Ovenden's body under three to four feet of snow at 20:00. A searcher apparently located the victim with a probe. He was still on, or next to, his snowmobile when uncovered.

AVALANCHE DATA

The avalanche released on the east side of Pagoda Peak, with the fracture a little below 11,000 feet elevation. The avalanche was classified as SS-AMu-R3. The avalanche was 300 to 400 feet wide by 400 feet vertical. No fracture depth was recorded.

COMMENTS

This avalanche is another instance of snowmobilers highmarking but not being prepared for the consequences of an avalanche. As mentioned in the narratives of many other avalanches involving highmarking, riders must understand that they are playing on a slope that can slide when snow conditions are unstable. To give them a safety advantage, they should be riding the slope one at a time, and all riders should have—and know how to use—full rescue gear, which includes beacons, probes, and shovels. Airbags, once they came into common use, have added an extra safety margin.

20020318 JACKSON PEAK, EAST OF JACKSON, WYOMING

March 18, 2002

One backcountry skier caught, buried, and killed

ACCIDENT SUMMARY

Traveling alone

Jackson Peak, at 10,741 feet elevation, is situated in the Gros Ventre range east of Jackson, Wyoming, On March 9, Mike Dollarhide (32) left on a solo backcountry ski excursion into the Jackson Peak area. At some point in his multi-day tour, Dollarhide triggered an avalanche that buried and killed him. We cannot know even the date this occurred, but eventually he was reported overdue.

On Thursday, March 21, volunteers from the Teton County Search and Rescue team recovered Dollarhide's body from avalanche debris near Jackson Peak, about six air miles east of the town of Jackson. Searchers found several clues on the debris, and a search dog located the victim.

AVALANCHE DATA

The avalanche was approximately 150 feet wide and 300 feet in length, with a crown depth of three to four feet. It occurred on a north-northeast aspect at an elevation of around 9,800 feet.

COMMENTS

The Search and Rescue team found no clues or tracks that would help determine what the victim was doing or where he was on the slope when he apparently triggered this avalanche.

20020322 EAST FORK TARGHEE CREEK, NORTHWEST OF BIG SPRINGS, IDAHO | March 22, 2002

One snowmobiler caught, buried, and killed

WEATHER AND SNOWPACK CONDITIONS

This avalanche occurred in the drainage of the East Fork of Targhee Creek. This area is in the Henry's Lake Mountains, 12 miles northwest of West Yellowstone, Montana, and five miles northeast of Henry's Lake. It is right on a ridgeline, which happens to be the state line between Montana and Idaho and is also the Continental Divide. It is a popular snowmobile area, and on the other side of the ridge (and state line) is Montana's Lionhead area, which has been the site of several avalanche fatalities.

In the five days preceding this avalanche, a small storm cycle had deposited 0.7 inches of water (perhaps 10 inches of snow) in this area. For most of the storm cycle, winds were light, except for a 24-hour period on the March 19 and 20, during which southwest winds averaged 20 to 30 mph, with gusts into the 50s. Temperatures had been exceptionally warm for two days prior to the avalanche, with daytime highs reaching 48°F on the 21st, and 53°F on the 22nd.

This was not a significant snowstorm, but there had been some loading from blowing snow. During the first week of January (10 weeks prior to this acci-

Doug Chabot, Gallatin National Forest Avalanche Center, standing in the hole where the victim was buried 20 feet deep. *Photo Gallatin National Forest Avalanche Center.*

dent), a layer of surface hoar and near-surface facets had formed. Once buried, these two different weak layers had been responsible for two other avalanche burials (in both cases, the victims were recovered alive) earlier in the season. Avalanche forecasters had been tracking these weak layers, anticipating they could cause further avalanches. However, by March, these layers had gained significant strength, and they were no longer producing failures in snowpit stability tests, even following some large storm events.

Still, earlier in the afternoon on the day of this fatal avalanche, several large, natural slides had released in the East Fork drainage.

ACCIDENT SUMMARY

Matt Blumer (26) of Pierre, South Dakota, was riding with six friends in the East Fork of Targhee Creek. They all carried avalanche rescue gear. It is unclear whether the group rode up the Targhee Creek drainage or dropped into the basin from the Lionhead ridge, but once in the drainage, they started highmarking a southwest-facing slope.

At 14:27, Blumer made a pass above a steep rollover approximately halfway up and triggered an avalanche on the slope. The avalanche from a first fracture carried Blumer and his sled through a thin stand of trees at the top of the rollover and deposited him on a bench at the bottom of the slope. The initial fracture continued to propagate uphill another 400 feet vertical. This led to a second wave of avalanche snow, which came down from the top of the slope. That snow, too, stopped on the bench, making a debris pile more than 20 feet deep.

RESCUE SUMMARY

The other party members started a search, except one, who rode to Targhee Pass to initiate a call for search and rescue. Because the location of the avalanche was not initially clear, search teams from both Montana and Idaho responded. A helicopter with two dog teams was dispatched from Bozeman, about 70 miles away.

At the site of the avalanche, the other party members found no visible clues and started a beacon search. They honed in on the signal and started digging. It took two hours to finally get down to the victim, who was buried under 20 feet of avalanche debris. He had long since died. They had recovered the body by the time the search-and-rescue helicopter arrived.

AVALANCHE DATA

Persistent Slab avalanche

The avalanche released on a southwest-facing slope at an elevation of about 9,300 feet, and it fell 800 feet vertical. The crown was three to four feet deep and 300 feet wide. The slope angle at the crown was 32 to 35 degrees, and the alpha angle measured 24 degrees. The avalanche was classified as SS-AMu-R4-O. The debris was so deep because a bench in the track stopped the moving snow before it got to the lower runout.

The weak layer was the facet layer that had formed in January. The following day, forecasters from the Gallatin National Forest Avalanche Center visited the site and made an interesting observation. In the small basin where this avalanche occurred, five large avalanches had released within a half-mile of each other. They knew of no other avalanches that released elsewhere in the range. The forecasters speculated that the tight confines of the drainage acted as a reflector oven and thus enhanced snowpack heating at the surface.

The Avalanche Handbook[3] describes this phenomenon in this way: "Under unstable conditions, it is not necessary to have warming penetrate to the weak layer; reduction in slab stiffness by warming can provide the trigger." In other words, surface warming can reduce slab stiffness, making it less stable.

COMMENTS

This group was experienced and probably had traveled in avalanche terrain often. They also knew that avalanches were the chief danger in highmarking—thus, their investment in avalanche rescue gear. But when avalanches break big and bury their victims deeply, traditional rescue gear is often ineffective, because it is designed to hasten recovery after a burial. In more recent years, the avalanche airbags have been hailed as the best device to prevent burials altogether—or at least make them less likely to occur. Time and statistics of 21st century avalanche accidents will help answer this claim.

20020322 TARGHEE CREEK, IDAHO

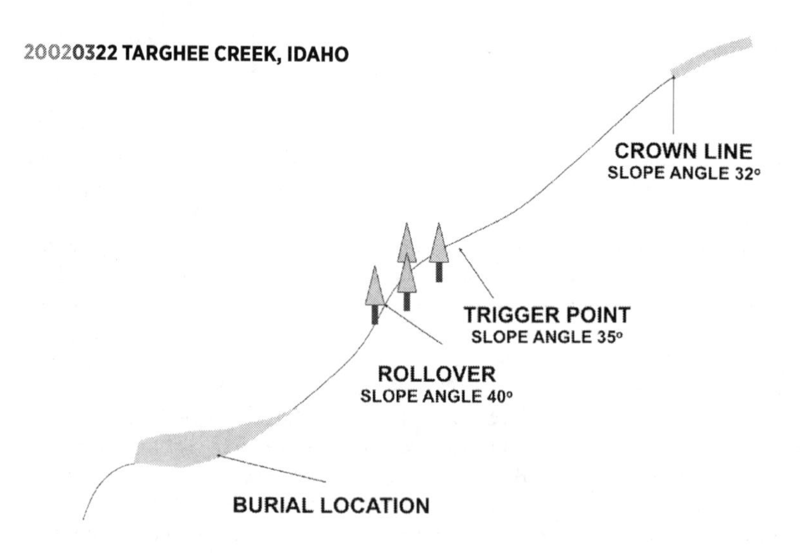

A profile of the avalanche slope. *Gallatin National Forest Service Avalanche Center.*

THREE BOWLS, SOUTHEAST OF EAGLE RIVER, ALASKA

20020328

March 28, 2002

One backcountry skier caught and buried; two dogs buried and killed

WEATHER AND SNOWPACK CONDITIONS

The Eagle River lies a few miles east of Anchorage and flows out of the Chugach Mountains. The north and south forks of the river merge above the town of Eagle River, northeast of Anchorage.

The South Fork area received 26 inches of snow during a storm on March 16 and 17. Ten days later, on March 26, another storm deposited 14 inches of snow. These storm layers, which comprised the slab, rested on a shallow layer of intermediate facets formed during an extended cold period earlier. The weather on the day of this incident was calm, clear, and sunny, with temperatures in the mid-20s.

ACCIDENT SUMMARY

On Thursday afternoon, March 28, Skip Repetto (38), and John Stroud (33), both from Anchorage, were telemark skiing on the east side of the South Fork of Eagle River, roughly seven miles southeast of Eagle River. Stroud had brought along his two large dogs (each weighed about 130 pounds). Both men carried beacons, probes, and shovels.

They were in what the locals call the Three Bowls area—essentially one large west-facing bowl, but with aspects facing north, west, and south. The men and dogs started up a ridge near the northern-most bowl. Near the top of their climb—above 4,000 feet elevation—they dug a quick pit with their hands, isolating only the top two layers. The two concluded that the top two layers were well bonded, so they skied from the ridge to the bottom without incident.

Then they climbed their skin track back to the top and traversed south along the ridgeline to a different ski line near the south bowl. They skied down about 1,500 feet to about the 2,600 foot elevation, and both noted a change in the snow conditions that somehow felt less stable. Repetto was feeling uncomfortable with the consistency of the snow, so they talked it over and decided to change to a more northerly aspect. This required crossing a deep V-shaped creek bed to get to a steeper slope to get in a few more turns.

Terrain trap

Around 15:15, Repetto told Stroud to stay in his current safe location—they would cross the next slope one at a time. Repetto crossed the creek bed and onto the north aspect. He proceeded about 50 feet, only to look back to see Stroud and his two large dogs following his track on the suspect slope, about 125 feet back. The weight of the two skiers and the two large dogs triggered the slide, which propagated above the skiers and dogs and across the drainage to steeper terrain.

Because of his position on the slope, Repetto was able to stay on his feet and ski to safety. Stroud attempted to ski to the opposite side of the drainage with his two dogs, but was quickly knocked off balance and overcome by the moving snow. His skis and poles acted as anchors, pulling him down as he fought to stay on top. Several times, Stroud grabbed at the stand of alders near the edge; investigators later noted hand and finger marks left in the bed surface. His attempts were unsuccessful, and he was swept down the drainage and buried. He traveled an estimated 500 feet, eventually coming to a stop on the right side of the debris, near the toe. Stroud later remembered that while he was buried, that the only thing he could move was his left index finger, and that, less than an inch. Neither he nor his dogs were visible to Repetto.

RESCUE SUMMARY

With no visible surface clues, Repetto skied to the toe of the debris, put on his climbing skins so he could ski more easily on the debris, and switched his transceiver to receive. He immediately picked up a signal and followed it to an area at the edge of the debris. He pulled out his probe and shovel, and pinpointed his friend's location. After a few random probes, he hit Stroud in the back.

Stroud was buried beneath three to four feet of debris, lying across the slope, head slightly downhill. Repetto estimated it took him 35 to 40 minutes after burial to gain an airway, by which time his friend appeared to have quit breathing. Repetto cleared the snow from Stroud's head and mouth, at which point Stroud started to gasp for air. Stroud did not respond to verbal communication for around 10 minutes, but eventually came around. It took Repetto another 20 minutes to excavate enough snow to remove Stroud. His skis and poles were still attached.

By coincidence, Kip Melling, a resident of Eagle River, was looking out his kitchen window and noticed a fresh avalanche in the Three Bowl Path. Melling was an avalanche instructor with the Alaska Mountain Safety Center and a member of the Anchorage Nordic Ski Patrol. He was also the first responder for another accident earlier the same season, 20011111. Earlier in the day, he and a friend had skied in the Three Bowls area, and they had seen the two men and two dogs.

Melling gathered up his ski and avalanche gear and drove the 1.3 miles to the trailhead. The red Toyota truck he had noticed earlier in the day was still parked there. He climbed 10 minutes up to the avalanche area and saw the two men at the toe of the debris. Stroud and Repetto were visibly shaken by the event. There were no serious physical injuries to either, though both dogs were still missing. Melling brought Stroud and Repetto back to his house to recuperate, warm up, and talk before they made the drive back to Anchorage.

Stroud and several friends attempted to recover Stroud's two dogs on Friday, March 29, without success. Lacking an accurate last-seen area and sufficient resources, they called off the search for the dogs.

AVALANCHE DATA

Persistent Slab avalanche

The accident site consisted of a steep, northwest-facing bowl, with a slope angle of 35 degrees in the starting zone. The slope was steep, smooth, and uniform, and then it narrowed into a high-consequence terrain trap (a creek drainage) at the base. The avalanche released at an elevation of about 4,000 feet and fell 1,600 feet vertical. The crown was one to two feet deep and 1,500 feet wide. It probably would be classified as SS-ASu-R3-O, though the debris was a mix of soft slab and hard slab snow. Debris depth in the runout zone ranged from two feet to over 10 feet and consisted of pencil-hard slab blocks and soft-slab debris, intermingled with unconsolidated, faceted snow.

Had the men dug a pit on the slope that avalanched, they likely would have seen two separate layers of weak facets. One or both of these layers was where the avalanche failed.

COMMENTS

This avalanche incident is a remarkable account of experienced skiers traveling in high-risk avalanche terrain. They knew the terrain was dangerous and accepted that risk. They carried full rescue gear, they dug a hand pit to check layering (though this did not provide data on the slope that avalanched), they were paying attention to changing snow conditions, and for the most part, they tried to ski one at a time.

But a few lapses in their data-gathering and safe-travel procedures contributed to the accident. First, the hand pit done earlier in the day and near the top of the bowl gave no data whatsoever to the snow stability on the slope where the avalanche released. A few minutes digging a second pit might have revealed the facet layer(s) where the avalanche released.

Second, there was a breakdown in communication between the two men that led to both men and two large dogs crossing the avalanche path at the same time. That certainly was not what Repetto had intended, which was to cross one at a time. The weight of two skiers and two big dogs—the equivalent of four people—was more stress than the slope could withstand.

Repetto's experience and skill at using his beacon was the ultimate lifesaver.

MT. MAGNIFICENT, EAST OF EAGLE RIVER, ALASKA

20020331

March 31, 2002

Three snowshoers caught; one partly buried, two buried and killed; two dogs buried and killed

WEATHER AND SNOWPACK CONDITIONS

Sunday, March 31, was a warm and sunny day in the Anchorage area. Rangers at Chugach State Park, east of Anchorage, were nervous that the snowpack was thawing and weakening, and therefore could pose an avalanche danger to park visitors.

ACCIDENT SUMMARY

Mt. Magnificent is a 4,271-foot peak in Chugach State Park. The peak is situated five miles east of the community of Eagle River, which is essentially a suburb of Anchorage.

March 31 was Easter Sunday. That morning, under cloudless skies, Bill Crouse (44), his stepson, Don Zimmerman (26), and Doc Crouse, Bill Crouse's brother, were snowshoeing above timberline on a flank of Mt. Magnificent. They had two dogs with them. The group had followed the switchbacks to the road's end, and from there, they proceeded to snowshoe—breaking trail through deep snow—on a trail that winds into a bowl on the mountainside.

At about 10:00, they were about halfway across the snowy amphitheater, traveling in a line, when they collapsed a buried weak layer of depth hoar, which triggered an avalanche that released above them. Everyone was caught, and when the avalanche stopped, only Doc Crouse was on the surface. He could see no sign of Bill Crouse, Don Zimmerman, or the dogs.

More than one person on a slope

Doc dug himself out from about a foot of debris and made a surface search, which yielded nothing. He then walked out to the family's home to report the avalanche.

No rescue equipment

RESCUE SUMMARY

The Alaska State Troopers got the emergency call at 12:45. Fifty rescuers responded, including troopers, firefighters, Chugach State Park rangers, and Doug Fesler and Jill Fredston of the Alaska Mountain Safety Center. A trooper helicopter ferried Fesler and Fredston in to assess the danger before allowing rescuers to access the site. The area of debris was large—Fesler estimated it was the size of three football fields. Once the decision was made that rescuers could safely enter the area, many had trouble getting there, especially those on snowmobiles, which bogged down in the wet snow.

Fesler and Fredston asked Doc Crouse to accompany them and point out where his relatives and the two dogs had triggered the avalanche. Avalanche rescue dogs and their handlers led the search that eventually located the two buried men, who had not survived. The accident report did not mention whether the rescue dogs were able to locate the buried dogs.

COMMENTS

Wet Slab avalanche

It appears that several distractions kept this group from even thinking about avalanches. It was a beautiful spring day, and it was Easter Sunday—a great day for a snowshoe tour with friends, relatives, and the dogs. The group was probably unaware that they were in avalanche terrain, and that a rapid thaw had warmed and weakened the snow cover to its breaking point. Their lack of awareness led to an unforgiving outcome.

20020613

MT. FORAKER, DENALI NATIONAL PARK, ALASKA

June 13, 2002

Three climbers caught and killed

ACCIDENT AND RESCUE SUMMARY

Mt. Foraker is about eight miles southwest of Mount McKinley in Denali National Park. At 17,400 feet, it is the second-highest peak in the Alaska Range. On or around June 13, it is believed that three climbers roped together triggered an avalanche that carried them to their deaths, though it is not certain they died because of an avalanche. Regardless, the following report is based on rescuers' observations when the victims were overdue.

Three Anchorage-area brothers, Kevin (27), Travis (21), and Colby (15) Strawn, had planned an ambitious 17-day expedition to climb both Mt. Foraker and Mt. McKinley in June 2002.

The Strawns were flown to the mountaineering base camp on the Kahiltna Glacier on Tuesday, June 11. On Thursday the 13th, the third day of their climb, they radioed the base camp, reporting that they had climbed to the 10,500-foot level of the mountain on the southeast ridge. Sometime after that call, they fell to their deaths, probably because of an avalanche. Park rangers had described the snow conditions as so unstable that other groups trying to summit had decided to turn around.

On Sunday, June 16th, no one had heard from the party for several days, so the pilot that had dropped them off flew over their route. He grew concerned when he did not see the brothers, and noticed evidence of avalanche activity in the area. Concern grew further on Monday at the McKinley base camp. The brothers had not radioed in, and no other pilots flying in the area reported spotting them.

The Park Service sent up its high-altitude rescue helicopter at 15:30 with two rangers. They spotted tracks on Mount Foraker at 10,500 feet. About 16:40, they saw the three bodies on a slope at 8,500 feet. The brothers were still roped together and plainly visible on top of the snow. There was avalanche debris in the area, but it could have been that the climbers fell and the debris fell after them.

The helicopter returned to Talkeetna for recovery equipment and returned to the mountain on Monday evening, June 17, to retrieve the bodies and fly them to the base camp.

COMMENTS

The three brothers were experienced climbers. Before their family had moved to Alaska, they had climbed Mt. Rainier together and had climbed several peaks in the Tetons. In Alaska, they climbed together in the Chugach Mountains. Kevin and Travis had both made successful Denali climbs.

The slope they were crossing on the southeast ridge of Foraker had a pitch of 40 degrees—a prime angle for avalanches. One possible scenario is that they were traversing an avalanche starting zone, and they triggered the avalanche. With no belay, there was nothing to stop them from a fatal fall. Another scenario is that one of the three fell on that slope and dragged all three to their deaths. Either way, a snow anchor may have saved them.

2002–2003
SEASON

20021129 TUCKERMAN RAVINE, MT. WASHINGTON, NEW HAMPSHIRE | November 29, 2002

Seven ice climbers caught; four buried, one injured, two killed

WEATHER AND SNOWPACK CONDITIONS

Mt. Washington, at 6,289 feet elevation, is the highest peak in the northeastern United States. It's known for its winter recreation opportunities, especially skiing and ice climbing. It's also known for its brutal weather. Hurricane-force winds blow an average of 110 days per year, and Mt. Washington holds the record for the highest wind speed ever recorded over land—231 mph!

The winds on Mt. Washington are perhaps the most important weather ingredient for its avalanche danger. A broad plateau known as Bigelow Lawn stretches below the mountain's summit, and this plateau lies above several glacially-carved bowls. Tuckerman Ravine is one of these bowls, and when the wind blows from the west following a storm, it strips snow from the plateau and loads it into Tuckerman Ravine. The avalanche danger this day was rated as Moderate.

ACCIDENT SUMMARY

On Friday morning, November 29, three groups of climbers arrived in Tuckerman Ravine to go ice climbing. At roughly 10:00, Tom Stryker and Tony Tulip began climbing the Open Book, which is directly under the Lip. The Lip is often used as an easy exit out of the ravine compared to the ice pitches towards the center headwall. Stryker climbed the first pitch of the Open Book and, belaying off of three ice screws, brought Tulip up. From his belay point, Stryker was surprised—and suddenly more cautious—when he noticed that about 24 inches of wind-drifted snow had accumulated at that spot.

At that time, a second group consisting of three soloists—Matt Couture, Tom Burke (46), and Rick Coyne—began climbing. Couture climbed to the right of Stryker and Tulip, while Burke and Coyne climbed on the left. The three soloists caught up with Stryker and Tulip at the top of the first pitch, and the three soloists pushed ahead. Stryker and Tulip decided they didn't like all this activity above them and decided to bail out by traversing right, then walking down and around back to the floor of the ravine.

While this was going on, two other climbers arrived at the bottom and began to plan where they would go on their own roped climb. These men were Scott Sandberg (32), and Richard Doucette (43). Altogether, there were now seven climbers in three groups in the Open Book area of the ravine.

Back on the climb, Tom Stryker remained anchored and was belaying Tony Tulip as he traversed the slope to get them both out of what they thought had become a dangerous situation. They then heard a shout. Tom Burke had been hit by a sluff and was cartwheeling down the gully. He fell 100 feet and landed in a large low-angle snowfield, got up, and staggered a few steps. Burke then yelled to his friends above—Matt Couture and Rick Coyne—"I'm done for the day! I've had enough!"[1] One of the climbers made note of the time; it was 11:15.

Scott Sandberg and Richard Doucette, the two men at the base of the climb, saw Tom Stryker belaying Tony Tulip as he traversed off the route to the right and waited for them to clear before they started up.

20021129 TUCKERMAN RAVINE, NEW HAMPSHIRE

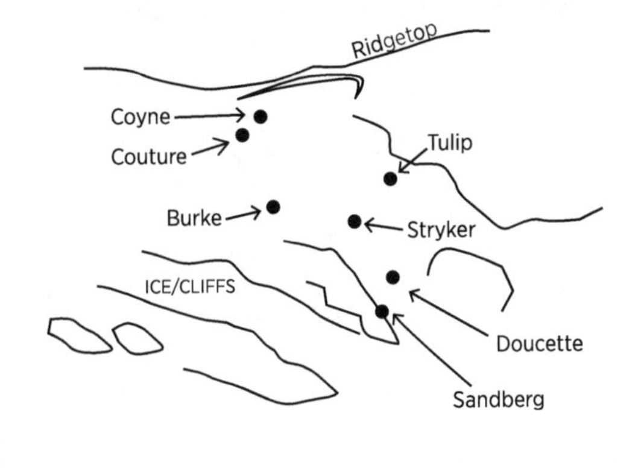

A diagram illustrating the location of the climbers at the time of the slide, based on a diagram found in *Rock and Ice Magazine*.

The time was now 11:25, and near the top of the gully, Rick Coyne started over the lip of the headwall and found himself wading through waist-deep snow. Matt Couture was about 50 feet below him. And that's when the avalanche fractured above Rick Coyne. A cry of "Avalanche!" went out.

The avalanche hit Coyne and Couture and carried them down the ravine. Below, Tom Burke, who had just survived a fall 10 minutes earlier, was also engulfed and swept away. As the avalanche fell, it entrained more snow as it flowed over other snowfields and over ice and rock.

More than one person on a slope

Tom Stryker heard the cry from above and hunkered against his anchor as the snow hit him. His anchor held. At the other end of the rope, Tony Tulip had made it far enough to the climber's right to be beyond the avalanche.

At the bottom of the climb, Richard Doucette was up close against the steep ice as the snow shot over his head, some of it hitting him but leaving him unharmed. Scott Sandberg, standing only four feet from Doucette, took the whole force of the avalanche; it swept him downslope.

RESCUE SUMMARY

When the avalanche stopped, Tom Stryker and Tony Tulip were still on the route and were unhurt; they began making their way down to the debris pile. Richard Doucette was at the bottom of the climb, but the avalanche debris had gone another 200 feet beyond his position. Two other men witnessed the avalanche from further downslope. They were caretakers for the Appalachian Mountain Club and were equipped with radios, beacons, shovels, and probes. These men made a radio call for help and then assisted in the rescue, first by sending bystanders to a first aid and avalanche rescue cache five minutes down the trail to bring up probes to the debris. None of the ice climbers had avalanche rescue gear.

No rescue equipment

Doucette had begun searching immediately after the avalanche and spied a hand sticking out of the debris 100 feet downslope. He ran to the area and started digging with his hands, thinking this was his friend, Scott Sandburg. But it was Rick Coyne instead. Coyne was in obvious pain but was breathing. Doucette then continued his search and saw a second hand sticking from the snow. This time he uncovered Matt Couture, who had suffered no serious injuries, so was able to become a rescuer himself. Rick Coyne had suffered significant rib and shoulder injuries. He was treated on scene and then assisted down the trail.

There were still two buried climbers—Tom Burke and Scott Sandberg. Searchers saw a climbing rope on the snow surface and knew it had to belong to Sandberg, who had not yet tied into his partner, Doucette. They followed the rope, pulling it out of the snow, and found Sandberg under two to three feet of snow. Rescuers immediately started CPR and continued that for about 20 minutes; Sandberg, who had been buried about 25 minutes, did not respond. He had suffered injuries in the avalanche that may have been the cause of death.

The search continued for Tom Burke. The debris field was about 400 feet long, and the searchers set up a probe line involving other hikers and climbers who had come into the area. The probe line worked its way up from the toe of the debris while a rescue dog and handler worked another part of the debris. One of the probers made the strike about 60 feet from the toe of the debris. Burke was under three feet of snow and had been buried about an hour and 45 minutes. He died from head and neck injuries.

AVALANCHE DATA

The avalanche released at an elevation of 5,200 feet in an east-facing ravine known as the Open Book. The crown was 12 to 18 inches deep and 140 feet wide. The starting zone area where the fracture occurred had slope angles that varied from 43 to 47 degrees. The avalanche ran about 1,000 feet slope distance, and the debris pile was 400 feet long, 55 feet wide, and up to 12 feet deep.

The avalanche was classified as SS-AFu-R3 (AF is the trigger classification for ice climbers on foot, in this case.)

COMMENTS

This accident resulted from a chaotic climbing scene. Two groups were on terrain that could accommodate only one party at a time, with a third group waiting its turn in an unsafe location directly below the first two groups. It became a competition for climbing space.

There was some thought given to avalanche danger, at least among the first party of two climbers. But there was no avalanche preparedness made by anyone in the three groups—shown by their lack of rescue gear. It seems many ice climbers do not carry avalanche rescue gear because they are climbing on ice, not snow. That's faulty reasoning. The very gully or bowl that produces ice can often have snow slopes above, putting those climbers in danger of avalanches.

Lastly, consider one more reason for ice climbers carrying beacons. Two of these climbers survived only because they had a hand sticking from the avalanche debris. Had their hands been buried as well, they would have likely died from asphyxiation before being found by a probe line or rescue dog, bringing the death toll to four.

20021215 THE CHUTES, EAST OF MT. ROSE SKI TAHOE, NEVADA

December 15, 2002

One sidecountry snowboarder caught, buried, and killed

WEATHER AND SNOWPACK CONDITIONS

Mount Rose Ski Tahoe is located in the Carson Range—an eastern extension of the Sierra Nevada—near the north shore of Lake Tahoe. A storm system moved into the region on Thursday, December 12. Three inches of snow fell on the 12th, followed by

A portion of the fracture line of the December 15, 2002, avalanche. It varied from 12 to 20 inches in depth. *Photo Mt. Rose Ski Patrol.*

seven to eight inches the following day, and an additional 10 to 14 inches by Sunday morning, December 15. The snowfall was accompanied by winds gusting to 90 mph. On December 14, the Reno airport—20 miles to the northeast—measured a record gust of 82 mph. The ski area closed on Saturday because of the winds.

ACCIDENT SUMMARY

On Sunday, December 15, much of the ski area reopened; however, the Northwest Magnum Chair (also called simply the Magnum lift) remained closed because of wind.

Three snowboarders, all off-duty employees of the ski area, had been riding the lift-served area much of the day. One of these men was Scott "Clint" Sappenfield (26); the other two were identified only as Smith and Howey. In the afternoon, they decided to make one last run—into "The Chutes." The Chutes area was out-of-bounds terrain roped and closed off. They dropped a car on the ski area road so that they could ride back to the lodge when they finished the run.

The group rode the Lakeview Chair and hiked on snowshoes to the top of The Chutes. They ducked a rope and passed a sign that read "Avalanche Area Do Not Enter." They decided to ride a chute known as the Hornet's Nest. Howey went first because he was the most experienced. Sappenfield went second, and Smith quickly followed. Smith was right on Sappenfield's tail, so he made a hard break on his board, and that's when the avalanche released.

Smith was able to stop before being caught in the slide. Further downslope, Howey looked up and saw the avalanche coming at him. In a split second, he was able to turn across the slope and avoid being caught. Sappenfield, however, could not escape, and the avalanche carried him downslope and buried him. It was just after 15:00.

RESCUE SUMMARY

No rescue equipment

None of the group was carrying avalanche rescue gear. The two survivors called out Sappenfield's name, but didn't get a response. Howey headed down the slide path and didn't find any sign of Sappenfield. Smith headed down next, but he did not find any

The debris in the lower third of the avalanche path. *Photo Mt. Rose Ski Patrol.*

clues, either. The two survivors spotted a Nevada DOT snowplow on the road below and flagged it down to catch a ride back to the lodge, where they reported the avalanche.

The ski patrol got the call at 15:35, and apparently the caller mistakenly identified the slide area as being in Yellow Jacket Chute. Three ski patrollers were in the hasty rescue team, but they did not find evidence of an avalanche in Yellow Jacket. As they checked the terrain, though, one of the patrollers triggered an avalanche, which took him for a short ride.

It took a few minutes to sort out the confusion over the location, but eventually the rescuers were redirected to Hornet's Nest. Soon, two more patrollers—with explosives—joined the hasty team, along with the witness, Howey, who confirmed the location.

The patrollers threw three hand charges, one of which released a slide. They then entered the slope to begin their search. An avalanche rescue dog and handler accompa-nied them. They searched for an hour without finding the victim. Two new search dog teams eventually replaced the original dog team.

The search continued until 18:00 without finding the victim, by which time the searchers were working by headlamp. At this point, Mike Ferrari, the patrol director and rescue leader, decided to end the search within the hour because of deteriorating weather conditions.

A little before 19:00, Ferrari began to pull the rescuers out. As they headed downhill and toward the road, Ferrari assigned the two dogs to work the right and left halves of the remaining shallower debris near the avalanche runout. Below a thick stand of four- to six-inch saplings in an area that had not been thoroughly searched, Zephyr, one of the rescue dogs, alerted. Rescuers probed the spot and found Sappenfield wrapped around a tree. His head had been under about four feet of snow, and he had been buried about four hours. He did not respond to resuscitation efforts; an autopsy later determined he had died of suffocation/hypothermia.

AVALANCHE DATA

This avalanche was classified as SS-ARu-R2-I. The crown varied from 12 to 20 inches deep, and the layer of slab snow slid on an ice crust that had formed during the third week of November. The Hornet's Nest slope has a slope angle of 38 degrees and faces north. The avalanche released at an elevation of 8,750 feet and fell 600 vertical feet to an elevation of 8,150 feet.

Storm Slab avalanche

COMMENTS

The Chutes area was closed for good reason—high avalanche danger created by heavy snowfall and gale-force winds. The three men involved in this avalanche fell to the temptation of first tracks in deep snow beyond the ski area boundary. And they did so with no avalanche rescue gear whatsoever. That decision took a young man's life. Beginning in the 2004-05 winter season, the Chutes area became open terrain at Mt. Rose, with access only via designated gates and served by a new chairlift.

NORTH TWIN LAKE, WEST OF LARAMIE, WYOMING

20021226

December 26, 2002

One snowmobiler caught, buried, and killed

ACCIDENT SUMMARY

The Snowy Range of southern Wyoming is situated about 30 miles west of Laramie and is a popular area for snowmobiling. On Thursday, December 26, a number of riders were near North and South Twin Lakes on the west side of the Snowy Range crest. One group of two—Matt Gillingham (34) and a friend—were highmarking a steep, northwest-facing slope. The time was about 10:00 when Gillingham triggered an avalanche that carried him down the slope and totally buried him. At the time, the other man was stuck and was digging out his snowmobile; he was out of the way of the avalanche.

RESCUE SUMMARY

Neither of the two men had any avalanche rescue gear. The friend searched for about an hour, finding nothing, and then got the attention of other riders nearby. One of these rode out for help while the others searched. Some used tree branches to probe, but they found nothing.

No rescue equipment

Before the search and rescue team arrived, searchers on site located Gillingham beneath four feet of snow. Some of the searchers apparently carried avalanche probes. The victim had not survived.

AVALANCHE DATA

The avalanche released at an elevation of about 10,600 feet on a northwest-facing slope. The slope angle was approximately 41 degrees. The avalanche was about 450 feet wide and fell about 600 feet slope distance. Fracture depth averaged two feet deep, and the slide was classified as SS-AMu-R3-G.

COMMENTS

This is one more instance of riders highmarking without avalanche rescue gear. With beacons, probes, shovels, and a rescuer who had practiced with a beacon, this could have been a live recovery.

20021228 TRINITY MOUNTAIN, NORTHWEST OF FAIRFIELD, IDAHO

December 28, 2002

Two snowmobilers caught and buried; one killed

ACCIDENT SUMMARY

Few details are available on this fatal avalanche. The following report is based on a brief story from the Idaho Statesman.

Trinity Mountain, at 9451 feet elevation, is the highest peak in the Trinity Mountain Range in south-central Idaho. The range is situated west of Fairfield and north of Mountain Home and is a popular snowmobile area.

High avalanche danger

On Friday, December 27, the Sawtooth Avalanche Center, based east of Trinity Mountain in Ketchum, issued an avalanche warning for High avalanche danger; this warning included the Trinity Mountain Range.

No rescue equipment

On Saturday, December 28, several groups of snowmobilers were riding the slopes around Trinity Mountain, reportedly near Big Roaring River Lake to the northwest of the peak. One group of four riders included Chase Travis Swenson (18) and his brother. This group triggered an avalanche that completely buried Swenson and his brother. Apparently, neither man was wearing an avalanche beacon, and the group had no rescue gear.

The two surviving snowmobilers in the Swenson's group were joined by three others who had witnessed the avalanche. Together they began searching the avalanche debris in the vicinity of the victims' snowmobiles. The searchers eventually located both men, though the duration and depth of burial were not recorded. Chase Swenson did not survive his burial, while his brother did.

COMMENTS

The lack of information on this accident gives little opportunity for comment, except for the obvious: A lack of avalanche awareness seems apparent. There is a good possibility that rescue gear of beacons, shovels, and probes may have saved Swenson's life.

20021229 CEMENT BASIN, NORTHEAST OF CRYSTAL MOUNTAIN RESORT, WASHINGTON | December 29, 2002

Four backcountry skiers caught; three partly buried, one injured, one buried and killed

WEATHER AND SNOWPACK CONDITIONS

The layering in the snowpack of Washington's Cascades that contributed to this avalanche accident began to develop on December 14. On that day, heavy rain soaked the snow cover and then froze into a hard crust. Then two nights with clear skies formed a layer of surface hoar on the crust.

A series of storms followed. These deposited 20 to 40 inches of snow on top of the crust. Between these storms and December 29, the Northwest Avalanche Center received reports of skier-triggered avalanches the length of the Cascades, from Mt. Baker to Mt. Hood; the center rated the avalanche danger as Considerable. On the morning of the incident, the Crystal Mountain Patrol used explosives to trigger several relatively large slides, two to five feet deep, that released on the buried surface hoar layer.

ACCIDENT SUMMARY

On Sunday afternoon, December 29, seven members of the Seattle Mountaineers skinned out of the Crystal Mountain Resort base area for a day of backcountry skiing. The members of this group had all taken avalanche awareness courses, and all were carrying beacons, shovels, and probes. They had looked at the Northwest Avalanche Center avalanche forecast from the previous day, December 28, and knew the danger rating of Considerable.

They planned to head east from the parking lot and climb the East Peak ridge and drop into Cement Basin. There they hoped to find good powder skiing on northeast-facing slopes. One member of the party had talked to a friend who had skied in Cement Basin the day before without incident.

On their climb, they did a few hand pits but no deeper snowpits to look at the upper snowpack layering. They jumped on the snow on their uptrack's switchbacks and saw no signs of instability. They skied their first run in Cement Basin on a lower-angled slope with no incident. They then climbed to the ridge again to ski a different, steeper slope.

More than one person on a slope

At about 13:00, two members of the group skied the slope without incident and waited at base of the slope and off to the side. Three other skiers stopped on the slope approximately a third of the way down and were standing about 15 feet apart. The final two skiers entered the slope from the top. The avalanche broke almost beneath the skis of the top skier. He escaped, but the slab caught the skier below him and then hit the three skiers standing part way down the slope. The avalanche was two feet deep, 200 feet wide, and fell about 500 vertical feet. Three of those four skiers were partly buried, and one was totally buried.

RESCUE SUMMARY

The three skiers who were not caught began a rescue. They helped dig out the three who were partly buried. One of those partly buried was Ken Madden (44), and he had sustained a broken left leg.

The five uninjured skiers began a beacon search and quickly picked up a signal. They pinpointed the burial spot near a tree and uncovered the victim, Dan Dovey (37), from three to five feet of snow. He had been buried for 15 to 20 minutes, was face-down, was not breathing and had turned blue. One of the survivors was a doctor who attempted to revive the victim, but CPR was unsuccessful.

Two skiers from a separate party witnessed the accident and assisted in the rescue. They then skied back to Crystal Mountain Resort and notified the ski patrol at 14:50. The patrol sent a ground team to the site with one witness. The patrol team provided first aid to the skier with the broken leg. At 16:30 (after dark) an army MAST helicopter was dispatched to the site with Crystal Mountain Ski Patrol personnel on board. They extracted and airlifted Dovey's body back to Crystal Mountain, arriving at 17:00. The medical examiner determined that death occurred as a result of asphyxiation, not trauma.

AVALANCHE DATA

Persistent Slab avalanche

The avalanche released on a north-northeast-facing slope at an elevation of about 6,500 feet. It was two feet deep, 200 feet wide, and fell 500 feet vertical. It was classified as SS-ASu-R3-O, and it released on the buried layer of surface hoar atop the ice crust.

COMMENTS

The members of this group had all been through some level of avalanche safety training, and they had the right rescue gear. But their decision-making and procedures did not prove adequate for the conditions. First, they read the avalanche bulletin, which alerted readers to the presence of several potential weak layers, including the buried surface hoar. Second, hand pits are a good way to assess near-surface avalanche problems but provide little information about potential failures deeper in the snowpack. A couple of hasty pits would have been more likely to find the weak layer; the information from testing it may have altered their ski plans. Lastly, they did not ski one at a time, which is standard procedure when in avalanche terrain. The three skiers in the middle could have stopped in a safe zone to the side of the slope, not in it, or at the bottom.

The net result of these errors was four of seven skiers getting caught in a single avalanche at the same time, instead of one, or no one. Six people searching for one buried victim would have given that victim a much better chance of survival.

20030104 SKI LAKE, TETON PASS, WYOMING | January 4, 2003

One backcountry snowboarder caught and killed

WEATHER AND SNOWPACK CONDITIONS

Winds on January 4 were strong in the Teton Pass area. Because the winds were causing blowing snow, the Bridger-Teton National Forest Avalanche Center rated the avalanche danger at Considerable.

ACCIDENT SUMMARY

Ski Lake is situated in an east-facing bowl to the northeast of Mt. Glory, the prominent peak near the summit of the Teton Pass highway. The lake is at an elevation of 8,650 feet with steep slopes above it. On Saturday, January 4, a group of seven was using snowmobiles to access two side-by-side chutes on the northeast side of Peak 9584 above Ski Lake.

One member of the group was Tristan Picot (19). Picot was a professional snowboarder visiting from France. On the day of the accident, he was riding with a group of seasoned locals. Around 14:00, Picot started his second run down one of the two main chutes above the lake. He triggered a hard-slab avalanche that released snow in both chutes. He was caught and carried on a fast fall, full track, down the rocky, cliffy chute. Picot was not wearing a helmet. He was not buried, but was killed by head and neck trauma sustained in the fall. Members of his group gave CPR, but Picot did not respond.

RESCUE SUMMARY

Late that afternoon, the victim's body was flown out via a helicopter and long-line evacuation.

AVALANCHE DATA

Persistent Slab avalanche

The hard slab avalanche released at an elevation of about 9,450 feet on a northeast facing-chute. The crown was two to three feet deep and about 250 to 300 feet wide. The avalanche fell about 700 feet vertical. The slope angle in the starting zone ranged from 36 to 40 degrees. The slide was classified as HS-ARu-R3-O.

The weak layer beneath the slab was a layer of faceted snow topped with surface hoar, all of which had formed during a dry period in November.

COMMENTS

This was high-risk terrain where any avalanche—or a fall—could lead the victim into high-speed collisions with rocks and/or cliffs, and that's exactly what happened.

CORRAL CREEK LAKE, EAST OF AFTON, WYOMING

20030105

January 5, 2003

Two snowmobilers caught and buried; one killed

ACCIDENT SUMMARY

The Salt River Range is situated in far western Wyoming, just east of the town of Afton. On Sunday, January 5, a group of snowmobilers was riding in the vicinity of Corral Creek Lake, which sits at an elevation of 9,544 feet and is about seven miles southeast of Afton.

One of the riders was Joshua Roy Richins (16). Richins triggered an avalanche that completely buried him. None of the group wore beacons or carried any other avalanche rescue gear. After a futile search, his companions called local search and rescue, who located the victim under four feet of snow.

No rescue equipment

AVALANCHE DATA

The snowpack in this area was the classic slab-over-weak-layer profile. At the ground there was about one foot of depth hoar, and to add to the weakness, a layer of large surface hoar from a late November dry spell had formed on top of the depth hoar. This was topped with five feet of firm, slabby snow, most of which was one-finger hardness.

Persistent Slab avalanche

The avalanche released on an east-facing slope of 36 to 40 degrees at an elevation of 9,800 feet above Corral Creek Lake. The crown was two feet deep, and the avalanche was classified as SS-AMu-R3-O.

COMMENTS

The report on this fatal avalanche was minimal, but one thing can be said with certainty: with no beacons, probes, and shovels, this group was not equipped for an avalanche rescue, and it cost a life.

WOLVERINE PEAK, NORTHWEST OF COOKE CITY, MONTANA | January 22, 2003

20030122

One snowmobiler caught, buried, and killed

WEATHER AND SNOWPACK CONDITIONS

Wolverine Peak is a 10,479-foot mountain in the Beartooth Range of Montana, about five miles northwest of Cooke City. During a period of fair weather in the first two weeks of January, a layer of near-surface facets and/or surface hoar formed on the snow surface in the Beartooths. Twenty inches of snow then fell from January 14 to 17. Widespread

This view of the avalanche area shows the locations of the victim and his sled. The fracture line is barely visible near the ridgeline. *Photo Gallatin National Forest Avalanche Center.*

natural avalanche activity occurred immediately after this storm on slopes where the surface hoar was present, and a snowmobiler was injured in an avalanche on January 18.

Weather data showed that three inches of snow fell on January 20, followed by another five inches on the night of January 21. Strong winds accompanied the new snow, adding a layer of wind-blown snow on the slope that later avalanched. On the day of this accident, the weather conditions were deteriorating and visibility was poor.

ACCIDENT SUMMARY

On Wednesday, January 22, Andrew Greicar (21) and Jamie Bennington, both from North Dakota, were snowmobiling near Wolverine Pass. The two riders were highmarking on separate slopes out of sight from one another, and both men were wearing transceivers. By 14:30, Bennington had not seen Greicar for 10 to 15 minutes, so he followed a snowmobile track to the base of a slope on the shoulder of Wolverine Peak. There, he found a fresh avalanche and part of Greicar's snowmobile sticking out of the debris. He did a beacon search and located Greicar's burial position, but he did not have a probe or a shovel.

Traveling alone

Inadequate rescue equipment

Bennington had started digging with his wind screen when he heard another sledder in the distance. He stuck a stick in the snow to mark the location and rode to get the other sledder to help him dig.

RESCUE SUMMARY

The snowmobile Bennington heard was that of Yellowstone National Park Ranger Chan, who was in the area testing a portable radio repeater. Chan immediately called the Cooke City SAR Group. In a stroke of luck, three members of the Cooke City SAR were already in the area looking for a group of lost snowmobilers (that group was eventually found to be safe). Those SAR members responded and overtook Chan and Bennington as they made their way back to the accident site.

Poor visibility made it difficult to find the avalanche and the stick protruding from the snow, but the rescuers finally located the site. They located the victim with a beacon and struck him with a probe—within one foot of where Bennington had placed the stick.

The first responders uncovered Greicar from beneath five feet of avalanche debris. He did not respond to resuscitation efforts.

AVALANCHE DATA

Persistent Slab avalanche

The avalanche released on a wind-loaded slope with a northeast aspect. The slope angle, which averaged 34 degrees, increased to 42 degrees at the crown. The crown was three feet at its deepest point, and 250 feet wide. The avalanche ran approximately 450 feet vertical, with an alpha angle of 27 degrees. The avalanche was classified as SS-AMu-R4-O.

The snow that fell during the period of January 21 to 22 triggered a cycle of natural avalanches on many slopes in the Wolverine Peak area. Stability tests performed adjacent to the slope that avalanched on January 24 found the faceted weak layer to be extremely sensitive.

COMMENTS

Avalanche educators always stress several points for group safety in avalanche terrain, and these safety points fall into two categories. The first category includes ways to avoid avalanche terrain altogether, or ways to minimize risk by proper travel habits or behaviors. The second category includes proper rescue gear and procedures that, should an avalanche occur, improve chances of survival.

This duo of snowmobilers got it wrong in both categories. First, they violated a commandment of safe travel, which states, "Thou shall not travel alone." It may not have been their plan, but when they got separated they were effectively traveling alone. When Greicar was buried, he was alone and any chance of a fast recovery was gone.

Second, they got it wrong with their rescue gear. In an avalanche burial, the rescuers must be able to locate, pinpoint, and uncover in a minimal amount of time. This requires three pieces of gear: a transceiver (beacon) to locate, a probe to pinpoint, and a shovel to uncover. (Some people think a probe is not required. Not true. If you locate with a beacon and don't pinpoint, you run the risk of mis-digging by a few feet, wasting valuable minutes and energy.)

In this avalanche burial, two broken rules—traveling alone and the lack of a probe and shovel—gave the victim almost no chance to live.

KETTLE CREEK, SOUTH OF TOGWOTEE PASS, WYOMING

20030125

January 25, 2003

Two snowmobilers caught; one injured, one buried and killed

ACCIDENT SUMMARY

On Saturday, January 25, a group of 12 snowmobilers was riding in the Kettle Creek area, south of Togwotee Pass, Wyoming. The group was made up of experienced, skilled riders, but only a few carried avalanche rescue gear. This area is about nine miles south of Cowboy Village Resort, and the incident happened in a spot known as the narrows of Kettle Creek, at an elevation of about 9,000 feet.

More than one person on a slope

Around 13:30, one member of the party, Gregory Roth, became stuck while highmarking. His friend, Marshall Hevelery (43), rode up to help dig Roth out, and the weight of the two men and their sleds triggered the avalanche. The avalanche fell about 600 feet, and both men and their machines were carried downhill. When the snow stopped, Roth was on the surface with an injured knee. Hevelery was completely buried. He was not wearing an avalanche transceiver.

Inadequate rescue equipment

Seven riders from the original group of 12 began a search for the victim with limited gear. They had a few shovels and probes. It took 20 minutes, but one of the rescuers struck Hevelery under two to three feet of snow. Friends and rescuers performed CPR to no avail.

AVALANCHE DATA

The avalanche was 100 feet wide, 2.5 feet deep, and fell about 600 feet, though the report does not specify whether that was vertical or slope distance. The slope faced northeast, and the angle was 38 degrees in the start zone. The slide was probably classified as SS-AMu-R2.

COMMENTS

For experienced riders, this group had little avalanche awareness or preparedness. Few carried beacons, probes, or shovels. And the actions of the two victims showed little awareness of their situation. Tim Ciocarlan, the search and rescue director at the site, said the incident does teach some lessons. He noted that getting highmarking riders unstuck should be a delicate operation. "The worst thing you can possibly do is go up there and get them," he said. "You're looking for trouble. Let them get themselves unstuck."[2]

20030129

AVALANCHE BOWL, SOUTH OF TETON PASS, WYOMING

January 29, 2003

One backcountry snowboarder caught, buried, and killed

ACCIDENT SUMMARY

Avalanche Bowl is a popular backcountry ski slope in the Snake River Range on the south side of Teton Pass, Wyoming. It's about a 30-minute skin or snowshoe in from the parking area on Highway 22. It is a steep, open bowl that faces northeast. At the bottom of the bowl is a long gully.

On Wednesday, January 29, a snowboarder, Pavel (Paul) Volf (27) went on a solo trip into the backcountry terrain south of Teton Pass. Sometime that day, he entered the top of Avalanche Bowl and triggered a large slab avalanche. The slide carried him the entire length of the slope and into the gully, where he was totally buried.

Traveling alone

Later that same day, Keith Benefiel was skiing solo when he saw a track cutting off the crest of the ridge into Avalanche Bowl. Benefiel followed that track a short way and saw that it led into the crown of a fresh avalanche. He could see the pile of avalanche debris, about 200 yards long, in the gully below the bowl.

Benefiel, a former search and rescue volunteer, thought: "I'm looking at the tracks of a dead man." He skied down the safety of a ridge above the gully, looking for signs of the victim. He shouted down. There was no response, and there was no track coming out.

RESCUE SUMMARY

That evening, Benefiel reported his finding to the Teton County Search and Rescue Team, but the team waited for a missing persons report before sending in a search team. The next day, Thursday, Peter Volf—Pavel's older brother—sensed trouble when Pavel didn't show up for work. Peter then drove up to Teton Pass and found Pavel's car in the parking lot. It had snow on it and had been plowed in.

Peter then got two friends and geared up to search for Pavel that night. It was now near midnight on Thursday, and the three men headed toward Avalanche Bowl (where apparently Pavel had told them he was headed). Peter was hoping his brother might have just been injured and was still alive.

They took a safe route along the ridge above the gully. They saw the avalanche but no sign of Pavel. Then the group caused a huge collapse of the snowpack. The sound convinced them to abandon their quest and wait for a search and rescue team to take over.

On Friday, January 31, the Bridger-Teton Avalanche Center was rating the avalanche as high. Teton County S&R geared up for the search, but for their own safety, they waited for a hand-charge mission to clear the area of avalanche danger. Explosives released several avalanches, which covered the previous avalanche debris.

At 13:00, searchers and two avalanche dogs set foot on the debris field. Rescuers started with a beacon search, hoping Pavel had been wearing a beacon, but they did not pick up a signal. The dogs and their handlers took over and quickly caught a scent. One dog began digging, and a probe strike confirmed the location. Pavel Volf was buried under four feet of snow—two feet from the avalanche he had triggered and two feet from the avalanche recently released with explosives. His body was airlifted out by helicopter.

COMMENTS

Backcountry snowboarding and skiing alone has its rewards. Sometimes people simply prefer their own company. But if an accident happens—any kind of accident—the problem is far greater if alone. Without partners, Pavel Volf needed luck to be on his side. The luck of not being buried wasn't there.

COPPER CREEK BOWL, NORTH OF LINCOLN, MONTANA

20030201

February 1, 2003

Two snowmobilers caught and buried; one killed

WEATHER AND SNOWPACK CONDITIONS

An estimated 18 inches of snow fell in the area on January 30 and 31, and this snow fell on a layer of surface hoar. The backcountry avalanche danger was rated High by the West Central Montana Avalanche Center in Missoula.

High avalanche danger

ACCIDENT SUMMARY

Copper Creek Bowl is located about 15 miles north of the small town of Lincoln, Montana, which is 40 miles northwest of Helena. Copper Creek Bowl is on the edge of the Scapegoat Wilderness Area and is a popular spot for snowmobilers and backcountry skiers.

On Saturday, February 1, several groups of snowmobilers were riding in Copper Creek Bowl. Around 11:45, Jason Troyer (21) got stuck partway up the bowl. Wendell Baer (27)

Inadequate rescue equipment

rode up to help Troyer. They got the stuck machine out and had started their engines when the avalanche broke above them. Both men and their snowmobiles were carried down the slope, and both were buried. Baer was wearing a beacon; Troyer was not.

RESCUE SUMMARY

There were six other riders in the group, and they rode to the rescue immediately. Several of the rescuers picked up Baer's beacon signal and quickly zeroed in on his burial location. When they got close, they spotted Baer's hand sticking out of the snow. His helmet was visible just under the surface. They had Baer uncovered within a few minutes, and he was okay.

Rescuers were called to the site, but there are no details on how or when Troyer's body was recovered.

AVALANCHE DATA

A significant snowfall on top of a surface hoar layer had created a dangerous snowpack. The avalanche released on a northeast-facing slope at about 8,000 feet elevation. No further details on the avalanche are available.

COMMENTS

The victim of this avalanche may have been highmarking, but that was not specified in the limited reports available. Regardless, the lack of a beacon was the greatest cause of a preventable death.

20030202

ELK CREEK, NORTH OF LIVINGSTON, MONTANA

February 2, 2003

One snowmobiler caught, buried, and killed

WEATHER AND SNOWPACK CONDITIONS

In the second week of January, a layer of surface hoar, or near-surface facets, formed on the snowpack of the mountain ranges of south-central Montana. This included the Crazy Mountains, which is a small range situated 25 to 30 miles north of Livingston. That layer was buried under eight inches of wind-transported snow. Then, on February 1, another storm dropped 12 inches of snow, creating about 20 inches of soft slab snow resting on the faceted weak layer. The avalanche danger issued by the Gallatin National Forest Avalanche Center had been either High or Considerable for several days prior to and including February 2.

High avalanche danger

ACCIDENT SUMMARY

On Sunday, February 2, a group of three snowmobilers, including Bryan LaHaye (33), was riding in the Elk Creek drainage of the Crazy Mountains. At approximately 15:30, LaHaye rode partway up a north-facing slope. Conflicting reports make it unclear if he became stuck or simply stopped on a bench partway up the slope. Either way, the slope failed under the weight of LaHaye and his snowmobile.

The fracture broke 200 feet vertical above him and overran the bench where LaHaye had stopped. He and his snowmobile were carried to the bottom of the slope. LaHaye was completely buried approximately 50 feet above his snowmobile, which was partially buried at the toe of the debris. No one in the party was wearing a transceiver or carried rescue gear.

No rescue equipment

RESCUE SUMMARY

One of the two remaining men rode five miles to a ranch house, where he initiated the call for SAR personnel. This call came in at approximately 16:30. The other survivor remained on the scene, looking for surface clues.

Four SAR personnel arrived on the scene at about 18:30. LaHaye was located by a coarse probe line and recovered about an hour later.

AVALANCHE DATA

Persistent Slab avalanche

The slope that avalanched faced north and had an average angle of 32 degrees, but that angle increased to 42 degrees at the crown. The shallower-angled bench halfway up the slope apparently acted as a support to hold the snow in place—that is, until the weight of the snowmobile and rider caused it to fail. The crown was 1.5 feet deep and 200 feet wide. The avalanche fell 400 feet vertical, and was classified as SS-AMu-R4-D3-O.

Stability tests performed on February 3 by the investigating team found the weak, faceted layer to be very sensitive.

COMMENTS

This avalanche is one more instance of a group not being prepared for rescue. If all these riders had been properly equipped, a beacon search may have led to a recovery in time to save LaHaye's life.

HATCH PEAK, HATCHER PASS, NORTH OF PALMER, ALASKA | February 9, 2003

20030209

Two backcountry snowboarders caught; one partly buried, one buried and killed

WEATHER AND SNOWPACK CONDITIONS

Hatcher Pass is situated in the Talkeetna Mountains, about 13 miles north of Palmer. It's a local favorite for winter recreation—skiing, snowboarding, snowshoeing, and snowmobiling—and its terrain varies from mellow to steep. It's been the site of a number of avalanche fatalities including two others on or just below this same peak (19971109 and 2001111).

From February 4 through 9, about 24 inches of snow fell in the Hatcher Pass area, accompanied by winds that had caused blowing snow and had loaded east and northeast-facing slopes.

ACCIDENT SUMMARY

Inadequate rescue equipment

Hatch Peak is a 4,811-foot mountain immediately south of Hatcher Pass. On Sunday, February 9, two snowboarders were on Hatch Peak, but only one had come prepared for an avalanche rescue. Anthony Watters (24) was wearing a transceiver and had a probe and shovel in his pack. His 18-year-old friend had no avalanche rescue gear at all.

The two men had climbed up the mountain and were on their first run down on a steep northeast-facing slope. The time was about 13:00, and they were nearing the bottom of the slope when it avalanched from above. The avalanche hit both men. Watters was completely buried, while his friend was buried to his chest.

RESCUE SUMMARY

The second snowboarder was able to dig himself out. He started searching the debris. When he found no sign of Watters, he began a hike out to get help. He crossed a gully, and on the other side, he ran into a group of four skiers. Two of these skiers had beacons, and they went to the slide area. The survivor and the other two skiers went out to the Hatcher Pass Lodge to report the avalanche and get more help. (The accident report is unclear as to whether only two of the four skiers had beacons, and whether the two skiers with beacons also had probes and shovels.)

At the lodge, there were two park rangers with snowmobiles. The rangers, the survivor of the avalanche, and several other volunteers returned to the site of the avalanche. By that time, the first two skiers had gotten a beacon signal and located the burial area. The rangers had probes and shovels and were able to pinpoint the burial spot and dig the victim out from three to five feet of snow. Watters had been buried 90 minutes and did not survive.

COMMENTS

This fatal avalanche almost raises more questions than it answers, but there is one critical detail to focus on. These two men failed in the concept of companion rescue, which demands that all party members be equipped with beacons, probes, and shovels—and be competent in their use. In this avalanche, the rescue gear became useless, both for the survivor and for the buried victim.

The take-home message: Travel in steep terrain only when all party members have the right rescue gear and know how to use it.

20030210 HOURGLASS COULOIR, JACKSON HOLE MOUNTAIN RESORT, WYOMING | February 10, 2003

Two lift skiers caught; one injured, one buried and killed

WEATHER AND SNOWPACK CONDITIONS

On the night of Sunday, February 9, into Monday morning, February 10, seven inches of snow fell at Jackson Hole Mountain Resort in Wyoming. Strong northwest to southwest winds accompanied the snowfall.

ACCIDENT SUMMARY

The Hourglass Couloir is an inbounds area of the Jackson Hole Mountain Resort, but the chute is permanently closed because of the threat of avalanches, not only to people who would enter the area but also to skiers and snowboarders on the open terrain of Tensleep Bowl below.

At about 13:00, three local skiers entered the Hourglass Couloir. The men were Steve Haas (41), Tom Burlingame, and Morgan Wion. All three were strong skiers and had beacons, probes, and shovels. Haas went first, while Burlingame watched from near the top. Wion was also at the top, but was standing further back than Burlingame.

Haas triggered the avalanche, which broke near the top of the chute and caught Burlingame as well. The avalanche carried Haas the entire length of the couloir—about 600 feet vertical—into a remote corner of Tensleep Bowl below and completely buried him. Burlingame was swept 100 feet down the chute, riding the surface of the avalanche. He slammed into a rock, breaking two ribs. Wion watched from above.

RESCUE SUMMARY

Burlingame was in pain, but got up and slid down the couloir looking for Haas. He turned his beacon to receive, and saw that it had been damaged when he smashed into the rock. Burlingame worked his way down the path and eventually picked up a signal, but it was erratic. He would pick up a signal, and then lose it, which slowed his search. He figured he had lost six or seven minutes before Wion came down and was able to latch onto the signal coming from Haas.

Finally, the men got a signal they could follow, and it led them to Haas' burial location. The rescuers probed and struck Haas. It took about 10 minutes of digging to uncover him from three to four feet of snow. Altogether, Haas had been buried about 20 minutes, and he was not breathing when Burlingame and Wion dug him out. The two rescuers tried CPR without success. Some minutes later, the Jackson Hole Ski Patrol arrived and took over CPR efforts. They used a toboggan to transport the victim to the resort medical clinic. An ambulance brought him to St. John's Hospital, where he was pronounced dead.

AVALANCHE DATA

Hourglass Couloir has been described as a "very active and dangerous avalanche path," and therefore mountain management decided to make it a permanently closed area for the danger it posed to skiers and their potential rescuers. The couloir faces northeast, leeward of the recent prevailing winds, and it had been loaded with about two feet of fallen and wind-transported snow. The avalanche was classified as SS-ASu-R2, with a two-foot crown. The slide began at about 10,100 feet elevation and fell about 600 feet vertical down the 40-degree chute.

COMMENTS

These men were risk-takers and were known and respected for their ability to ski technical lines in unforgiving terrain. Because avalanches were an ever-present threat, they always carried—and were proficient in using—avalanche rescue equipment. But on this day, it was a cruel twist of fate that a rescuer's beacon broke, which delayed the recovery too long for the victim to survive.

GOBBLERS KNOB, NORTH OF BIG COTTONWOOD CANYON, UTAH | February 15, 2003

20030215

One backcountry skier caught, buried, and killed

WEATHER AND SNOWPACK CONDITIONS

The winter of 2002-03 had been a lean snow season in the Wasatch Range east of Salt Lake City. Two different weak layers had formed in the thin snowpack, the first during a spell of clear weather in December and the second in January, again during clear skies. These were layers of faceted snow that had been buried by snow storms that followed.

From about February 10 to 14, a warm storm system had moved into the Salt Lake City and Wasatch area. The snow line was around 8,000 feet, and the six to eight inches of snow that fell above that elevation was heavy and damp. Winds, though, had been mostly from the southwest and had formed areas of shallow slab, and the Utah Avalanche Center had described the snow surface as a mix of firm crusts and damp powder. On Saturday, February 15, the UAC stated, "there is a 'Moderate' danger of triggering an avalanche into deeper weak layers on northwest through easterly facing slopes, steeper than about 35 degrees and above about 9,000 feet elevation, and on very steep rocky slopes with hard wind deposits." This would prove to be accurate.

ACCIDENT SUMMARY

Gobblers Knob, at 10,246 feet elevation, is the highest summit on the ridge separating Big Cottonwood Canyon, to the south, from Millcreek Canyon, to the north. On Saturday, February 15, a party of five experienced and avalanche-trained backcountry skiers was touring in the Gobblers Knob area. All were equipped with beacons, probes, and shovels. One of the party was Alan Davis (46), who did volunteer work for the Friends of the Utah Avalanche Center.

They had successfully skied several other steep slopes in the area earlier in the day without incident. Near the end of the day, on their last run, they descended the northwest face of Gobblers Knob to get to their car in Mill Creek Canyon. Around 17:30, Alan Davis skied first while the others waited in the trees at the top. After a few turns, he triggered a one-foot hard slab avalanche on the 40-degree slope. Though initially small, the avalanche quickly widened to 400 feet across. This larger volume of snow funneled into a narrow, twisting gully and fell 1,700 feet vertical. Davis was buried in the debris field in the gully.

RESCUE SUMMARY

The rest of the group descended as fast as they could, their beacons on receive. It became slow going in the narrow gully, where the snow had made a jagged pile. Nevertheless, they eventually picked up the beacon signal and pinpointed the burial spot. They dug out Davis from four feet of debris after a 25-minute burial. He did not respond to CPR.

The survivors made a 911 call on a cellphone and waited for the rescuers. Darkness had fallen when a LifeFlight helicopter flew into the area, but survivors guided it to the site with their headlamps. The rescue mission concluded after midnight when Davis's body was brought out by sled through Mill Creek Canyon.

AVALANCHE DATA

Persistent Slab avalanche

The avalanche was triggered in a steep, rocky area with a thin, weak snowpack. It released at an elevation of about 10,100 feet on a 40-degree north-northwest-facing slope. The crown initially was only one foot deep and 100 feet wide, but after descending a short distance, it broke out additional slabs on either side, making an avalanche about 400 feet wide. It fell 1,700 feet vertical, with the debris funneling into a gully in the lower track. The slide was classified as HS-ASu-R3-O.

On the slope that avalanched, the snow cover was shallow, and the rocky ground underneath made a good environment for facets to grow—in other words, a facet farm. A similar slope with a deeper snow cover may not have avalanched.

COMMENTS

This was an experienced group of skiers who knew the terrain and avalanche potential of the Wasatch Range well. They carried rescue gear and were skiing one at a time. A combination of a snowpack feature and a terrain feature contributed to this fatal avalanche—despite the safety measures taken by the group. First, the shallow snow cover made it easy for the snow to turn to facets, and second, the gully below was a terrain trap that squeezed the debris into a long and deep deposit.

DRY GULCH, NORTH OF LOVELAND PASS, COLORADO

20030217

February 17, 2003

Two climbers caught; one buried and killed

WEATHER AND SNOWPACK CONDITIONS

The first two weeks of February brought dry and windy weather to the Front Range of Colorado. The winds, though, created blowing snow and widespread slab formation near and above timberline. Then, from February 13 to 17, Loveland Ski Area recorded 14 inches of new snow. Winds during this period were from the northwest, west, and southwest, and wind speeds averaged 15 to 20 mph, with gusts to 45. There was plenty of blowing snow above timberline that loaded all east-facing slopes. On February 17, the Colorado Avalanche Information Center rated the avalanche danger as Considerable.

ACCIDENT SUMMARY

Interstate Highway 70 (I-70) passes through the Eisenhower Tunnel 55 miles west of Denver and at an elevation of 11,000 feet. Skiers and riders at Loveland Ski Area are cruising the mountainside above the tunnel, and the terrain surrounding the ski area offers a wide expanse for backcountry skiing, climbing, and snowshoeing.

Monday, February 17, was the Presidents' Day holiday, and early that morning, Ken Booker (48) and John Brill (46) left Denver for a snowshoe climb of a summit north of Loveland Ski Area. They parked at a pullout off of I-70 and started their trip by following the Herman Gulch Trail to the saddle east of Point 13,294, between Herman and Dry Gulches. This peak is known in climbing circles as the Citadel, but its lesser-known name is Snoopy, because of its resemblance to the Peanuts character lying on his doghouse.

Booker and Brill climbed the east ridge toward the summit of the peak. At some point below the summit, they removed their snowshoes in order to climb the rocky ridge below the summit. On their descent, they did not follow their ascent route, and instead dropped onto a broad southeast-facing snow slope to traverse back to where they had left their snowshoes. Around 15:15, and the two men were kicking in steps when they triggered the avalanche.

It was a large avalanche. John Brill recalled what happened: "Ken was 50 feet behind me. It happened before you could blink an eye. After hearing a huge, thundering boom, we were going downhill. I just out of pure luck caught myself with my pickax and fell only about 50 yards."[3] Booker was not able to self-arrest and was swept far down the slope and buried. The debris field covered six acres (about 4.5 football fields) and was up to 12 feet deep.

Neither man had avalanche rescue gear, and Brill was not able to spot his friend anywhere on the slope. He made a 911 call on his cell phone at 15:21.

No rescue equipment

RESCUE SUMMARY

The Clear Creek Sheriff's dispatcher notified the Alpine Rescue Team, the Loveland Ski Patrol, and the Keystone Ski Patrol (with an avalanche rescue dog), but it took more

View of the avalanche from the runout. The skier is standing near the burial site. The diamond at upper right marks where the climbers stashed their snowshoes. *Photo Dale Atkins, CAIC.*

than an hour for these teams to arrive by snowmobile and helicopter. In the meantime, Brill searched the surface in vain.

The dog did not alert, and 10 rescuers probed some of the debris until after 18:00. The search was then suspended because of darkness and cold.

Rescuers returned to the site on Tuesday morning. Avalanche dogs alerted in a few spots but their efforts failed to locate the buried man. Very dense avalanche debris may have been the reason the dogs struggled to detect a strong scent. Finally, a little after 14:00, a probe line located the victim under four to five feet of snow.

AVALANCHE DATA

Persistent Slab avalanche

This large, hard slab avalanche was classified as HS-AFu-R3-O. The men triggered the avalanche (artificial foot), which ran on old snow. The crown depth generally ranged from two to three feet but was six feet in places, and the crown was 550 feet wide. The avalanche released at an elevation of 12,880 feet and fell approximately 640 feet vertical down the southeast-facing slope. The slope angle ranged from 34 to 37 degrees. The alpha angle (angle from the toe of the debris to the fracture line) was 25 degrees. The field of debris was approximately six acres and up to 12 feet deep.

COMMENTS

Perhaps the only mistake these two climbers made was not recognizing that they had stepped onto an avalanche starting zone—once they'd already stepped off the rocky terrain. The easier (and perhaps more comfortable, since it was more likely out of the wind) route was not the safer route.

In a side note, Brill said that Booker usually carried an avalanche beacon, but that morning a last-minute car problem forced them to change from Booker's car to Brill's car, and the beacon got left behind. But one beacon (and no shovels) would not have changed the outcome; it just would have quickened the body recovery once the rescue teams arrived.

The most essential point to be made of these men's actions is that they did not think through the danger posed by avalanches on much of their route, both going up and going down. Triggering an avalanche was a distinct possibility, given the terrain and snowpack. They were not prepared for an avalanche rescue—no beacons, probes, or shovels—and kicking in steps in an avalanche starting zone was unreasonable.

ELKHEAD PASS, NORTHWEST OF BUENA VISTA, COLORADO | February 22, 2003

20030222a

Three backcountry skiers caught; two partly buried, one buried and killed

WEATHER AND SNOWPACK CONDITIONS

Mid-February was a snowy period in the Colorado Rockies as a series of storms moved over the mountains. There is no way to know actual snowfall in the area of Elkhead Pass in the Sawatch Range, but snow measured at three other sites—Monarch, 33 miles to the south; Gothic, 33 miles to the west; and Aspen, 33 miles to the northwest—serves as an estimate. A rough guess would be that about two feet of snow fell at Elkhead Pass from February 14 to 22. Winds above timberline would have formed widespread slab conditions.

ACCIDENT SUMMARY

Elkhead Pass, at an elevation of 13,220 feet, is one of the highest hiking trails in Colorado. The pass is situated in the Sawatch Range of central Colorado and is 10 miles northwest of Buena Vista. It separates Missouri Gulch to the north from Pine Creek to the south. Because of its remote location and high elevation, it sees little winter recreational use.

A group of three backcountry skiers began a three-day, two-night ski mountaineering trip on Friday, February 21. The three were Curt Dale (57), his son, Chris Dale (25), and Bob Redwine (55). Their planned route was to begin at the Missouri Gulch trailhead, climb into Missouri Basin, cross over Elkhead Pass, and then descend and exit out Pine Creek. These three were experienced mountaineers and skiers and had been planning this trip for several months. (Over the years, Curt Dale had climbed all 53 of Colorado's fourteeners as well as Washington's Mt. Rainier and Alaska's Denali.) On this trip, the men had probes and shovels, but no beacons.

Inadequate rescue equipment

On Friday, they made it into Missouri Basin and camped above 11,000 feet. The following day, Saturday, February 22, they were on a steady climb and arrived at the north side of Elkhead Pass around 15:00. Breaking trail across the basin had been difficult, plus it was cold, snowing, and windy. At the pass, they searched for a safe way to descend the steep south side. They talked about the avalanche danger and decided to not follow the summer trail because it traversed a steep southeast slope that they thought would be covered with a wind slab. Instead, they descended to the skier's left onto a south-facing slope with some vertically-oriented rock bands, which they hoped would provide some protection.

At the base of the first rock band, the men chose to take their skis off, thinking it would be safer to proceed on foot. They had dropped down 80 feet vertical from the pass and were grouped together on an estimated 40-degree slope. They talked over their situation and decided to keep going, because they had this one slope to get down to the flats, where they could camp for the night.

With their skis strapped to their packs, they had taken just a few more steps when the slope avalanched, catching all three and carrying them down the slope. When the avalanche stopped, Chris Dale and Bob Redwine were buried to their waists. The two men could not see Curt Dale, and it took a little more than 10 minutes for them to dig themselves out, at which time Chris saw a backpack, barely visible, sticking out of the debris.

Chris moved up the debris while was Bob was still digging himself out. It took Chris another five minutes to dig out his father, who was lying face-down in the snow. Once Chris got his father uncovered, he noticed his face had turned blue. There was no snow in his father's mouth, so Chris started with rescue breaths. He checked for a pulse and there was none. He then started CPR, continuing for 10 to 15 minutes, and it successfully brought back his father's pulse. Chris then continued with rescue breathing for another 10 minutes, at which point Curt Dale began breathing on his own.

While Chris was reviving his father, Bob Redwine set up the tent in a level spot and got sleeping bags ready. They got Curt in a sleeping bag in the tent, and Chris got in with him to keep him a little warmer. By now, Curt was breathing on his own, but was unconscious. They stayed in the tent for many hours, keeping everyone as warm as possible. Around midnight, Chris noticed that his father was having difficulty breathing—and then stopped breathing altogether. Chris checked for a pulse and then started CPR again, continuing for about 30 minutes with no success. Curt Dale had died.

Chris and Bob decided to pack enough to ski out Pine Creek to the trailhead. They left Curt wrapped in a sleeping bag in the tent. It took Chris and Bob 21 hours to ski out and notify the Chaffee County Sheriff.

RESCUE SUMMARY

The two survivors did not get out of the backcountry until Monday, at which point they contacted the sheriff. The following two days, bad weather and risky flying conditions thwarted helicopter missions to extract the body. Finally, on March 1, Curt Dale's body was recovered by the Chaffee County SAR team, with help from the Colorado Air National Guard helicopter team.

AVALANCHE DATA

The avalanche released on a south-facing slope of about 40 degrees and at an elevation of about 12,800 feet. The crown was two to three feet deep and 100 feet wide. The avalanche fell 150 feet vertical and was classified as SS-AFu-R2.

COMMENTS

There are no shallow-angle slopes on the south side of Elkhead Pass. The three men had gotten themselves into a difficult situation. They were aware of and concerned about the avalanche danger, not only on the slope they were on, but also on the surrounding slopes. It was a case of seeing safe terrain a tantalizingly short distance away, but not having a safe route there. What to do?

In retrospect, backtracking would have been a better option. No doubt they were tired and cold after a long day of hard travel, so climbing up the slope they had just come down and backtracking was a dispiriting thought. Again, what to do?

If they continued down, it would have been better to do so one at a time. An avalanche in that situation would have meant only one person caught, with two companions left to search. But without beacons, even that becomes an unappealing option: an avalanche death caused by not being able to locate the victim. Our conclusion, with the help of 20/20 hindsight: backtrack.

KEOKEE PEAK, NORTHWEST OF SANDPOINT, IDAHO

20030222b

February 22, 2003

One backcountry skier caught, buried, and killed

WEATHER AND SNOWPACK CONDITIONS

The Selkirk Mountains are a north-south-oriented range that extends from British Columbia into the Idaho panhandle, ending just north of Sandpoint and Lake Pend Oreille. Keokee Peak (6,448 feet) sits on the crest of the Selkirks 11 miles northwest of Sandpoint. Caribou Mountain Lodge is a commercial lodge a few miles east of Keokee Peak.

February 15 through 17 was the extended weekend of Washington's birthday holiday, and it brought a period of warm weather and rain that created a two-inch-thick crust on snow surfaces on all aspects in the Selkirks. This was followed by several days and nights of clear skies during which surface hoar formed on the crust. Next came a storm on the February 19 and 20, which dropped 10 to 12 inches of snowfall containing 1.6 inches of water, as measured at the Schweitzer Basin SNOTEL site, 3.5 miles southeast of the accident site. The storm also brought strong southwest winds that gusted to 70 mph, which meant all east-facing slopes were heavily loaded with blowing snow. Dry and cold weather returned on February 21 and 22.

ACCIDENT SUMMARY

On Saturday, February 22, Tim Parnow (45) was one of a group of six skiers in the area of the Caribou Mountain Lodge near Keokee Peak. This was an experienced group; all were avalanche savvy and carried beacons, probes, and shovels. At about 11:30, they reached the slope they wanted to ski. They dug a snow pit on a 35-degree southeast-facing slope and got a Rutschblock score of 3, which means the slope is unstable, and it's likely that slopes with similar snow conditions could be triggered by a skier. The group also noticed the presence of the buried layer of surface hoar.

These data made them suspicious of the stability of the snow on this slope, so they traversed eastward across the slope to where the slope angle was a little less steep. Parnow was the first to ski, and he picked a line near the trees along the east edge. Parnow skied over a roll in the fall line onto a steeper portion of the slope, and skied out of sight of his friends waiting above. After about 30 seconds, the group above saw an avalanche running across the runout at the bottom of the slope.

RESCUE SUMMARY

The group above skied to the rollover and saw no sign of Parnow, so they immediately initiated the rescue by switching their beacons to receive and skiing down the bed surface of the avalanche. In about a minute, they picked up the signal from Parnow's transceiver and honed in on it. The signal led them to a tree, where they probed and struck his boot. By now, five minutes had passed. The rescuers began digging, but the tree branches made it difficult. Making it worse, Parnow had been buried head down, so it took 15 to 20 minutes to get him uncovered from five feet of snow.

One of the rescuers made a 911 cell call. Big Sky Paramedics in Sandpoint got the call at 11:54 and dispatched a helicopter, which arrived on scene at 12:37. In the meantime, the rescuers on site could not get any life signs from Parnow. Once the helicopter arrived, he was airlifted back to Sandpoint, where it was determined he had probably died instantly from blunt trauma.

AVALANCHE DATA

Persistent Slab avalanche

The avalanche released on an east-facing slope at an elevation of about 6,200 feet. There was no data taken on the depth of the crown, but it was estimated to be 1,000 feet wide. The slide was classified as SS-ASu-R3-O.

The weak layer was the one-inch-thick surface hoar layer that had been buried prior to the most recent storm, and the bed surface was the two-inch-thick ice crust that formed after the rain about a week before.

COMMENTS

This group of skiers had the training, knowledge, and equipment to look for and find instability in the snowpack. Their pit revealed the weak layer, and their Rutschblock revealed the instability. But their response to this information was inadequate. They merely moved to a lower-angled part of the same slope, which may have been a safe move if the slope hadn't steepened below.

This accident also shows the limitations of the standard rescue gear of beacons, probes and shovels. The group of five used their rescue equipment expertly, but that couldn't save the victim from a high-speed collision with a tree.

Given the known instability, this was a day for skiing low angle terrain.

Ninety minutes after this avalanche accident happened, another avalanche killed a snowmobiler about 10 miles to the north (20020222c.)

20030222c

ECHO BOWL, EAST OF PRIEST LAKE, IDAHO

February 22, 2003

Five snowmobilers caught; four partly buried, one buried and killed

WEATHER AND SNOWPACK CONDITIONS

This avalanche accident occurred on the same day, an hour and a half later, and 10 miles north of 20030222b, so similar weather conditions existed at both sites.

ACCIDENT SUMMARY

The Echo Bowl area of the Selkirk Mountains is east of Priest Lake in the Idaho panhandle. It is a hugely popular area with snowmobilers. On big weekends, there can be hundreds of riders in the area, and the slopes of Echo Bowl are used mainly for highmarking. (Check out YouTube videos to get a picture of the terrain.)

On Saturday, February 22, Patrick Kopczynski (42) was one of five snowmobilers who triggered an avalanche while highmarking. Kopczynski was buried and killed in the avalanche. The other four riders were partly buried, and all survived. One of those four was Kopczynski's five-year-old son, who was on the back of the sled when the avalanche hit. He was buried next to the snowmobile and had one leg out of the snow. This led rescuers to a quick recovery that saved his life.

COMMENTS

There was no on-site report available for this fatal avalanche, only a short newspaper story. Therefore, our comments are limited to one obvious thing. The group had no avalanche rescue gear—an omission that may have cost a life.

No rescue equipment

SMITHS FORK, SOUTHEAST OF AFTON, WYOMING

20030224

February 24, 2003

One snowmobiler caught, buried, and killed

ACCIDENT SUMMARY

The Salt River Range lies in far western Wyoming, east of Star Valley and the town of Afton. On Monday, February 24, a group of five snowmobilers was riding in the Poker Hollow area of the Smiths Fork drainage. It was late in the day, and the group was on its last run of the day, heading back to the trailhead.

Mark Loveland (41) was one of the five riders, and he was the only one who was not wearing an avalanche transceiver. The group was on the west side of Poker Creek, at the top of an avalanche slope. They decided to descend this slope one at a time, and the first four riders made it to the bottom without incident. The time was 17:10 when Loveland started down, and he triggered an avalanche that broke two feet deep across the top of the slope. The avalanche swept Loveland and his snowmobile down the slope and buried both.

Inadequate rescue equipment

RESCUE SUMMARY

The four riders at the bottom of the slope immediately went into rescue mode. Three headed for the debris in the runout while the fourth man found a spot where he could make a 911 cell phone call.

The three searchers began probing and quickly hit the victim's snowmobile, near the toe of the debris. They continued to probe for Loveland, initially in the area around the snowmobile and then spreading out, but they were unable to strike the victim.

Members of the Lincoln County Search and Rescue team arrived and set up a probe line to search for the victim. Eventually, at 19:45 and almost in the dark, they struck Loveland's body, buried four feet deep and about 10 feet upslope of his snowmobile. He had not survived.

AVALANCHE DATA

This avalanche was triggered on an east-facing slope at an elevation of 8,100 feet. The slope angle in the starting zone was 36 to 40 degrees. The crown was two feet deep, and the avalanche was classified as SS-AMu-R3. The avalanche danger was rated Considerable.

COMMENTS

Four men in this group wore avalanche beacons. One did not, and it cost him his life. These men appeared to be avalanche savvy. They carried rescue gear, and they recognized their final slope as being an avalanche path, which they descended one at a time.

It is interesting that four snowmobilers safely descended this slope, while the fifth triggered the avalanche. Let's take a look at the best thinking on how this can happen. When the snowpack is "absolutely unstable," it doesn't take an external trigger to release an avalanche: they release naturally. But when the snowpack is "conditionally unstable," it requires an external trigger to initiate release. (This is often called an artificial trigger.)

Research has shown that the mountain snow cover is almost never uniform in strength, but rather is a complex quilt of strong and weak spots. A snowmobiler or skier can (unwittingly) miss all the weak spots or hit one that causes local snow failure only, and no avalanche occurs. But if a local failure is able to propagate to other weak spots, an avalanche does occur. This explains why, say, four snowmobilers or skiers can travel on a slope with no avalanche release, but the fifth person can hit one additional weak spot that links to the others, at which point the entire slope avalanches.

Is there a teaching point here? Probably not, other than always be cautious on potential avalanche slopes.

20030305 HANCOCK PASS, NORTH OF MONARCH PASS, COLORADO

March 5, 2003

One snowmobiler caught, buried, and killed

WEATHER AND SNOWPACK CONDITIONS

Snowfall in February was above normal throughout the Colorado mountains. Crested Butte, about 28 miles northwest of the avalanche site, had gotten 152% of its normal February snowfall; Monarch, nine miles to the south, had gotten 184% of normal. This kept the avalanche danger hovering in the "Considerable-to-High" range for much of February and March.

Snowfall measured at Monarch was 30 inches between February 21 and 28, followed by another 13 inches on March 1 and 2. There was no lull as the storm track remained aimed at Colorado, and snow began falling once more on March 4. This storm system would bring snowfall lasting until March 7 along with strong winds, blowing snow, and high avalanche danger. Avalanche warnings were posted from March 4 to 7.

High avalanche danger

ACCIDENT SUMMARY

Hancock Pass sits at an elevation of 12,160 feet on the Continental Divide of the Sawatch Range in the central Colorado Rockies. It is about nine air-miles north of Monarch Pass. Hancock Pass sees a lot of jeep traffic in the summertime and gets its share of snowmobile use in the winter.

On Wednesday, March 5, a group of four men left Colorado Springs early in the morning for a day of snowmobiling up Chalk Creek, one of the canyons on the east slope of the Sawatch Range. They arrived at the Chalk Creek trailhead in the ghost town of St. Elmo at 08:00.

This group included Seth Chiddix (31), Jeff Rusk (33), Rod Snow, and Shane Chiddix. Seth, Rod, and Shane were skilled riders with up to 10 years' experience each; Jeff Rusk had less experience—this day would be only his third snowmobile trip. They carried extra warm clothing, food, water, and first aid kits in their packs. However, none had any formal avalanche training. They all carried shovels, but they only had one probe pole among them. Also, there were only two beacons among them, and those belonged to the Chiddix brothers. Since there were not enough beacons for the four riders, Seth Chiddix left them turned off in his pack.

Inadequate rescue equipment

Their intended trip that day was to ride up Chalk Creek to Hancock Pass. Seth clearly said on several occasions that they should not go over Hancock Pass, because there would be more dangerous avalanche terrain on the other side. Everyone agreed.

As they rode in, Seth rode his snowmobile on several short but steep slopes to test the snow. Nothing happened on those tests, but in late morning they stopped in a meadow and caused a widespread collapse of the snowpack. After that, Seth voiced his concern and said, "We're going to stay off of steep slopes and we're not going over the pass."[4]

As they approached the north side of Hancock Pass, Rod Snow decided to play in the powdery flats well below the pass. The other three riders approached the steeper terrain as it rose up toward the pass. This was a steep slope with several bands of trees on it.

The riders were on the climber's left of the summer road and were near a thick band of trees. Seth told the others that he had never seen avalanches on this slope, but had seen them on the slope on the other side of the summer road. So he proceeded climbing, working hard to push a route up and across the slope. He could feel the firm base beneath 18 inches of powder snow, and he made it to a stopping point on a bench, with his brother Shane behind him. From there, they were going to wait for Jeff Rusk to join them, and then all three would continue to the pass. They could see Rod Snow in the flats below.

The time was about 13:00, and Seth and Shane could not see Jeff below them because of a rollover on the slope. They suddenly felt the snow around them move, and they accelerated off to the climbers' right. They and/or Jeff below had triggered the avalanche. Seth and Shane watched as the powder cloud billowed 80 to 100 feet into the air. From far below, Rod was watching and could see Seth and Shane high on the slope and Jeff gunning his snowmobile up the track set by Seth and Shane—until the avalanche released and the powder cloud obscured his vision.

RESCUE SUMMARY

Seth and Shane rode down the avalanche slope, looking for any sign of Jeff. The last they had seen of him was on the east (climber's left) side of the slope next to the tree line. At the same time, Rod was riding up from below. They all scanned the snow for clues and saw none. One man rode out the way they had come in to summon help while the other two began searching below Jeff's last-seen area, looking for clues, scuffing the snow surface with their boots, and randomly probing with the only probe they had.

By late afternoon, about 30 rescuers had been assembled, but they did not go in because darkness was coming on, the wind was increasing, and the temperature was plummeting.

The following morning, March 6, a large rescue team with three avalanche dogs was on site. At 09:20, one of the dogs alerted, and the rescuers uncovered Jeff Rusk's body from three feet of snow and wrapped around a tree. He had died of trauma. His snowmobile was later found 23 feet farther uphill.

AVALANCHE DATA

This avalanche was triggered by the snowmobilers on a north-facing slope at an elevation of 12,760 feet. The slope angle in the starting zone was 39 degrees. It was a large

Deep Persistent Slab avalanche

avalanche with a crown that was initially three to four feet deep and 100 feet wide, but that slide then widened below the rollover to ultimately be about 700 feet wide. The avalanche fell 1,100 feet vertical. It produced a large powder cloud and was classified as HS-AMu-R4-D3-G. The alpha angle was measured at 22 degrees.

The snowpack consisted of 18 inches of fresh powder snow on top of a hard wind slab in the middle pack and a layer of depth hoar at the ground.

It cannot be ascertained where the trigger of the avalanche occurred. The two snowmobilers at the top may have triggered the slide, but they were able to escape. Equally likely, Rusk could have triggered the avalanche from the middle of the slope, and he had no way to escape.

COMMENTS

This group was concerned about the wrong terrain. They had convinced themselves that the avalanche terrain was on the other side of the pass, and because Seth Chiddix had not previously observed avalanches on the slope where the avalanche occurred, they took their eye off the problem right in front of them and rode right into the jaws of an avalanche. A heavily loaded 39-degree slope fits every definition of an avalanche slope.

Compounding the problem, because they intended to avoid avalanche terrain, they chose to ride with no one wearing avalanche beacons. They were conceptually aware of avalanches as deadly threats—something to be avoided—but did not recognize when that threat was before them.

After the rescue was completed, Seth Chiddix spoke with the news media. Chiddix had employed Rusk at his company, and he praised Rusk as being a good employee, father, and friend who would be missed. As written in *The Denver Post*: "Chiddix, facing the pain of loss and the regret of a nagging conscious, said 'Take avalanche classes. Know the snow conditions. Know the weather reports. Get updates from the Avalanche Center. Have beacons, probe poles, safety kits, first-aid kits. And know the area where you're going.'"

20030309a PTARMIGAN LAKE, WEST OF BUENA VISTA, COLORADO

March 9, 2003

One snowmobiler caught, buried, and killed

WEATHER AND SNOWPACK CONDITIONS

This accident came just four days after—and 10 miles north—of a fatal avalanche triggered on Hancock Pass (20030305). The Weather and Snowpack Conditions leading up to these events were almost identical.

Snowfall in February was above normal throughout the Colorado mountains. Crested Butte, 25 miles west of the avalanche site, had gotten 152% of its normal February snowfall; and Monarch, 20 miles to the south, had gotten 184% of normal. This kept the avalanche danger hovering in the "Considerable-to-High" range for much of February—a trend that continued into March.

On March 1 and 2, new snow measured at Monarch was 13 inches, and this was followed by continued snowfall from March 4 to 7. Equally important for creating a high avalanche danger was the winds, which were strong and persistent, and created slab

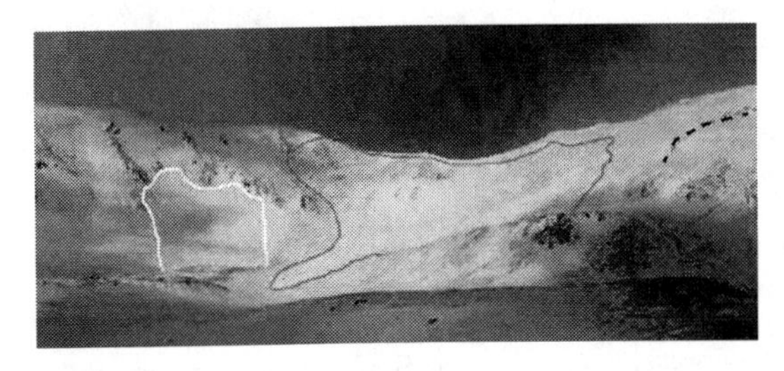

The fatal avalanche is the center gray outline. The dashed line to the right is a very small part of the sympathetic release. The left outline is the natural avalanche three days prior. *Photo Dale Atkins, Colorado Avalanche Information Center.*

conditions especially on north through southeast aspects. Avalanche warnings were posted from March 4 to 7. On March 9, the avalanche danger was rated Considerable.

ACCIDENT SUMMARY

Ptarmigan Lake sits above timberline at an elevation of 12,132 feet. It's in a large east-facing basin on the Continental Divide in Colorado's Sawatch Range. The lake is four miles south of Cottonwood Pass and 14 air-miles west of Buena Vista. The mountain rising above the lake is Jones Mountain, and it tops out at 12,995 feet. Ptarmigan Lake is a popular hiking destination in the summer, and the basin provides good snowmobiling in the winter.

On Sunday, March 9, Wayne Wilkinson (42) and his wife Teri were snowmobiling in the east-facing Ptarmigan Lake Basin area. The Wilkinsons were in Buena Vista for a snowmobile convention. They were the only two of their group in the Ptarmigan Lake area; the rest were several miles away, near Cottonwood Pass.

Three days earlier, an avalanche had released toward the south end of Jones Mountain above Ptarmigan Lake. The fracture line and debris area, though partially filled in, were still visible—a pretty good clue of unstable snow.

Around 10:00, Wilkinson was riding in the basin north of this previous avalanche while his wife watched from below. He was hill climbing when he triggered a large avalanche that released about 300 feet above him. He and his snowmobile were carried back down the mountainside and totally buried. Teri Wilkinson was beyond the runout area and witnessed the entire avalanche. She was the only witness.

RESCUE SUMMARY

No rescue equipment

Other riders came onto the scene, but Wilkinson was not wearing an avalanche beacon, so the searchers scanned the debris for any sign of the victim or his snowmobile. There were no signs. One of the searchers called the Chaffee County Sheriff, who received the call at 10:48. A search team was dispatched from Buena Vista, plus a call was made to Sue Purvis, an avalanche dog handler in Crested Butte.

The avalanche was 1,100 feet wide. Even when the searchers focused in the area where Teri Wilkinson had last seen Wayne, it was still a large area to search. Probing had located nothing by the time Sue Purvis and her dog Tasha arrived on scene at 14:20. Tasha alerted after a long search, and Wilkinson was dug out from under six feet of snow at 16:00. He had long since died. His snowmobile was later found with a probe.

AVALANCHE DATA

Deep Persistent Slab avalanche

This avalanche was classified as HS-AMu-R3-G, and it was a classic hard slab: the debris field looked like a rocky scree pile—with some blocks the size of cars. The slide released on an east aspect at an elevation of 12,800 feet and fell about 600 feet vertical. The crown ranged in depth from 1.5 to 10 feet, with most of the crown being eight feet deep. It was 1,100 feet wide. The slope angle in the starting zone ranged from 34 to 39 degrees.

At the same time this avalanche was triggered, the adjacent slope to the north on Jones Mountain also released sympathetically. This sympathetic hard-slab avalanche was about 3,000 feet across.

The initial report on the size of this avalanche was that it was a mile wide. It was not, but the area of instability was a mile wide when three avalanche releases were linked together. The first release was the natural avalanche on the south end of Jones Mountain that ran some three days before, the second release was the fatal avalanche in the middle, and the third was the sympathetic release on the north flank of Jones Mountain.

COMMENTS

The victim in this avalanche was not wearing a beacon, but in an avalanche of this size—and the resulting deep burial in dense debris—rescue could not have come fast enough for a beacon to have saved his life. The main fault in this accident was a lack of avalanche awareness. Wayne and Teri Wilkinson were not locals. It would be most interesting to know if the current avalanche danger level—Considerable—was brought up at the convention they were attending.

20030309b

MT. ABUNDANCE, NORTH OF COOKE CITY, MONTANA

March 9, 2003

Three snowmobilers caught; two buried, one killed

WEATHER AND SNOWPACK CONDITIONS

The Absaroka and Beartooth Ranges north of Cooke City, Montana, experienced an exceptional temperature warm-up in late February, and this created a melt-freeze crust on the mountain snowpack. Then, as often happens with these crusts, facets formed on the surface, only to be buried by the next snowfall, which came on March 1. This was followed by a major snowstorm on March 5 to 9, which dropped 60 inches (five feet!) of snow. This snow contained five inches of snow-water equivalent. That's an inch of water per day for five days.

High avalanche danger

During this storm period, west winds averaging 20 to 40 mph—and gusting above 50 mph—created heavy blowing snow, which loaded all slopes with easterly aspects. On March 9, it was still snowing and blowing hard, and the avalanche danger was rated High.

ACCIDENT SUMMARY

Mt. Abundance is a 10,098-foot peak about eight miles northwest of Cooke City, Montana. It's a popular area for snowmobilers, but its slopes are steep and avalanche prone. Mt. Abundance has been the site of several fatal avalanches triggered by snowmobilers (see 20020216).

More than one person on a slope

On Sunday, March 9, a party of four snowmobilers was riding on the southwest flank of Mt. Abundance. All four carried full avalanche rescue gear of beacons, probes, and shovels. The time was 11:15 when one of the riders was climbing a slope and got stuck. Two of the other three riders went up to help dig out the stuck machine, and that's when the avalanche released. All three men were caught and carried down the slope. One managed to stay on the surface and was not buried. A second man was totally buried, but he had a hand on the surface and was able to clear the snow from around his face. The third victim, a 52-year-old man, was totally buried. All three snowmobiles were also buried.

RESCUE SUMMARY

The rider who had stayed at the bottom of the slope was not caught in the avalanche. He started uphill and joined the man who had been caught but not buried. One of those dug out the man with a hand out who had cleared the snow from around his face. The other survivor started a beacon search and quickly got a signal. Two other survivors joined him, and together they pinpointed the burial location of the fourth man and started digging.

The rescuers dug out the buried man in about 15 minutes. He had been buried two feet deep and was not breathing when uncovered. The rescuers started CPR immediately and continued it for an hour. The victim never responded. They then called Cooke City SAR, who responded and evacuated the victim.

AVALANCHE DATA

This was a fairly small avalanche that was classified as HS-AMu-R3-D2-O. It released on an east-facing slope at an elevation of 9,200 feet and fell 250 feet vertical. The crown was 2.5 feet deep and 200 feet wide. The avalanche had been triggered in the lower third of the path, where the slope angle was 30 to 33 degrees, but the slope angle at the top of the slope where the fracture occurred was 40 to 41 degrees. The alpha angle was 26 degrees. The debris in the runout was seven feet deep.

COMMENTS

The avalanche report does not mention whether this group was highmarking or rather climbing the slope to get to other terrain. That is not an important distinction in analyzing this accident. What is important is that this group broke a cardinal rule of riding—if one rider gets stuck on a steep slope, do not go to his aid. Let him get himself unstuck.

Though this seems unkind, it is well grounded as safe procedure. A steep, unstable slope is more likely to avalanche if stressed by several riders and machines as opposed to only one. Digging out a stuck snowmobile on a steep slope is exhausting work, but for safety's sake, it's a job best left to one rider.

PORCUPINE PEAK, WEST OF ARAPAHOE BASIN, COLORADO | March 20, 2003

20030320

Two sidecountry skiers caught and partly buried; one injured, one killed

WEATHER AND SNOWPACK CONDITIONS

A storm that may come around once in 20 or 30 years hit the Front Range of Colorado on the morning of March 17. A deep low-pressure set up over southeast Colorado and pumped in copious moisture from the Gulf of Mexico. The result was four days of snowfall for the Front Range. By March 21, some areas on the east slope of the mountains got seven feet of snow. Arapahoe Basin ski area, on the crest of the Front Range, got 63 inches.

ACCIDENT SUMMARY

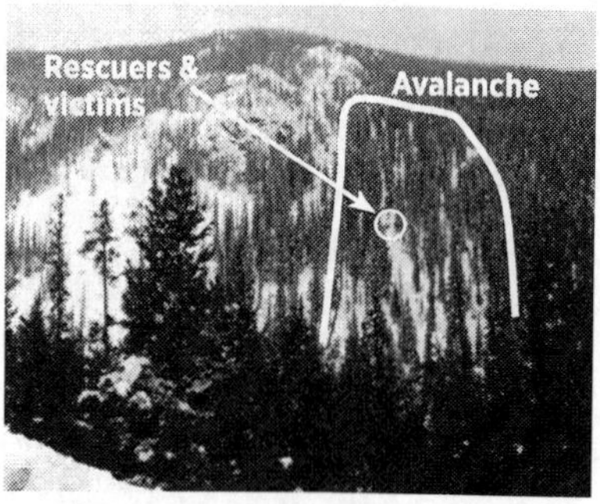

During the storm on Thursday, March 20, a party of four skiers left the boundary of Arapahoe Basin via a backcountry access gate. The four men were K. C. Ratcliff (30), Russ Sikorski, Garrett Seal (36), and Tim Putz (33). All were experienced backcountry skiers, were avalanche savvy, and were equipped with beacons, shovels, and first-aid kits. They had called the local avalanche hotline that morning and knew the avalanche danger was rated High to Extreme. They took this information into consideration when discussing where and how they would ski.

High avalanche danger

Looking south from US 6 to Porcupine Peak. The white line marks the approximate location of the crown and flanks of the March 20, 2003 avalanche. *Photo Nick Logan, Colorado Avalanche Information Center.*

From the ski area boundary, they traveled west about a mile and a half, traveling the ridgeline toward Porcupine Peak. This ridgeline parallels US Highway 6, and the group's plan was to ski a northwest-facing slope to the bottom, cross the north fork of the Snake River, climb some 100 vertical feet to the highway, and hitchhike back to Arapahoe Basin. While they traveled toward Porcupine Peak, they observed no signs of imminent avalanche danger, such as fresh natural avalanches, shooting cracks, or a collapsing snowpack.

The group chose to avoid open slopes and decided to stay in the trees because of the avalanche danger. They normally skied one at a time and spotted each other on potential avalanche slopes. That was not possible in the treed area that they chose to ski, so the group decided to ski one at a time to the creek bottom by going in two-minute intervals.

The time was about 15:00 when Tim Putz went first and made it to the bottom with no problems. Garrett Seal went second, also encountering no problems, and stopped before reaching the bottom.

More than one person on a slope

Ratcliff started downhill; Sikorski followed a few seconds later. After a few turns, one or both of these skiers triggered an avalanche. The avalanche caught both skiers and swept them through the trees at high speed, and both had high-impact collisons with trees.

Near the bottom of the slope, both Seal and Putz heard trees snapping and saw the avalanche coming at them. Seal turned and headed toward the creek. Putz tried to ski to the side, but saw the avalanche bearing down on him. He bent over and flipped the heelpieces loose to get rid of his skis and "shinnied up a tree" as the avalanche rushed under him. The avalanche stopped a short distance below his tree perch.

When the avalanche stopped, the two skiers down below made voice contact with Ratcliff. Putz was able to make a 911 call on his cell phone and then went to the highway to summon other help, if available. Seal dropped out of the tree he had climbed and found both of his skis and one pole. He put his climbing skins back on and rushed up the debris.

He found that Sikorski had broken both legs, and that Ratcliff had hit a tree and was in agony, curled around the tree. Sikorski, despite his injuries, had slid downhill to Ratliff to offer aid, if possible. Sikorski and Seal did what little they could for Ratcliff; Seal wrapped his body around the victim to keep him as warm as possible.

RESCUE SUMMARY
Dan Burnett of the Summit County Rescue Team got the page at 15:20 and was the first rescuer to reach the site. It took him 20 minutes to drive to the site on the highway, and another 20 minutes to snowshoe uphill to reach the victims. Ratcliff told Burnett that his head and back hurt and that he was very cold. Burnett gave extra clothing to Ratcliff and then wrapped him in a space blanket and got him in a sleeping bag lined with chemical heat packs.

Other rescuers arrived, including paramedics and members of the Arapahoe Basin Ski Patrol. They put Ratcliff in a toboggan and lowered him down to the creek, and then lifted him to the highway. There a Flight-for-Life Helicopter flew him out. At some point during this rescue process, Ratliff lost consciousness and went into cardiac arrest. He died of head, skeletal, and other internal injuries.

AVALANCHE DATA
The victims triggered this avalanche on a northwest-facing slope at an elevation of 10,800 feet, and the slide fell 600 feet vertical. The crown was four to six feet deep and 200 feet wide. The avalanche ran to ground in places and was classified as HS-ASu-R3-D2 G.

Persistent Slab avalanche

COMMENTS
This group of four skiers was experienced and was used to skiing slopes that can avalanche. They all had rescue gear, they knew the avalanche danger was high to extreme, and they made a plan on how they would ski the slope one at a time. They knew an avalanche on this day on this slope was possible, even likely; but the lure of an exceptional powder run was strong. Essentially, they rolled the dice and lost. The snowpack on this day was just too unstable.

Two further comments are warranted. First, it seems the group broke their safety procedure of skiing one at a time, for two men were moving in the staring zone at once. That's twice the load on the snowpack, which made it more likely to overload the weak layer.

Second, slopes having trees usually become more dangerous once an avalanche releases. The reason? Those trees become battering rams that can injure or kill victims being rapidly swept downhill.

BURRO MOUNTAIN, NORTHWEST OF DURANGO, COLORADO | March 22, 2003

20030322

One snowmobiler caught, buried, and killed

ACCIDENT SUMMARY
The La Plata Mountains are located in southwest Colorado and are the southernmost extension of the large expanse of the San Juan Mountains. Burro Mountain, at 11,575 feet elevation, is situated 20 miles northwest of Durango and 14 miles south of the small town of Rico.

Saturday, March 22 was a sunny day over most of Colorado and the Four Corners region. However, southwest winds of about 25 mph were causing blowing snow, which was loading the steep north side of Burro Mountain. Locals know this slope to be avalanche prone.

A group of nine snowmobilers was riding in the area, and some were highmarking on the north slope. The time was about 13:00 when Lee Austin (22) climbed the slope and became stuck halfway up. Austin's brother rode up to assist but had to turn back down when he could not make it high enough. As Austin's brother was descending, the avalanche broke above Lee Austin. The brother was able to outrun the avalanche, but it hit Lee and carried him down the slope. He and his snowmobile were totally buried. Neither he nor any of his group were equipped with avalanche rescue gear.

No rescue equipment

RESCUE SUMMARY

Numerous other riders in the area witnessed the avalanche. One of Austin's friends called 911 on his cell phone at 13:09. Minutes later, the Miguel County Search and Rescue dispatcher called Colorado Helitrax, a heli-ski company based in Telluride that also assists in rescues in the San Jan Mountains. Helitrax was flying skiing clients at the time, and they returned to base to drop off their clients and flew toward the avalanche site. Additional rescue groups also responded.

In the meantime, searchers scoured the avalanche debris and had located Austin's snowmobile and his helmet, both near the toe of the debris. The Helitrax helicopter flew the 20 miles from Telluride and landed at about 14:00 with two avalanche dogs with handlers, two Helitrax guides, and four members of San Miguel County SAR.

The dog teams and probe lines began a systematic search of the debris, and in 20 minutes a probe struck the victim at a spot near the toe of the debris but 40 feet laterally from his snowmobile. Rescuers uncovered Lee Austin from five feet of snow. He was unresponsive but showed no signs of trauma, and rescuers initiated CPR. A paramedic also used a defibrillator, but without success. Austin was pronounced dead after about an hour of resuscitation efforts.

AVALANCHE DATA

Persistent Slab avalanche

The avalanche occurred on the north-facing slope of Burro Mountain at an elevation of about 11,450 feet and fell about 600 feet vertical. The crown varied from four to six feet deep and was 700 feet wide. The slide was classified as HS-AMu-R3-O.

COMMENTS

This is a popular area for snowmobiling, and several of the riders in Austin's party and other parties riding in the area had seen avalanches on Burro Mountain slide before. Yet few, if any, of the riders in the area carried avalanche rescue gear. This terrain demands that riders—especially those who are highmarking—be equipped for avalanche rescue. It's not a matter of *if*; it's a matter of *when*.

20030410 VERDE PEAK, SOUTHEAST OF CHITINA, ALASKA

April 10, 2003

One guided backcountry skier caught, buried, and killed

ACCIDENT SUMMARY

Alaska's Wrangell–St. Elias National Park and Preserve is the largest national park in the United States, covering 13 million acres. About 40 miles southeast of Chitina, the eastern end of the Chugach Mountains extends into the park. Verde Peak, at 7,250 feet elevation, is in this remote area of the Chugach Mountains.

Two Anchorage doctors, Robert Pulliam III (55) and Hedric Hanson (61), were staying at a lodge on the Chitina River. They were taking guided day trips, skiing in the nearby mountains. Their guide was Drew Lovell (27), who worked for Ultima Thule Outfitters. For several days, Pulliam skied right behind Lovell, making turn for turn. Every day, all three wore beacons and carried probes and shovels.

It was early Thursday afternoon on April 10 when the group of three was descending a ridge off the south side of Verde Peak. Lovell, their guide, was in the lead and skiing the ridgeline when Pulliam suddenly turned off the ridge and dropped into the top of a steep gully. Neither Hanson nor Lovell knew why Pulliam veered off the ridge, but they stopped skiing and looked back.

Pulliam had stopped on the steep slope and was some distance behind Lovell and Hanson. They watched from the ridge as Pulliam turned around, probably to climb out on the track where he had come in. That's when the avalanche released. Initially, it was a small avalanche, but after a few seconds, the fracture propagated across the top of the gully and became a large avalanche. In places it scoured the snow cover down to the rocks. Pulliam was carried in a massive pile of debris down about 1,700 feet to the bottom of the gully.

RESCUE SUMMARY

Lovell was able to descend the avalanche path, and near the bottom, he got a beacon signal. Lovell dug Pulliam out from under several feet of avalanche debris, but Pulliam had been killed by "severe head trauma." The following day, a rescue team made up of Ultima guides and the owner and employees of the lodge was able to recover Pulliam's body.

AVALANCHE DATA

The fracture of this avalanche was described as five feet deep. It broke to the ground, and it fell about 1,700 feet. The classification probably was HS-ASu-R3-G.

Persistent Slab avalanche

COMMENTS

Neither Hanson nor Lovell could understand why Pulliam had suddenly veered into terrain that Lovell was guiding them to avoid. Whatever the reason, it was a fatal mistake. We keep preaching that rescue equipment is required to give victims a chance to survive (and that is very good advice), but this avalanche was too big and he fell too far to survive.

In a strange coincidence, this avalanche has a link to another fatal avalanche in *The Snowy Torrents*. The victim, Robert Pulliam, was a cardiologist and a member of the Alaska Heart Institute, and was medical director for cardiology at the Providence Alaska Medical Center in Anchorage. Two years earlier, on April 28, 2001, another doctor at Providence Alaska Medical Center—Scott Dull (39)—died in an avalanche in Utah (20010428). Dull was an emergency room physician and was also the state medical director of emergency services.

20030426

CHARITY VALLEY, SOUTH OF LAKE TAHOE, CALIFORNIA

April 26, 2003

One snowmobiler caught, buried, and killed

WEATHER AND SNOWPACK CONDITIONS

April had been a very snowy month in the Sierra Nevada of California. Squaw Valley Ski Area, near the north end of Lake Tahoe, had reported about 10 feet of snowfall thus far in the month of April, and about 20 inches of snow fell in the two or three days prior to the avalanche.

ACCIDENT SUMMARY

Charity Valley is located in California about 10 miles south of South Lake Tahoe and five miles west of Markleeville. It is a mountainous region east of the Sierra Crest and is a popular area for snowmobiling, with riders coming in via the Blue Lakes Road and playing in the terrain around the Upper and Lower Blue Lakes.

No rescue equipment

On Saturday afternoon, April 26, Louis Magnotti (43) was riding with friends. None in the group had any avalanche rescue gear. At some point, Magnotti triggered an avalanche that threw up a powder cloud, enveloping him and his snowmobile. When the snow settled, his friends could find no sign of Magnotti. Witnesses searched for 45 minutes and found only his snowmobile, which had one skid sticking out of the snow.

RESCUE SUMMARY

It was almost evening before a search and rescue team arrived at the scene. Forty rescuers worked the area with probes, but evidently that was difficult work because the debris was loaded with large blocks of hard-slab snow. It wasn't until 23:15 that they found Magnotti's body under five feet of snow.

AVALANCHE DATA

Persistent Slab avalanche

The avalanche released at an elevation of 8,200 feet and fell 200 feet vertical down a northeast-facing slope. The avalanche evidently released on a steep rollover with one estimate of the slope angle at the crown being 50 degrees, and that would account for the crown being estimated at seven feet deep and 200 feet wide. This was a hard slab avalanche, with the debris field being up to eight feet deep and with numerous blocks of hard snow four to five feet in diameter. It was classified as HS-AMu-R3-O. The alpha angle was measured at 25 degrees.

COMMENTS

The Charity Valley area did not have a reputation of posing a high avalanche hazard, despite plenty of steep terrain. To the trained eye, however, tree damage is evident, which means there have certainly been big avalanches in the past. But there was no history of avalanche accidents in the area, and as best as could be determined, this was the first avalanche death known to have occurred in this part of the Sierra Nevada—at least in several decades. Perhaps for this reason, many of the snowmobilers who rode here did not carry avalanche rescue gear such as beacons, probes, or shovels. But this fatal avalanche was deep and fairly large, which might be what it takes to boost the local level of avalanche awareness and safety.

2003–2004
SEASON

20031212 ARTIST POINT, MT. BAKER, WASHINGTON | December 12, 2003

Three snowshoers caught and buried; two injured, one killed

WEATHER AND SNOWPACK CONDITIONS

The first week of December in Washington's Cascade Range had been warm enough for thaw-freeze conditions to form a crust on much of the snowpack. Then, beginning on Thursday, December 11, temperatures dropped and snowfall began. By Friday morning, about a foot of low-density snow had fallen in the Mt. Baker area of the North Cascades, and snowfall continued on Friday.

On Friday morning, the Mt. Baker Ski Patrol reported a number of natural avalanche releases about 10 inches deep and shallow, easily-triggered slabs. The Northwest Avalanche Center was rating the avalanche danger as Considerable above 4,000 feet elevation.

ACCIDENT SUMMARY

On Friday morning, December 12, three students from Western Washington University in Bellingham took off on a snowshoe day-trip to celebrate the end of finals. They were Greg Bachmeier (22), Laurie Ballew (21), and Jacqueline "JP" Eckstrom (21). They drove to the Mt. Baker Ski Area; just past the ski area is the designated parking lot for Artist Point. They strapped on their snowshoes and began the trek to Artist Point, which is south of the ski area. At an elevation of 5,100 feet, Artist Point is slightly west of Mt. Baker and Mt. Shuksan and offers spectacular views—but not on this day, since it was snowing heavily and visibility was marginal.

These three students were well equipped for the weather and snow conditions. They were warmly dressed and had food, water, and extra clothing in their packs. They had not considered avalanche danger as a possibility. As Bachmeier later said, "It's a common trail; it's a road in the summertime. It didn't strike me as an area that would be prone to avalanches. Snowshoeing, you basically think of as safe." So they never considered that they should be equipped with avalanche rescue equipment as well.

No rescue equipment

The first hour of their trip was uneventful, though it was starting to become more strenuous than anticipated, as they were breaking trail in two feet of new snow, and that snow was deepening the higher they went. Then they ran into some backcountry skiers who were descending. This group mentioned that it could be a little dangerous going all the way to Artist Point, so Bachmeier, Ballew, and Eckstrom agreed to head for the top of a saddle not too far away, near the summer road's last big switchback before Artist Point. That seemed like a good lunch spot. Bachmeier gave his ski poles to Eckstrom because she needed them more than he did for walking in the deep snow.

The time was about 11:00. The group had been on the trail about two hours and had climbed up about 700 feet in elevation. They were close to their destination but had one last slope to climb. This one was steeper than any they had encountered. Bachmeier started up but couldn't get traction, so he retreated to where Ballew and Eckstrom were standing to look for a better route.

That's when the slope silently fractured about 50 feet above them and 80 feet wide.[1] The avalanche hit all three, carried them a short distance, and completely buried them. Ballew remembers being buried in a sitting position and the snow setting up quickly. She was able to move her hands to clear an airspace around her face, but that's all she could move. Her body and legs were cemented in the snow and she could breathe, but barely. She could see it was slightly brighter above her head, which she estimated was three feet below the surface.

The avalanche knocked the breath out of Bachmeier and buried him flat on his back, four to five feet deep. He could see dim light above and could move his arms, and then was able to punch upward and clear the space around his face. He yelled from beneath the snow. There was no answer.

He tried to move his body to make room so that he could reach down to move snow to free his body and legs, but his snowshoes, still attached, were locked in the snow. Every so often, he yelled out hoping for some response, but none came. As darkness was approaching, he heard a snowmobile, but the sound faded. Later, he learned that was the Mt. Baker Ski Patrol on sweep, checking the ski-area boundary.

Darkness came and Bachmeier kept working to free himself, helped by pressing the light button on his watch. Finally, at 02:30, after being buried for more than 15 hours, he was able to wiggle out of his backpack to get food, water, and extra clothing. With the light of dawn approaching, he had moved enough snow from around his legs to reach down and release the bindings on his snowshoes. Once freed, he could move his legs and gain enough purchase to sit up and dig his way to the surface. He emerged from his snow tomb at 09:00, 22 hours after being buried.[2]

When he scanned the snowscape, he saw that another eight inches of snow had fallen while he had been buried. What he didn't see was any sign of Ballew or Eckstrom. With his snowshoes still buried deeply and no shovel to dig down to them, Bachmeier was stranded. Since he had given his ski poles away before the avalanche, he had no way to probe to search for his companions. He tried wallowing down the trail, but it was too exhausting. Then he heard voices, and he shouted out. Two backcountry skiers came into view. Bachmeier told them what had happened and that the two women were still missing. One skier, Barrett Gribble, stayed with Bachmeier while the other, Aaron DeBoer, skied to the ski area to summon help.

RESCUE SUMMARY

DeBoer reached the ski area and contacted Duncan Howat, the general manager. Those two tried to return to the avalanche site on a snowmobile, but it bogged down in the deep snow. DeBoer got off and skied the rest of the way to the site, while Howat returned to the ski area to get a snowcat—fully expecting this would be needed for the inevitable body recovery.

Back at the avalanche site, several other snowshoers had arrived and offered help. DeBoer and Gribble put Bachmeier in the care of the snowshoers until the snowcat arrived, and then they skied to the hole in the snow where Bachmeier had been buried. They began searching the area with the probes they were carrying in their packs. It took an hour, but one of the searchers struck a leg and then a body under three to four feet of snow. It was Eckstrom, and both rescuers knew she was dead.

As the two men were uncovering Eckstrom's body, Gribble's foot suddenly sank into a hole and hit the head of the other victim, Ballew. When they cleared the snow from what they thought was a second frozen body, Ballew spoke: "Hello," and then she was able to say her name.

Ballew was taken by snowcat to the ski area first-aid room, where her core temperature was measured at 85.5°F. Then she was transported by ambulance to the hospital in Bellingham. Her lasting injuries were not severe—minor frostbite and nerve damage in one leg. Bachmeier suffered frostbite on his hands and a wrenched knee.

AVALANCHE DATA

Storm Slab avalanche

The avalanche was classified as SS-AIu-R1-I. The fracture was 10 to 18 inches deep and about 80 feet wide. It probably fell 100 to 150 feet vertical. The slope faced northwest and was at an elevation of 4,700 feet. It was probably a Storm Slab avalanche, sliding at the interface of the old crust.

COMMENTS

It is a miracle that Bachmeier and Ballew had survived burials of 22 and 24 hours. A few favorable circumstances allowed this to happen. First, the victims were dressed well, with several layers of insulation and breathable, waterproof shells. Second, the avalanche was small and the snow was low density. This helped in two ways: it kept the avalanche debris from packing tightly around the victims, giving them a slight amount of movement, and it allowed for a flow of air so they could breathe. Many avalanche victims die from re-breathing the oxygen-poor, carbon dioxide-rich air they just exhaled.

This group did not recognize the danger posed by this steep slope with a fresh load of storm snow. A more seasoned group would have been suspicious enough to avoid it altogether, or at least cross it one at a time.

20031213 SOUTH FORK SNOQUALMIE RIVER, NORTHWEST OF SNOQUALMIE PASS, WASHINGTON | December 13, 2003

One snowshoer caught, buried, and killed

WEATHER AND SNOWPACK CONDITIONS

Snoqualmie Pass is located 50 miles east of Seattle and is the site of several ski areas and plenty of backcountry terrain for skiing and snowshoeing. I-90 runs over the pass. On December 10 to 12, 19 inches of snow fell at the pass, and on Saturday December 13, heavy snow fell all day, with 14 inches accumulating from 9:00 to 15:00. The avalanche danger was rated as Considerable to High, and the Northwest Avalanche Center issued an avalanche warning that morning. Snowfall continued throughout the day and was heavy enough to cause the closure of I-90 over Snoqualmie Pass.

High avalanche danger

ACCIDENT SUMMARY

Late morning on Saturday, a group of several snowshoers headed up toward Snow Lake, which is the headwater of the Middle Fork of the Snoqualmie River. The snowshoe group was not on the main Snow Lake Trail, which is on the east side of the river, but were rather on the west side of the valley—the same side as Alpental Ski Area.

The time was about 11:30 when the avalanche released. This was either a natural avalanche or it was triggered by the snowshoe group. The group was traveling beneath an area known as the Mushroom Couloir when a 38-year-old woman was hit and carried off the trail and completely buried. Her companions were unable to locate any sign of her. No one in the group was equipped with avalanche rescue gear. One person called 911.

No rescue equipment

RESCUE SUMMARY

At 11:51, the Alpental Ski Patrol got a call on the avalanche and as quickly as possible dispatched a team of patrollers to the site. Due to the high avalanche danger, the responding ski patrollers traveled the safer route up-valley on the ski area side (east side of the South Fork of the Snoqualmie River), attempting to locate the scene of the avalanche through visual or verbal contact. En route, further reports indicated that the scene was indeed on the ski area side of the valley.

At 13:09 the first ski patrollers arrived on scene after traveling up-valley about three quarters of a mile and breaking trail through many days of snowfall. Members of the Ski Patrol Avalanche Rescue Team (SPART) soon joined this initial team. Also by this time, 26 backcountry recreationists (all without transceivers, shovels, or probes) were at the scene, helping to search for the victim. To reduce the chaos, the rescue site commander sent all these people out of the area and to the checkpoint in the parking lot.

A ski area grooming machine cut a road half a mile up the valley floor to transport personnel and equipment. The area of debris was about 150 feet by 150 feet and varied in depth from 1.5 feet to seven feet. Initially, a transceiver search was made of the entire debris field twice with no signal detected. Then, 45 rescuers fine-probed the area with no strikes. At the same time, six rescue dogs also worked it, with only a few moderate alerts. All alerts were probed further and excavated to various depths, finding nothing.

On the extreme left flank of the path was a gully/terrain trap consisting of a large rock outcropping on the right of the gully, a cliff on the left, and constriction between them measuring 11 feet at its narrowest. This particular area was probed and partially shoveled out by 12 to 18 rescuers, but that, too, yielded nothing. Finally, at 17:35 (one hour after dark), with continued snowfall and increasing avalanche hazard, the search was terminated, with the intent to resume the next day.

The search continued on Sunday, December 14. Almost two feet of snow had fallen since the avalanche occurred, so rescuers used explosives to mitigate for avalanches before teams were sent into the debris. Teams totaling 37 rescuers and multiple rescue dogs (some new to the scene) worked the area for seven hours with fine probing and dog coverage. Again, nothing was found. Rescuers repeated the search on Monday, again with negative results.

The search was suspended for five days until December 20, when a RECCO device was brought to the site. RECCO is a hand-held radar unit that sends a signal that is reflected by a RECCO tab sewn into clothing or embedded in ski boots. The reflected signal can be traced to its source. This was something of a long shot, hoping that the victim was wearing clothing with a RECCO tab sewn in, but once more, a search of the entire debris area produced nothing.

During the search period of December 13 to 20, rescuers were mystified as to how multiple organized searches with dozens of people and 11 different rescue dogs could have missed someone—especially considering the relatively small size of the slide and area of deposition. However, following the RECCO search, several rescuers stayed on site on December 20 to further probe the area along the left flank of the debris where the gully/terrain trap could be hiding the body.

Terrain trap

Four men began trenching in this 11-foot-wide swath of snow between two vertical rock bands. They trenched six feet down and they saw that the rock on the skier's right side was undercut, creating a large cavity that had been filled by snow from the avalanche. They probed at an angle beneath the undercut and got an immediate strike. They began shoveling and soon uncovered an ice axe, a trekking pole, and the tip of a snowshoe. Finally, after searching for seven days, they found the woman's body. The undercut in the rock wall went in four feet and was large enough to entirely trap a human body.

AVALANCHE DATA

The avalanche was a shallow soft slab with a crown depth of less than a foot. It released on an east-northeast-facing slope at an elevation of about 3,400 feet. The slope angle was 35 to 37 degrees, and the avalanche fell 200 to 300 feet slope distance.

A definitive classification for this cannot be made. It was either triggered by the snowshoers and therefore a SS-AIu-R2, or it was triggered by sluffing snow off the cliffs above and therefore a SS-N-R2.

COMMENTS

The avalanche danger this day was rated High. This group of snowshoers carried no avalanche rescue gear, and their route was below a very steep area of cliffs. So it is probably safe to say that they had not considered the possibility of an avalanche on their outing to Snow Lake. We can say the same about the 26 other people—none of whom had rescue gear—who showed up to help search.

This avalanche was small, and in other circumstances—an open run-out area, for example—it would have been easily survivable. However, a fluke terrain trap led to a deep burial with little chance of survival.

20031217 NAVAJO PEAK, NORTHWEST OF BLEWETT PASS, WASHINGTON | December 17, 2003

One snowmobiler caught, buried, and killed

WEATHER AND SNOWPACK CONDITIONS

In early December, rain fell on the snowpack of the Cascades in central Washington. The snow surface then froze into a crust which—as so often happens—provided the perfect environment for a thin layer of surface hoar and/or near-surface facets to form. In the four days leading up to the avalanche, an estimated twelve inches of snow fell on Navajo Peak. The snowfall was accompanied by west winds that would have helped to load leeward slopes (northeast through southeast). The Northwest Avalanche Center rated the danger on December 17 as Considerable above 5,000 to 6,000 feet elevation.

ACCIDENT SUMMARY

Navajo Peak is a 7,223-foot mountain in the Wenatchee Mountains, which is a subrange of the Cascades in central Washington. The peak is located about 12 miles west-northwest of Blewett Pass on Highway 97.

Inadequate rescue equipment

On Wednesday, December 17, a group of four very experienced snowmobilers was highmarking on the southeast flank of Navajo Peak. The local snowmobile community knows that this slope slides frequently. Three of the four riders had beacons, probes, and shovels, but the victim was not wearing a beacon. In any case, the victim was reported as riding "very well" that day and was near the top of the slope at 13:00. He was in the midst of making his turn back downhill when he triggered a medium-sized slab avalanche. The victim turned back uphill and "gunned it," attempting to ride uphill off the slab.

His effort was unsuccessful and despite his proximity to the crown, the victim was carried down-slope with his snowmobile. The avalanche took its victim 1,100 feet vertical and swept him into an area near the toe, where the debris field narrowed and deepened. Both the rider and his snowmobile were completely buried.

The victim's three companions were watching from the bottom of the slope in a safe spot. They tried to watch their friend as he was carried downhill, but quickly lost sight of him because "there was a big cloud of snow and we couldn't see anything."

RESCUE SUMMARY

When the avalanche settled and the victim's companions could again see the snow surface, there were no signs of either the snowmobile or the victim. One of the group called 911, and then all three began a visual and probe search. Unfortunately, they found nothing. In time, members of the Chelan County Sheriff's Department responded and coordinated the search effort. Through the afternoon, additional rescuers were flown in by helicopter. With limited personnel, probing made no strikes. A rescue dog and handler from the Mission Ridge Ski Patrol worked the debris briefly, with one so-so alert. Darkness prevented a thorough search of that area, and the search was suspended at nightfall.

At 6:00 on Thursday, December 18, rescue efforts were reinitiated, but low clouds delayed helicopter flights until later in the morning. The first flight was prepared to drop explosives into the avalanche starting zone to clear any hang-fire pockets. However, when they arrived on site, they saw several snowmobilers already in the area. These were friends of the victim who had ridden in early in the morning to conduct their own search. These volunteers had to be cleared from the area before any helicopter control mission could take place. One small slab was released during that mission, and then the rescue leader deemed the scene safe for the recovery effort to continue.

Once teams of rescuers were on site, several probe lines were established. Additionally, the rescue dog and handler from Mission Ridge worked the area, and that's how the victim was found. The dog alerted in the same general area where it had shown interest the evening before. The dog handler probed and made the strike. Shovelers uncovered the victim from beneath five feet of snow. A while later, probers located the snowmobile, 10 feet away and also five feet deep.

AVALANCHE DATA

This avalanche was classified as SS-AMu-R3-O. The crown was 19 inches deep and 120 feet wide. The slide released at an elevation of 6,600 feet and descended the 36-degree slope about 1,100 feet vertical. The slope faced southeast.

Persistent Slab avalanche

COMMENTS

This group of riders was known to be experienced, and—properly—they were riding one at a time on a slope they all knew had a history of avalanches. Yet inexplicably, one of the four was not wearing a beacon. As fate would have it, that was the man who became the victim. Would a beacon have saved this man's life, given the five-foot burial? Perhaps not, but a slim chance is better than no chance. A snowmobiler, also with inadequate rescue gear, was killed in an avalanche south of Blewett Pass in January 1998 (19980118c).

20031226

ASPEN GROVE, WEST OF SUNDANCE RESORT, UTAH

December 26, 2003

Five snowboarders caught; two partly buried, three buried and killed

WEATHER AND SNOWPACK CONDITIONS

High avalanche danger

A few days before Christmas 2003, the second-largest storm in the history of Salt Lake City began. When the storm ended a few days after Christmas, the city had gotten about three feet of snow—with four feet piling up on the "bench" on the east side of the city. The Wasatch Range got five to six feet of snow, with most of this falling in two days. On Friday, December 26, the Utah Avalanche Center rated the avalanche danger as High.

ACCIDENT SUMMARY

On the day after Christmas, Friday the 26th, a group of five young men set out for a day of backcountry snowboarding in the Provo area of Utah's Wasatch Range. From Provo Canyon, they went past Sundance Resort on Highway 92 and parked at the Aspen Grove Recreation Area. This area is on the lower northeast slope of 11,750-foot Mt. Timpanogos.

More than one person on a slope

The five men were Adam Merz (18), Mike Hebert (20), Rod Newberry (20), J. D. Settle, and Matt Long. They ended up snowboarding in the Robert's Horn Chute area—a chute between cliffs where avalanches that release from large slopes above must pass through. These five men were not alone in the area: an estimated 14 people were on lower slope when a natural avalanche released from high above.

J. D. Settle later recalled that the time was about 16:25 when the group of five stopped to take a break. They were well up the slope, above all the others in the area. A minute later, Settle heard a sound that he thought could be an earthquake. He looked up: "It looked like pure white coming at us. I've never seen anything like it."[3] A family snowshoeing near the bottom of the slope saw the avalanche hit the five men, who disappeared in the moving snow.

One of the witnesses made a 911 call that was received by the Utah County Sheriff's Office at 16:27.

RESCUE SUMMARY

No rescue equipment

None of the five men had avalanche rescue gear. Settle and Long were lucky. Settle was buried to the neck and was able to dig himself out; Long was under a foot of snow but was able to clear his face and breathe. They got themselves out and began the search for their three companions. Others in the area joined Settle and Long in the search for Merz, Hebert, and Newberry. There were no surface clues.

Settle grabbed a tree branch to scuff and probe the snow, and while he was searching, a second avalanche came down. "The second one hit me right in the back and brought me down right to the bottom," said Settle. "That's the one that trapped me and I got an air pocket. I could get my head above the snow, but I was trapped. My legs, I couldn't move them." Other searchers managed to dig him out. (Settle was briefly hospitalized for hypothermia and a knee injury, but was back at Aspen Grove on Sunday to join the search.)

Shortly after 17:00, the first SAR team arrived at the site, but they found no clues to the three missing men before authorities suspended the search because of darkness and the threat of more avalanches. On Saturday the 27th, prior to putting rescuers on the lower slope, a helicopter dropped explosives into the starting zone and triggered no further avalanches. Then several dog teams and probe lines went onto the debris area, which was enormous—estimated to be 22 football fields (about 28 acres) in size. The primary search area below where the three missing victims had last been seen was still overwhelming—estimated at 11 football fields (14 acres) and 10 to 20 feet deep. Probing was exceptionally difficult, first because the debris was often deeper than the length of the poles, and second because many poles broke in the hard snow. Searchers found nothing on Saturday, though an avalanche dog showed interest in one area.

The recovery mission resumed on Sunday morning the 28th. Dogs again alerted in one general area, and probing and shoveling uncovered a ski hat, backpack and snowboard within 100 feet of each other. A probe then struck the body of Mike Hebert under four feet of snow. He had been carried about 1,000 feet from where the avalanche hit the group. Further searching produced nothing, at which point the rescue effort was put on hold indefinitely.

It would be more than three months later that the recovery effort came to an end. On April 11, searchers recovered the body of Rod Newberry. Then, on April 17, they found the body of Adam Merz. The two men had been carried about 1,700 feet down the slope and buried about 90 feet apart in a ravine near a footbridge at the bottom of the slide.

AVALANCHE DATA

The continuing storm prevented good observations of the starting zone of this avalanche, so little data is available. We do know that the avalanche was a natural release, that it released on a northeast-facing slope and fell several thousand feet, and that the volume of snow was very large. Therefore, it was most likely classified as SS-N-R4. It may have been mostly storm snow.

Storm Slab avalanche

COMMENTS

When interviewed after the avalanche, J. D. Settle said his group talked about and was aware of the avalanche risk, but with so many feet of fresh powder, they couldn't resist. Once tasted, the lure of fresh powder is strong, but when people push the limits of gravity and physics, avalanches will happen, and some victims are going to die.

These young men dearly needed guidance, a responsibility that is both theirs and their parents'. Backcountry safety comes with experience and education. And the public school districts in Utah have bought into this idea: "Know Before You Go" is an avalanche awareness program created in Utah for middle and high school students. Part of the instruction is a lively and entertaining video showing the power and effects of avalanches, with the strong message that awareness and education are keys to avalanche safety. A video news clip of this fatal Aspen Grove avalanche is part of Know Before You Go's hard-hitting message that only awareness and training can prevent tragedies like this. With the schools starting the education process, parents of kids drawn to winter recreation should be certain they are prepared for rescue—which is inevitable in the long run—by having the equipment that may save their lives. In 2016, the Know Before You Go program expanded into Colorado, and has now been used internationally and presented in several languages.

20040101 CASTLE PEAK, DONNER SUMMIT, CALIFORNIA

January 1, 2004

Two backcountry skiers caught; one partly buried, one buried and killed

WEATHER AND SNOWPACK CONDITIONS

A major storm struck the Sierra Nevada Range of California in the last few days of 2003. In the Donner Summit area, snow fell heavily on December 31 and January 1, and strong westerly winds created whiteout conditions and high avalanche danger.

ACCIDENT SUMMARY

On December 31, two backcountry skiers from the Bay Area of California drove to the parking area along I-80 at Donner Summit. They skied northward on the Round Valley Trail toward Castle Peak for a multi-day tour. The two men were Drew Gashler (37) and Doug Hagan (40). They were experienced and had been in this area several times, and they both carried avalanche beacons. On this trip, though, they may have underestimated the strength of the storm they headed into.

Inadequate rescue equipment

On the night of December 31, they camped in the snow. It is not known whether they had a tent or dug a snow cave. The following morning, January 1, they headed, in blizzard conditions, for the Peter Grubb Hut at the foot of Castle Peak to wait out the storm. Traveling was a tiring slog: it took 30 minutes, breaking trail, to go the first 100 yards. For reasons unknown, they did not turn on their beacons.

They reached a point in their trek when they were traversing a side-hill slope, and for a moment the wind died. The two men could look up and see that the slope steepened above them and that a large cornice loomed over the slope. They tried to move faster to get off this slope, but that's when the avalanche released. It hit both men and carried them down the slope.

When the avalanche stopped, Hagan was mostly buried, and he could see no sign of Gashler. It took Hagan the better part of an hour to dig himself out, which left him exhausted. He also had only one ski, and so was barely able to move in the deep snow. But then he found one of Gashler's skis, which he put on, giving him mobility. Next, he turned on his beacon, which he may have inadvertently left in transmit mode—and thereby unable to receive a signal. In any case, it didn't matter, because Gashler's beacon was turned off.

Hagan searched only a short time. He found no surface clues, visibility was almost nil, and he began to worry about his own survival. He left the avalanche site and skied to the hut.

RESCUE SUMMARY

Hagan made it to the Peter Grubb Hut, where he spent two days in blizzard conditions. He found a stash of canned food that sustained him, and then skied out when the storm began to subside on January 3. On the trail, he ran into a group of skiers. They had a cell phone, which he used to call for help.

A rescue team came in later that day and found the avalanche site covered with storm snow, making it difficult to know the size of the slide and where to search. The search continued for several days, and on January 5, a rescuer with a probe found the Gashler's body pinned against a tree under three to four feet of snow.

Gashler's beacon had been damaged in the collision with the tree. Rescuers thought the beacon was set in the "off" position, but could not be absolutely certain.

AVALANCHE DATA

The slope angle where the men were crossing the slope was 28 degrees, but the slope steepened above their track. The avalanche was possibly triggered by an ill-timed natural cornice collapse and therefore classified as SS-NC-R3.

COMMENTS

This was an intriguing avalanche accident, mostly because of what we do not know. These two men were obviously intent on completing their multi-day tour, despite the blizzard. But the lack of visibility got them into trouble when they realized they were midway up an avalanche slope with a hanging cornice at the top. We cannot be sure whether the men triggered the avalanche—with the cornice fall being a result of the avalanche release—or whether a natural cornice fall triggered the avalanche.

The bigger question, though, is why both men's beacons were apparently turned off. Was it oversight? Carelessness? Distraction because of the weather? We don't have the answer.

SOLDIER CREEK, NORTH OF FAIRFIELD, IDAHO

20040102

January 2, 2004

Two residents caught, buried, and killed

WEATHER AND SNOWPACK CONDITIONS

From December 24 to 31, two storms dropped 1.5 to two feet of snow on Soldier Mountain Ski Area in the Smoky Mountains of south-central Idaho. Then, a third and more powerful storm hit on New Year's Eve. This was the same storm described in Accident 20040101; it trekked northeastward from the Sierra to Idaho. Heavy snow fell around Soldier Mountain Ski Area, Fairfield, and Ketchum, about 30 miles northeast of Fairfield. By noon on January 1, the storm had dropped 24 to 36 inches of snow in 15 hours, and the Soldier SNOTEL site had recorded 2.8 inches of water equivalent.

Winds recorded at the top of 9,150-foot Bald Mountain above Ketchum averaged 30 to 45 mph and gusted to 79 mph, with an initial direction of south-southeast. Winds then shifted to west at frontal passage.

High avalanche danger

At 13:30 on January 1, the Sawtooth National Forest Avalanche Center in Ketchum issued an avalanche warning, not just for backcountry travelers, but for residents as well. The bulletin stated, in part, that "very heavy snowfall and strong winds have caused the snowpack to become unstable on all elevations and aspects. Residents of communities that live in or near avalanche paths should take precautionary measures."

ACCIDENT SUMMARY

Marsha Landolt (55) was the Dean of the University of Washington Graduate School in Seattle. Her husband Robert Busch (58) was the director of research for a pharmaceutical company. They lived in Seattle but owned a two-story log cabin in Soldier Creek a mile from Soldier Mountain Ski Area and were staying at their cabin for the Christmas and New Year holidays. Also staying at the cabin were five other people, all relatives: Landolt's stepson Nick Cosan (24), Jenna (32), and Kelby Rovig, the Seattle couple's daughter and son-in-law, and the Rovigs' children, Tucker (5) and Emma (1). Two dogs—Shadow, a black lab, and Odie, a golden retriever—were also among the residents.

Behind the cabin was a steep hillside that rose about 550 feet. Landolt and Busch had owned the cabin for 26 years. Neither they nor any of their neighbors had ever seen an avalanche on the slope behind, but they also had never seen a storm like this. The couple's children had used the slope for sledding in past winters.

Mid-afternoon on Thursday, January 1, the storm knocked out power at the cabin. Cosan, the Rovigs, and their two children made plans to sleep on the first floor, in front of the fireplace. The grandparents, Landolt and Busch, had an adjacent bedroom on the first floor. Then, around 20:00, the power was restored, and all the younger folks moved back upstairs to the loft. The dogs stayed in front of the fireplace.

The time was 01:30 on the morning of January 2 when a natural avalanche released on the slope behind the cabin. The snow came downhill with great force and crushed into the back wall of the cabin, breaking windows and doors and completely filling the lower floor almost to the ceiling. The loft area was filled with one to two feet of snow, but the family members upstairs were unhurt.

RESCUE SUMMARY

In the loft, Nick Cosan initially thought the sound that woke him was a gust of wind hitting the cabin. Just down the hall, Jenna Rovig heard a crash and woke up with a scream, thinking her bed was collapsing. When her husband Kelby tried to push back the covers, he realized the bed was covered by snow and quickly knew what had happened—avalanche! He got out from under the load of snow and checked on his son, who had been in the same bed, and his one-year-old daughter, who was in a playpen. Both were okay.

Once the three adults on the upper floor verified that everyone there was accounted for, they began calling out for Landolt and Busch. Neither answered. The stairwell was packed with snow, so the two men broke a window and jumped into the snow. Cosan got to the front porch, which faced away from where the avalanche had come, found a shovel, and broke a window into the bedroom where Landolt and Busch had been sleeping. Cosan peered into the snow that was packed inside and saw movement. It was the nose of his black lab, Shadow. He reached in and was able to pull the dog free and through the broken window.

Cosan and Kelby Rovig, both armed with shovels they found on the front porch, broke more windows trying to find a way in. One of them eventually got a chainsaw from the shop nearby and began cutting the window frame to enlarge it—until the chain derailed on a metal bedpost.

At that point, the survivors knew they needed more help. Kelby strapped on snowshoes over his socks (his boots were buried inside the cabin) and hiked to a neighbors' house, a few hundred yards away.

While he was gone, Nick Cosan kept digging through the bedroom window. In his words: "I found the bedspread on the bed and by pulling on that was able to uncover the legs and torso of my mother. But I couldn't uncover any more because of the tightness of the snow. I realized from pushing, pinching, trying to get any response and from the color of her skin … I knew at that point it was over."

Cosan wanted to keep searching for Busch, but he had been digging in the snow for 90 minutes and was very cold and tired. At some point, he had cut his head, and blood had coated his glasses to the point he could barely see. He took a break in Busch's truck to warm up.

The January 2, 2004, avalanche released on the slope in the upper left and damaged the cabin at lower right. *Photo Janet Kellam, Sawtooth Avalanche Center.*

While the two men had been searching, Jenna, in the loft, had heard scratching and moaning sounds coming from her golden retriever, Odie. The sounds were coming up the chimney flue, but as time wore on, the sounds eventually stopped. Jenna realized her dog must have died.

Then Kelby returned. He had woken the neighbors, who called search and rescue and gave Kelby some warm clothing. Kelby got a ladder and helped Jenna and the two children down, and then got them into the shop, where Cosan had built a fire.

Soon, the first rescuers arrived via snowcat. They got Nick Cosan and Kelby Rovig to an ambulance, where the two men were treated for hypothermia, frostbite, and cuts. Next, Jenna and her children, Tucker and Emma, were evacuated.

The rescuers worked through the night, clearing snow and finding the body of Robert Busch. Both victims' bodies were evacuated, but the rescue team kept searching for personal belongings that the survivors would need, like clothing and car keys.

The rescue ended with a final miracle. It was shortly before noon when the rescuers heard barking from somewhere in the rubble under the snow. Odie had been sleeping in front of the fireplace, and the avalanche had pushed him through the glass screen and into the chimney. Odie had suffered severe burns from the fire but being pushed into the chimney had saved his life, for then he could breathe. The golden retriever was evacuated and treated for non-life-threatening wounds.[4]

Debris from January 2, 2004, in the damaged cabin. *Photo Janet Kellam, Sawtooth Avalanche Center.*

AVALANCHE DATA

This natural avalanche released at an elevation of 6,225 feet on a slope that faced east-southeast. The starting zone slope angle was 39 degrees, the mid-path slope angle was 30 degrees, and the angle just behind the cabin was 15 to 20 degrees. The crown was 375 feet wide and averaged two to three deep. The avalanche fell 575 feet vertical and was classified as SS-N-R3-I.

Storm Slab avalanche

The avalanche was made up of fallen and windblown snow from the series of storms that began on December 24. There was no discernible weak layer—no facets or buried surface hoar, just a slight density change between storm-snow layers. The alpha angle from the toe of the debris to the crown was measured at 18 degrees. The debris was seven to 14 feet deep around the cabin.

COMMENTS

Though this slope had no history of avalanches (as far as the locals knew), the one necessary ingredient for an avalanche had always been present—a 39-degree starting zone. It took a storm of rare intensity to produce the avalanche, but when it came, it did so with deadly consequence.

The result of this avalanche would have been even worse had one fortunate circumstance not occurred, and that was the electric power coming back on several hours before the avalanche. When this happened, five family members unwittingly moved out of harm's way up to the second story to their normal sleeping quarters, sparing them from being buried.

PORTAGE, ALASKA | January 22, 2004

20040122

One person at work caught and killed

WEATHER AND SNOWPACK CONDITIONS

The weather in Portage, Alaska, had been cold in mid-January, with the low temperature on January 18 reaching -26°F. Then a significant warm-up began, such that the high temperature on the January 20 reached +40°F, and the temperatures the next two days stayed mild with mixed rain and snow.

ACCIDENT SUMMARY

Jeffrey Nissman (23) was an employee of the US Forest Service and was stationed at a Forest Service work center in Portage. He also had developed and was maintaining the website for the Chugach National Forest Avalanche Center. On Thursday, January 22, Nissman was moving furniture from a building when a slab of snow and ice—estimated to weigh 650 pounds—slid off the metal roof above the doorway and crushed him.

Roof avalanche

The accident report did not specify whether anyone witnessed the roof avalanche or if there was a delay in getting Nissman uncovered. In any case, rescuers gave CPR for 45 minutes without reviving Nissman. It is not known whether his death was caused by trauma or suffocation.

COMMENTS

Fatal roof avalanches are uncommon, but they certainly do occur in the United States. Probably, there are many more fatal roof avalanches than the few that show up in the avalanche accident database. The reason is that some (most?) of these occur in an urban environment and therefore are not reported to avalanche centers.

Physically, there is no difference between the ingredients of a backcountry avalanche and those of a roof avalanche. They all must have a slab, a slope, a weak layer, and a trigger. For a roof avalanche, the weak layer is often the lubricated interface between the snow slab and a warming roof, while the trigger is a rise in temperature.

Lastly, metal roofs make excellent sliding surfaces (bed surfaces). And, quite frankly, it is a building design flaw to have a building entryway exposed to roof avalanches. Roof structures can be built to either prevent the snow from sliding off or divert the flow away from exterior doorways.

20040131 THE PYRAMID, NORTH OF WILSON, WYOMING

January 31, 2004

One backcountry skier caught, buried, and killed

WEATHER AND SNOWPACK CONDITIONS

In the Teton Range west of Jackson, Wyoming, an extended period of dry weather in mid-January had created a firm surface and sun crust on the mountain snowpack. Surface hoar then formed on top of the crust, creating a dangerous weak layer when the next storm appeared. This happened on January 25, which was the start of a six-day storm period that dropped 50 inches of snowfall containing 3.5 inches of water equivalent. During the storm, strong west and southwest winds formed widespread slab conditions. On January 31, the avalanche danger was rated as Considerable.

ACCIDENT SUMMARY

Peak 9670 is known locally as the Pyramid. This peak sits six miles north of Wilson, a small community below Teton Pass. The Pyramid is the high point on a ridge that separates Jensen Canyon from the North Fork of Phillips Canyon. It offers excellent backcountry skiing for those willing to make a long climb and risk the avalanche danger on its slopes.

On Saturday, January 31, Ray Azar (48) and his dog, Bomber, made the climb up the peak in order to ski the steep, open southeast face of the summit. All the local hardcore skiers knew Azar, who had acquired the nickname "Every Day Ray."

While climbing Azar met up with two friends, Jon Patterson and Beth Thebaud. The three skiers skinned together up the peak and then parted ways at the summit. Azar headed to the southeast face, and Patterson and Thebaud chose another descent.

Traveling alone

The time was 13:45 when a man working in his office in the valley saw the large "dust cloud" of an avalanche coming off the peak. With binoculars, he could see a single ski track leading into the crown. The observer called Teton County Search & Rescue and the Bridger-Teton Avalanche Center.

RESCUE SUMMARY

Patterson and Thebaud had completed their run and were climbing back up for a second lap when they saw a deep fracture line on the slope where Azar had skied. As they got closer, they saw Azar and Bomber's tracks going into the slide. They switched their transceivers to receive and started down the avalanche path.

The avalanche had run full track of about 1,600 feet vertical. Patterson and Thebaud checked tree wells on the way down and also had to negotiate a cliff band. Near the bottom, they got a signal and zeroed in on the location near the toe of the debris. With a probe, they struck Azar under three to four feet of snow. They uncovered him and began CPR. Azar had been buried for almost an hour, and CPR did not revive him. He had apparently died of suffocation.

The rescuers later found Bomber, who was unscathed.

AVALANCHE DATA

Persistent Slab avalanche

The avalanche released at an elevation of 8,900 feet and fell about 1,600 feet down a southeast-facing path. The avalanche was classified as SS-ASu-R4-O.

COMMENTS
Solo backcountry travel can bring good feelings of calm and serenity and suits many skiers' personalities, but it comes with a serious downside. In an emergency, there will be no help or rescue. Ray Azar knew the risks, both of skiing avalanche terrain and of skiing it alone. He was comfortable with this, but, sadly, his time ran out.

DALY CANYON, NORTHWEST OF PARK CITY, UTAH

20040226

February 26, 2004

One snowshoer caught, buried, and killed

WEATHER AND SNOWPACK CONDITIONS
On February 25 and 26, a strong winter storm hit the Park City area of Utah's Wasatch Range. It was a warm storm, and about two feet of heavy snow fell on those two days. On the east slope of the Wasatch, especially at lower elevations surrounding Park City, the snowpack had been shallow and weak prior to this storm. Early on February 26, a big windstorm overloaded many slopes, causing the avalanche danger to spike upward.

The black lines outline the crown and flanks of the February 26, 2004, avalanche. The black X in the lower left marks the burial site. *Photo Bruce Tremper, Utah Avalanche Center.*

ACCIDENT SUMMARY
On Thursday, February 26, two men were snowshoeing in Daly Canyon (also known as Empire Canyon) near the Judge Mine, on the outskirts of Park City. Jason DeLecour (34) was visiting from Houston, Texas, and was snowshoeing with a friend who lived in Park City. Late in the day, just after 18:00, DeLecour triggered a small avalanche in a narrow, wooded gully. The gully acted as a terrain trap, causing the snow to pile up deeply, completely burying DeLecour.

Terrain trap

A hasty team found the victim buried about 4 feet deep—a result of the terrain trap. *Photo Bruce Tremper, Utah Avalanche Center.*

RESCUE SUMMARY

No rescue equipment

These men were not prepared for an avalanche emergency and had no rescue gear at all. The surviving man rushed to some nearby houses for help. Several residents hurried to the site, and a call went to the Deer Valley Ski Patrol for an avalanche rescue dog.

Few details of the rescue were available, but the hasty searchers had found the victim before the patrol rescue team and dog got to the site. The rescuers uncovered DeLecour from three to four feet of snow, and he did not respond to resuscitation efforts.

AVALANCHE DATA

Storm Slab avalanche

Very little data was available on this avalanche. It probably would have been classified as SS-AI-R2-I.

COMMENTS

The thought of avalanches probably never crossed the minds of these two snowshoers, so they did not recognize that the small slope above the trail could pose a threat. Small avalanches can be deadly when the debris comes to a stop in a gully, where it can pile up deeply.

APOLLO CREEK, WEST OF KETCHUM, IDAHO

20040228a

February 28, 2004

One snowmobiler caught, buried, and killed

WEATHER AND SNOWPACK CONDITIONS

For about a week prior to this fatal avalanche, the Sawtooth National Forest Avalanche Center had been warning of several persistent weak layers from one to three feet below the snow surface, with a special "heads up" for backcountry skiers and snowmobilers. On February 26, about one foot of new snow fell and covered a layer of surface hoar that had formed a day or two before the avalanche. There were now three identifiable weak layers within four feet of the snow surface, and any one—or all—of them were possible weak layers for avalanche release.

ACCIDENT SUMMARY

Apollo Creek is located in the Sawtooth Range of Idaho, about 15 miles west of Ketchum and Sun Valley. On Saturday, February 28, a party of five snowmobilers was riding near the head of the drainage, in a steep east-facing cirque. Slope angles range from 30 to 50 degrees.

This was an experienced group, and all members carried beacons, probes, and shovels. Around 16:00, three riders idled in a safe location while the other two took turns high-marking. Those two would alternate their climbs: one would ride as high as he could, and when he peeled off, the second rider would climb in the same track and try to go higher.

One of the two riders, age 29, reached the apex of his climb a little higher than mid-slope. As he was turning off, the slope fractured, failing on the most recent weak layer, one foot down. This shallow slab avalanche started to pull the rider and his snowmobile down the slope, when a secondary fracture occurred on the older, deeper layer of buried surface hoar, three feet down. This fracture propagated wider and higher—all the way to the top of the ridge—and released a much larger avalanche.

This large avalanche engulfed the rider and his snowmobile and carried both downhill and through a group of trees. When the avalanche stopped, the other four riders could see no sign of the rider or his snowmobile.

RESCUE SUMMARY

The companions rode to the last-seen point and began their search downhill. They found fragments of the snowmobile stuck in several trees (not a good sign) and then saw the handlebars, barely visible on the surface. A beacon signal was coming from 25 to 30 feet down slope from his snowmobile. It took the rescuers 10 minutes to pinpoint the burial spot and another 15 minutes to dig through six feet of debris to reach the victim. He did not respond to CPR and showed signs of massive trauma from collisions with trees.

The victim's companions left the body at the scene at about 17:00 and rode to the trailhead to notify authorities. The body was recovered by helicopter the following day.

AVALANCHE DATA

This avalanche released on an east-facing slope at an elevation of about 9,500 feet and fell about 400 feet vertical. The crown was about three feet deep, but no width was recorded. The slide was classified as SS-AMu-R3-O.

Persistent Slab avalanche

COMMENTS
These riders were experienced, were equipped for avalanche rescue, and were using the best safety technique of riding one at a time with other party members waiting in safe locations. Still, the group underestimated the instability. There were no glaring red flags, such as recent natural slab releases. We do not know if this group had the skills—or inclination—to dig snowpits that most likely would have revealed the multiple buried weak layers, but they certainly had access to the bulletins that were warning of the exact conditions this group encountered. Had they heeded the message—stick to low-angle terrain—they would have had a better day.

20040228b

BYRON PEAK, SOUTHEAST OF PORTAGE, ALASKA

February 28, 2004

One climber caught, partly buried, and killed

ACCIDENT SUMMARY
Byron Peak is a 4,590-foot peak in the Portage Valley, about 50 miles southeast of Anchorage and 14 miles southeast of Portage, Alaska. Most visitors come to walk on Byron Glacier, but on Saturday afternoon, February 28, Joseph Neale (23) and Jesse Billmeier (24) came to climb the peak. They skied across the glacier to the base of the ridge, stashed their skis, and began climbing on foot. They wore helmets and crampons, and, being aware of avalanche danger, they carried beacons, probes, and shovels.

They climbed steadily and were nearing the summit by late afternoon. At around 18:00, they were working their way up a snow-covered ridge, which was essentially a long cornice. They took turns in the lead breaking trail. Several times Billmeier warned Neale that he was getting too close to the edge and urged him to get back to safer ground. But Neale, in the lead, did not move back far enough, and a large chunk of the cornice—about 30 feet wide and 35 feet deep—broke off beneath him.

Billmeier was five feet farther back from the edge and was not caught. He stepped to the edge and saw Neale as he was engulfed in the mass of snow that tore away down the mountainside and eventually went out of sight. When the avalanche stopped, Billmeier called out. Nothing. He thought about going down the path, but it was far too steep and dangerous, so he retraced their climbing route to get help.

RESCUE SUMMARY
It was 19:30 when Billmeier got to the US Forest Service Begich Boggs Visitor Center near the toe of the glacier. The building was closed, but a cleaning crew let him in, and he was able to call the Alaska State Troopers. The troopers dispatched a helicopter with a crew of the Alaska Mountain Rescue Group, but by the time it got to the accident site, darkness had closed in. They flew the helicopter over the avalanche area, but the area was large and they could not spot the victim.

The following morning, the rescue team returned, and flew over the area getting as close to the ground as possible. After 20 minutes, they spotted a dark spot in the avalanche debris and put a team on the snow. It turned out to be Joseph Neale, who had died of massive injuries sustained in the fall. The cornice fall had triggered a secondary avalanche, causing a very large volume of snow to fall 3,950 feet vertical down the mountainside.

AVALANCHE DATA

The avalanche was classified as C-AFu-R4, and, as noted, fell about 3,950 feet vertical.

Cornice fall

COMMENTS

When standing on top of a cornice, it often feels as though the snow is bombproof. But that feeling is a trap. Cornices are built up, layer by layer, by successive wind events, and similar to a slab avalanche, it merely takes a trigger of the right size at the right place and right time to cause it to break. In this accident, Neal's partner urged him to move farther back from the edge, but the victim did not heed this counsel quickly enough. This accident was easily preventable.

SALMON LA SAC, EAST OF SNOQUALMIE PASS, WASHINGTON | March 5, 2004

20040305

One snowmobiler caught, buried, and killed

WEATHER AND SNOWPACK CONDITIONS

On Wednesday, March 3, a storm moved into the Cascade Range of Washington and brought snowfall into Thursday morning. This snow fell on a crust, and strong west winds were loading leeward slopes (mostly northeast through southeast) with blowing snow. On Thursday and Friday—March 4 and 5—the Northwest Avalanche Center rated the avalanche danger as Considerable because of the likelihood of triggered avalanches one to three feet deep.

ACCIDENT SUMMARY

Little information could be found on this fatal avalanche, except the following: Salmon la Sac is located about 15 miles east of Snoqualmie Pass, Washington, and is little more than a campground in a wilderness area. In the winter, it is a popular area for snowshoeing, cross-country skiing, and snowmobiling. On Friday, March 5, a group of snowmobilers was highmarking when one rider triggered an avalanche and was totally buried. This group was equipped with beacons, probes, and shovels, and the other party members located the burial spot and uncovered the victim from eight feet of snow. He did not survive. The victim was identified as Dez Van Assche (29).

COMMENTS

The lack of information available on this accident precludes comment.

JERU PEAK, NORTH OF SANDPOINT, IDAHO | March 6, 2004

20040306

One snowmobiler caught, buried, and killed

ACCIDENT SUMMARY

Jeru Peak is a 6,368-foot mountain in the Selkirk Mountains of the Idaho panhandle. The peak is 20 miles north of Sandpoint and nine miles east of Priest Lake. On Saturday, March 6, a group of snowmobilers was highmarking on the west side of the peak. They were riding one at a time, and all had avalanche rescue gear.

It was shortly after 12:00 when one rider put his highmark on the slope, turned to descend, and triggered the avalanche. The slide carried him about 500 feet down the mountainside and completely buried him and his snowmobile.

RESCUE SUMMARY

After the avalanche stopped, the other members of the group rode to the debris area and began a beacon search. It took about 15 minutes for them locate and dig out the victim. He had been buried under five feet of dense debris. His rescuers gave CPR, but they could not revive him.

At 12:40, the Boundary County Sheriff's Office got the 911 call that reported the avalanche and told the dispatcher that CPR was in progress. A medical helicopter was called in, but the victim died long before it arrived on the scene.

While the rescue was in progress, a second avalanche buried three other snowmobilers on a nearby slope. All three were rescued, and no injuries were reported.

COMMENTS

This group was experienced and was prepared for an avalanche rescue. Additionally, they were highmarking one at a time, so that only one rider at a time was exposed to the avalanche danger. Despite all their preparedness, caution, and relatively quick search, they could not rescue the victim quickly from a deep burial, in which survival is often measured in a few short minutes.

20040310 MT. GUYOT, EAST OF BRECKENRIDGE, COLORADO

March 10, 2004

One snowmobiler caught, buried, and killed

WEATHER AND SNOWPACK CONDITIONS

Mt. Guyot is a 13,376-foot peak in the Front Range of Colorado and is located six miles east of Breckenridge. No particular weather event preceding this avalanche could be considered a key contributing factor. Rather, it was a combination of storms and lulls from November through February that created, by March, a backcountry snowpack that was a mixture of slab layers, which formed during storm and wind events, interspersed with faceted layers. The first week of March saw about 15 inches of snowfall, and with blowing snow at high elevations, a wind slab formed on easterly aspects.

ACCIDENT SUMMARY

On Wednesday morning, March 10, a party of three snowmobilers from the Denver area began a ride that started near the community of Jefferson in Park County (about 15 air miles southeast of Breckenridge). The trio of riders consisted of Darin Heitman (39), Heitman's brother Trent Waters (32), and Bob Hoff (58). They had ridden in this area before and were familiar with the terrain. They all carried two-way radios so they could stay in touch, but they did not carry avalanche rescue gear.

No rescue equipment

They traveled the summer road over Georgia Pass, at 11,585 feet, and dropped into Summit County. They spent the morning riding in the Georgia Pass area. Late in the morning, the trio followed a trail past a cabin—known by locals as the "Avalanche Cabin"—where two other riders were staying.

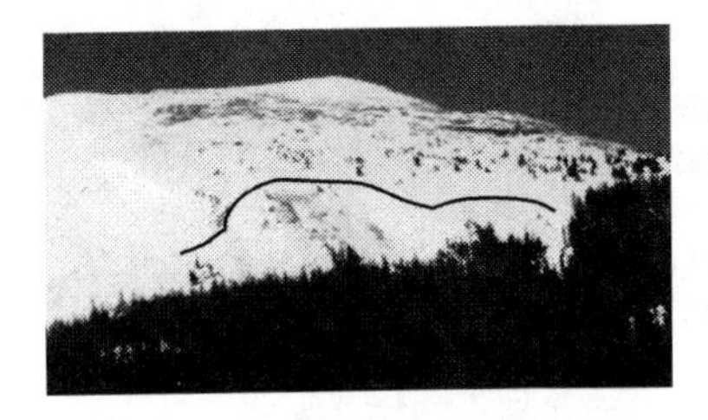

Panoramic view of the accident site with the fracture line highlighted by the black line. *Photo Brad Sawtell, Colorado Avalanche Information Center.*

Not far to the west of the Avalanche Cabin is a long flank of Mt. Guyot, which extends northward for half a mile and ends at Point 12,201. The large east-facing slope of Guyot's north flank is steep and prone to avalanches—thus the name of the cabin.

As the riders approached the bottom of the large, east-facing slope, they came upon the debris of an avalanche that had run naturally a few days earlier. The time was just before noon, and Heitman decided to highmark the slope north of where the avalanche debris lay. He began climbing the undisturbed snow while Waters was parked below a thick stand of trees near the bottom of the slope. Hoff was farther downhill and away from the avalanche slope.

Heitman got stuck but managed to get himself out. He started back downhill, and that's when the avalanche broke hundreds of feet above him. The avalanche carried Heitman and his snowmobile down the slope, and he disappeared. Only the trees around Waters kept him from being hit, while Hoff was low enough to be out of reach of the avalanche.

RESCUE SUMMARY

Hoff could tell that Waters had not been hit, so he yelled that he would go to the cabin to get the two men there while Waters began to search. Waters was on the debris, searching and yelling, when the three other men arrived a few minutes later. The two new searchers had beacons, probes, and shovels. They helped Waters search while Hoff rode off to a group of guided riders on Georgia Pass. From the top of Georgia Pass, a guide from Good Times Adventure Tours was able to radio in and report the accident. His office, in turn, called 911 at 12:28.

The Summit County Sheriff's Office mobilized the Summit County Rescue Group and the Flight for Life helicopter. The helicopter flew in several members of the Summit County SAR Team, plus several ski patrollers and a rescue dog from Breckenridge Ski Area.

While the Breckenridge avalanche dog searched, the others spot probed in likely burial areas. A searcher spied the handlebars of the victim's snowmobile in a treed area, and the searchers then concentrated in that area. Next, a rescuer performing a random probe 50 feet downhill from the snowmobile struck the victim's helmet several feet down.

Searchers recovered Heitman's body from under two feet of snow, sitting upright and pressed against a tree. The time of recovery was 13:58; Heitman had been buried for more than two hours, and resuscitation efforts failed to revive him. Death was later determined to be from severe trauma—a crushed chest and internal injuries most likely caused by his collision with trees.

AVALANCHE DATA

Persistent Slab avalanche

The avalanche triggered by the rider was classified as HS-AMu-R3-G. The crown ranged from two to six feet deep and was 1,000 feet wide. The slope faced east, the crown was at an elevation of 11,920 feet, and the avalanche fell 500 feet vertical. The slope angle at the fracture line was 39 degrees, but the victim triggered the avalanche from the lower half of the slope, where the angle was much smaller.

COMMENTS

The crown and debris field of a recent avalanche were apparent to this group of riders once they came into the area. This should have been the only clue they needed to tell them that the adjacent slope, if climbed, would likely avalanche as well. But the two surviving members of this trio later said they had not given any thought to the avalanche danger, so that neither the debris of the prior avalanche nor the steepness of the highmark slope registered "danger" to them.

20040320 LA PLATA PEAK, SOUTHWEST OF TWIN LAKES, COLORADO | March 20, 2004

Two hikers caught; one partly buried and injured, one buried and killed

WEATHER AND SNOWPACK CONDITIONS

Near the end of March, spring conditions prevailed in the Sawatch Range of central Colorado. La Plata Peak is Colorado's fifth-highest mountain and is 14,336 feet in elevation, according to the Colorado Mountain Club. It is located about six miles southwest of the village of Twin Lakes and seven miles southeast of Independence Pass. Spring conditions meant the snow cover would be frozen until late morning, and then thawing would begin on sunny south aspects and eventually spread to north-facing slopes. Once thawed, the snowpack would be more susceptible to wet avalanche releases.

One additional factor contributed to this avalanche accident in March (and to accident 20040409 on nearby Browns Peak). Snowfall in the Sawatch Range had been approximately 60% of normal for the winter of 2003-04. This led to a shallow snowpack, and in Colorado, that means a weak snowpack.

ACCIDENT SUMMARY

On Saturday, March 20, three Colorado Springs men parked their car on Highway 82 for a day-long climb of La Plata's north-northwest ridge. The group included David Bennett (39), Joel Sieberesma (27), and Kyle Fitzpatrick (22). They were well prepared for a day climb and carried basic outdoor gear, extra clothing and food, ice axes, and avalanche probes and shovels, but no beacons. The day before, a Friday, they had called the Colorado Springs avalanche hotline maintained by the Colorado Avalanche Information Center. Part of that message read: "Spring conditions rule. All mountain areas will see an increased threat of wet-snow avalanches in the afternoon and evening hours. Our danger rating is overall 'Low' morning and 'Moderate' afternoon, because of wet-snow instability."[5]

Inadequate rescue equipment

They began their 4,000-foot climb at 07:30, and they made steady time on snowshoes on the firm frozen snow cover. They reached the summit at 14:00. This was about an hour later than they had hoped, so they spent only a short time enjoying the summit views and warm weather.

For their descent, they decided to take a shortcut by making a sitting glissade down the snow-covered west face. Using their ice axes to control their speed, the men found the snow on the upper slopes to be firm and crusty—perfect for glissading. They glissaded two sections and then traversed over to another snow-filled gully. The snow surface was still crusty but just starting to thaw.

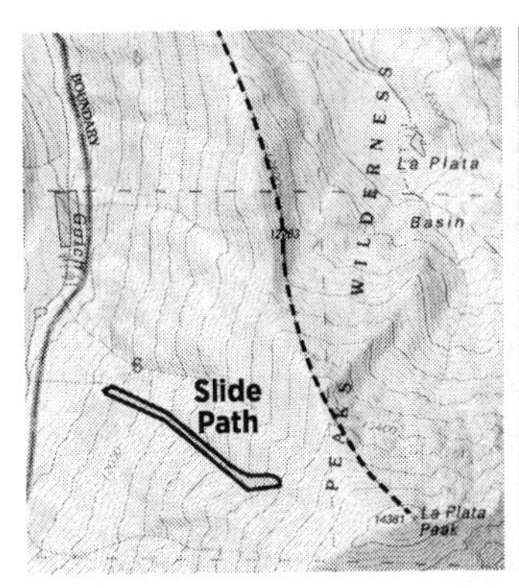

Left: The dashed black line represents the climbers' route to the summit and the start of their descent. The solid line outlines the path of the fatal avalanche.

Right: The avalanche released from the shallow gully-like feature on the upper far-left of the photograph, and the avalanche ran out onto the open slope. The roundish snowballs in the debris are characteristic of a wet snow avalanche. The snowshoe provides a sense of scale. *Photo Sue Purvis.*

More than one person on a slope

Kyle Fitzpatrick was the first to descend this pitch and was well down the gully when Joel Sieberesma started down. The time was about 15:00, and he had glissaded about 30 feet when the snow fractured around him. He tried to self-arrest, but was quickly tumbling out of control in the avalanche. For Sieberesma, it was the longest, scariest minute of his life. "My first thought was I'm going to die. It was like being thrown down a flight of stairs underwater, constantly being pushed and tumbled and turned. I was being bounced around and pulled up and pushed back down. It was light and dark, and light and dark. I was just trying to breathe while it was light."

From the top, David Bennett watched it all happen. "The avalanche broke about 10 yards below me. I saw Joel go down in the avalanche. I saw the big slide hit Kyle."

RESCUE SUMMARY

When the avalanche stopped, Sieberesma was bloodied and partly buried. He had lost his pack but was able to get himself out. He then ran down the debris, shouting for Fitzpatrick. Meanwhile, Bennett began to carefully work his way down the icy, rocky mountainside. The avalanche had fallen 1,600 feet vertical, and it took Bennett 40 minutes to get to the field of debris. The two men found trekking poles, a snowshoe, and a shovel handle, but no friend. After two hours without success, the two survivors started a lonely hike out. It took another six hours to reach their car because the snow in the valley was wet and cohesionless. With every step, they would sink in to their knees and it would be an effort to lift their snowshoes to take the next step.

The survivors reported the avalanche that night, and Sieberesma spent the night in the Leadville hospital for observation. On Sunday morning, a Flight for Life helicopter ferried in rescue teams from Lake, Chaffee, Gunnison, and Summit counties, and a rescue dog and handler came in from Crested Butte. The snow was dense and the surface layer had refrozen overnight. It was hard enough to break probe poles and apparently hamper scent from percolating upward, slowing the effectiveness of the dog. But at noon, the dog alerted, and searchers recovered Kyle Fitzpatrick's body from a three-foot burial.

AVALANCHE DATA

Persistent Slab avalanche

The slope faced west-northwest, and the avalanche released initially as a mostly-dry hard slab at an elevation of 13,200 feet. The fracture was 16 inches deep, and the slope angle at that spot was 37 degrees. After sliding about 400 feet vertical, the avalanche turned into a wet slab and altogether fell 1,600 feet vertical, stopping at 11,600 feet elevation. The wet flow entrained dirt and rocks, and it was confined to a gully that varied from 40 to 100 feet wide. The slide was classified as HS-AFu-R2-G.

COMMENTS

It seemed like a good idea: slide down the mountain instead of walk. The problem was that the snow structure had changed since their morning climb. A weak basal layer of well-developed and cohesionless depth hoar had been present all winter, but the morning crust was a strong layer that shielded the climbers' weights from activating the weak layer. As the day warmed, the snow cover warmed as well and lost the strength that the surface crust had provided. The men's ascent was on a far stronger snowpack than their descent.

20040409 BROWNS PEAK, SOUTH OF WINFIELD, COLORADO

April 9, 2004

One snowshoer caught, buried, and killed; one dog caught

WEATHER AND SNOWPACK CONDITIONS

Spring conditions had prevailed for several weeks in the Colorado high country, meaning that the snow cover was going through a daily cycle of being frozen and strong overnight and in the early morning, then thawing and becoming wet and weak from late morning until dusk. The avalanche danger also followed a daily flux, going from Low when the snowpack was frozen and increasing to Moderate or Considerable when the pack thawed.

One additional factor contributed to this avalanche accident in April (and to accident 20040320 on nearby LaPlata Peak). Snowfall in the Sawatch Range had been approximately 60% of normal for the winter of 2003-04. This led to a shallow snowpack, and in Colorado, that means a weak snowpack.

ACCIDENT SUMMARY

Browns Peak is a 13,523-foot mountain in the Sawatch Range of central Colorado. The peak is three quarters of a mile north of Huron Peak, one of Colorado's 14ers, and two miles south of the ghost town of Winfield. On Friday, April 9, a party of three men went for a tour by initially heading up the car road that follows the South Fork of Clear Creek. Just past Lulu Gulch, they began climbing a jeep road that switchbacks its way up a ridge to Point 13,044, which is 0.4 miles due west of the summit of Browns Peak.

Syd Schieren and Liam Gray were two of the men; one was on skis and the other was on snowshoes. The third man was Jigmet Dawa, who was on snowshoes. Also along was Dawa's nine-year-old Bernese mountain dog, Tiga.

At treeline, the road forked, and the men turned south toward the basin above the Banker Mine (abandoned since 1927). It was a perfect day for touring. Though a few brief snow showers rolled through, clouds on the surrounding peaks were gradually

The April 9, 2004, avalanche released on the right side of this basin and ran through the gully, spreading out in the runout zone. The group was traversing above treeline on the looker's right side of center. *Photo Nick Logan, CAIC.*

breaking and lifting. There was enough sun to make for great views, and at the same time, there were enough clouds to keep temperatures at treeline cool. Conditions on the trail made for easy travel. Several inches of new snow covered the firm, old snow.

The group left the jeep road to begin a traverse across an open basin. The lead man—the skier—had some concern about potential avalanche danger, so he suggested they spread well apart for the trek across the basin. The trio separated about 200 feet apart and continued their traverse.

The skier was nearly across when he heard a "shotgun blast" followed by his friends' yells. He turned around and saw the middle man pointing upslope. The group hesitated for a moment as they watched the slope start to fracture far above them. At first, one man thought it was only a sluff—the avalanche was slow to start as fractures propagated hundreds of vertical feet above their track. But after a few seconds, the entire slope was in motion. The middle man, on snowshoes, dropped his pack and sprinted to the trees a hundred feet away: he barely made it. The last man in line was Dawa, and he and his dog Tiga were swept away down the slope.

Schieren and Gray had not been caught. They stashed some equipment in a tree to mark their position and then started searching for their friend. After an hour they decided one would leave to get help. One man hurried back to Winfield; from there, he drove down the valley to a ranch and called 911. The Chaffee County Sheriff's Office received this call at 15:50.

RESCUE SUMMARY

The Chaffee County Sheriff's Office immediately mobilized the Chaffee County Rescue Group, Lake County Search and Rescue, and the Summit County Rescue Team. At least two avalanche dogs from the Copper Mountain Ski Patrol also responded. Rescuers arrived before dark and started searching the lower debris. The avalanche had released on an open slope, but the flow was channeled through a narrow gully. An initial wave of dry snow had shot out of the gully, but a secondary wave of wet snow surged from the gully and the debris split into two tongues. This lower debris was wet and very dense. The debris resembled ragged balls, and some were the size of cars. Overall, the avalanche had fallen 1,940 feet vertical.

As darkness crept over the rescuers, one avalanche dog worked the lower debris and the other worked the debris in the upper gully. Above the gully, a large bench—more than three football fields in size—was covered by debris. Search conditions for the rescue dogs were ideal. Down low, the debris was still wet, while up high, the debris was dry. More importantly, a very gentle breeze drifted down the gully. It had gotten dark, and just as the rescue was being called for the night, the upper dog alerted. The rescue dog bolted upslope and onto the bench and dashed out of sight. By the time the handler had scrambled upslope, her dog had found the buried man. Pinned against a tree, the man was buried about two to three feet deep. Rescuers evacuated Dawa's body, but because of darkness and deteriorating weather, they could not continue the search for the buried dog. Several rescuers agreed to return later in the week to continue the search.

Time had been crucial for the rescuers, even if it was a body recovery effort. Had temperatures cooled faster on Friday evening or if the rescuers waited until Saturday, the lower debris would have frozen solid, sealing in any scent. Probe poles would have been almost worthless as the frozen snow would have presented a nearly impenetrable surface.

Six days later, on Thursday, April 15, six friends of the victim (including Syd Schieren) returned to the site to search for Tiga, the buried dog. They spent the day searching the debris but failed to find the missing pooch. It was a quiet ski back to their cars in Winfield, but one man vowed to return every so often to find the dog as the snow melted out. As they approached Winfield, where their cars were parked, the last bit of snow gave out, and they saw a dog! Everyone exchanged startled looks as they looked to the dog and to each other and back to the dog; it sure looked like Tiga. They called her name but got no response. One man removed his skis and walked toward the dog. It ran. They gave short pursuit as the dog ran though the willows, woods, and a creek. Eventually the dog returned to the cars and let the humans approach. They saw the tags and the name "Tiga."

Tiga was very much alive, though a bit skittish and walking with a slight limp. She was pretty hungry, too. Her human friends could only wonder if she had been buried for days or if she had ridden out the avalanche and been too scared to show herself during the rescue. She wasn't talking, so we'll never know.

AVALANCHE DATA

Deep Persistent Slab avalanche

The three men—two on snowshoes—triggered this avalanche, which was classified as HS-AIu-R3-G. The avalanche started as a dry hard slab, and then ran into wet snow lower on the mountain. The men triggered the avalanche low in the starting zone as they traversed the bowl. At their position—11,700 feet—the slope angle was only 27 degrees, but steeper slopes loomed above. The fractures propagated upslope 300 to 900 feet vertical above the men. When the slab finally ripped free, it was generally one to two feet deep. Though the width of the avalanche was about 600 feet, the fracture line was 1,250 feet long as it extended diagonally along the west shoulder of Point 13,044. The slope faced northwest, and at the fracture line the slope angle was 34 to 38 degrees. The top of the avalanche was at 12,600 feet, and it stopped at 10,660 feet for a vertical fall of 1,940 feet. In the deeply incised gully near the bottom of the path, the debris was only 20 to 40 feet across, but below the gully the debris was 400 feet across.

COMMENTS

Several of the rescuers had also been involved with the fatal avalanche 20 days earlier on LaPlata Peak (20040320). LaPlata and Browns are separated by only five air miles, and the rescuers remarked at how similar this avalanche was to the previous one. Both avalanches were triggered on west to northwest aspects, and both occurred in a snowpack that was in the early stage of thawing. Both slides initially released in dry snow and swept into and released wet snow lower on the mountain.

The group of two snowshoers and a skier had considered the avalanche danger, and tried to lessen their exposure by spreading out as they traversed the slope. This worked to some extent: only one of them became a victim, rather than all three. But the group was not prepared for an avalanche emergency, for none had rescue gear. Beacons, probes, and shovels were the missing tools that might have saved Dawa's life.

GUN CREEK, NORTH OF PAXSON, ALASKA | April 10, 2004 20040410

Three snowmobilers caught; two partly buried, one buried and killed

WEATHER AND SNOWPACK CONDITIONS

The Arctic Man Ski and Sno-Go Classic is an annual spring event held at the Summit Lake area near Paxson, Alaska, which is in the Hoodoo Mountains, about 180 miles south of Fairbanks. It's a four-day bash that's attended by thousands. The competition combines snowmobiling, skiing, and snowboarding.

Weather conditions were very spring-like for the 2004 event, held on the second weekend in April. Saturday, April 10, was sunny and warm, and during the afternoon, the snowpack was softening and weakening.

ACCIDENT SUMMARY

Attending the 2004 Arctic Man weekend were Richard Staley (24), his friend Jake Wegner (22), and Jake's father, Ray Wegner (55). All three were from the Fairbanks area. While there was a break in the races going on with the Arctic Man events, this group was riding recreationally about a mile from the race course where the competitive events were being held.

Gun Creek is a narrow, treeless canyon with steep slopes rising high on both sides. As Ray Wegner recalled, "We were down there snowmachining like everyone else. We went up the canyon to look around. We were about ready to turn around and come back when it happened."[6]

More than one person on a slope

Around 15:00, Jake Wegner rode off the packed track and about 30 feet up a hillside to turn around—and got stuck in the soft snow. Ray Wegner and Richard Staley parked their snowmobiles and started walking uphill to help Jake get unstuck. That's when Ray looked up at the steep slope above them and recognized their danger. Ray saw it fracture: "I could see it was cracking. I yelled 'Get out of here. It's going to avalanche!'"

By then, it was too late. A slab of snow about 300 feet wide broke loose and came barreling down the mountainside, and the three men ran for their lives. Ray was about 50 feet ahead of Jake and Richard and watched as the snow hit them first before hitting him. Ray was partly buried and was able to dig himself out fairly quickly. As he looked around, he saw that Jake had been partly buried as well and was in the process of digging himself out. But there was no sign of Richard Staley, and none of them carried avalanche rescue gear.

No rescue equipment

RESCUE SUMMARY

The avalanche had filled the bottom of the canyon with snow. Ray Wegner's wife, Julie, had been riding with the three men but had stopped further down the canyon. Ray was able to signal for her to go for help. While she was gone, Ray and Jake walked over the debris, looking for any sign of Staley, but found nothing. The debris pile had plugged the bottom of the canyon and was about 150 feet wide and an estimated 13 feet deep in places.

About a dozen rescuers arrived by snowmobile, and an Alaska State Trooper helicopter dropped off more rescuers and equipment. Eventually, a rescuer struck Richard Staley with a probe, and his body was recovered.

AVALANCHE DATA

Deep Persistent Slab avalanche

This avalanche was triggered by the snowmobilers far below in the runout zone. It fell about 900 feet slope distance, was about 300 feet wide, and had a crown that appeared to be six feet deep in places. It also ran to ground in parts of its track. It would most likely be classified as SS-AMu-R4-D3-G.

COMMENTS

This was not the day to be riding in a narrow canyon where virtually every slope was steeper than 30 degrees. As temperatures increased, the avalanche danger was on the rise. With no rescue gear, this group of snowmobilers had not anticipated—nor were they prepared for—an avalanche emergency.

These men realized they were in a dangerous situation just minutes before they apparently triggered the avalanche from far below. Once it released, there was no escape.

See accident 20000408 for another fatal avalanche occurring in the vicinity of the Arctic Man event in April 2000.

20040426 TABLE MOUNTAIN, SOUTHWEST OF MT. BAKER SKI AREA, WASHINGTON | April 26, 2004

One backcountry snowboarder caught, buried, and killed

ACCIDENT SUMMARY

Traveling alone

On Monday, April 26, a backcountry snowboarder was traveling alone beyond the boundary of the Mt. Baker Ski Area in the north Cascades of Washington. Well, almost alone: he had the company of his two dogs. He was riding between the ski area boundary gate and Table Mountain, in the vicinity of a pitch called "10 Minute Trees" by the locals. This is a 35-degree slope on a northwest aspect at roughly 4,500 feet elevation.

The man completed a few turns over 150 to 200 feet of the slope and stopped in a narrow chute above a steep rock outcropping. Below the rock was a moat created where the snow had pulled away from the rock. Rescuers later suspected that a wet-snow avalanche caught the victim from behind, pushed him off the rock, and buried him head-first in the moat, leaving his snowboard and boots exposed.

RESCUE SUMMARY

At 18:00, the Whatcom County Sheriff's Office received a report that a snowboarder had been found buried in an avalanche outside the Mt. Baker Ski Area. The people who found the victim had tried to dig him out but could not. They also reported that the victim had died. A rescue team from the Mt. Baker Ski Patrol and Bellingham Mountain Rescue were able to retrieve the victim's body. Apparently, the victim's two dogs survived.

AVALANCHE DATA

The avalanche was a small wet slab and was classified as WS-ARu-R2. The slope angle was 35 degrees. The slope faced northwest and was at 4,500 feet elevation.

Wet Slab avalanche

COMMENTS

Backcountry snowboarding (or skiing) alone has extra risks, and this accident is a good example. There can be no companion rescue in the event of an avalanche burial.

LIBERTY RIDGE, MT. RAINIER, WASHINGTON | June 13, 2004

20040613

Two climbers caught and killed

The following report was written by Glenn Kessler, Climbing Ranger at Mt. Rainier National Park[7]. Kessler's report appears here with minimal editing.

Mt. Rainier is a 14,410-foot volcanic peak that dominates the skyline of Washington's Cascade Range. It is the most glaciated peak in the contiguous United States and is a challenging mountaineering achievement.

Luke Casady and Ansel Vizcaya departed the White River Campground on Friday, June 11, for a planned ascent of Liberty Ridge. The exact details of the subsequent 48 hours may never be known, but the facts uncovered during the subsequent search and body recoveries suggest the following sequence of events:

Casady and Vizcaya, both experienced and seasoned climbers, camped along Curtis Ridge on Friday night and began the ascent up Liberty Ridge early Saturday morning. It is likely the pair climbed past Thumb Rock around midday and continued on up the ridge as the first signs of incoming weather appeared. With the winds building and the visibility decreasing, the climbers continued pushing forward, hoping that the storms would be short-lived and benign. By early evening, however, the winds had increased to 70 mph, and the snow began accumulating. Casady and Vizcaya realized that they would have to hunker down and wait out the storm.

Through the night, the winds hammered the mountain at speeds approaching 100 mph, scouring the falling snow from certain areas and building large slabs in others. This was an uncomfortable night for climbers everywhere on Mount Rainier, with tents destroyed and nerves rattled.

On Sunday morning, somewhere between 12,200 and 13,200 feet, Casady and Vizcaya assessed their predicament. Several inches of snow had fallen, but more importantly, the high winds had deposited large slabs of snow on leeward slopes. The pair had to decide whether it was better to continue on up and over, or turn around and down-climb the most difficult part of the route. The visibility was still not very good, but there were breaks now and then where Casady and Vizcaya could get brief glimpses of the summit, a tempting sight.

Sometime midmorning, as the pair were preparing to make their move, but before they had roped up, Casady and Vizcaya were caught up in a large slab avalanche that released several hundred feet above them, below the bergschrund on Liberty Wall. The avalanche swept them down the slope they were on and then over steep bands of rock, coming to rest only when they had reached the base of the gully on the Carbon Glacier at 9,200 feet, a fall of approximately 4,000 vertical feet. Neither climber survived the fall.

The bad weekend weather had turned back many teams and significantly slowed the progress of others. Rangers were aware that several teams were overdue, but this was typical following harsh weather. On June 16, at approximately 13:00, rangers reported 10 climbers who were descending the Emmons Glacier route and were moving very slowly. Rangers interviewed six of the 10 on the morning of June 17. All had climbed Liberty Ridge, some beginning their trips before, and some after, the Casady/Vizcaya team. None of the climbers, however, had seen the Casady/Vizcaya party. This triggered a search.

On Thursday, June 17, Mt. Rainier National Park began intensive search efforts to locate the overdue climbers. Rangers were dispatched to Camp Schurman to interview any remaining Liberty Ridge climbers descending the Emmons Glacier route, while aerial reconnaissance with a helicopter commenced near Liberty Ridge and the Carbon Glacier. After nearly an hour of aerial search, a backpack and body were spotted on the Carbon Glacier at roughly 9,200 feet, below Liberty Wall. Winds prevented the helicopter from closely approaching or landing near the body, which rested near a large avalanche debris cone beneath Liberty Wall. The weather was very warm and many avalanches of significant size were noted from the 4,000-foot Liberty Wall. The location where the body was seen is particularly known for its rock and ice fall hazards. For this reason, ground recovery operations were planned for first light the next morning (during the coolest temperatures). An aerial search continued for the second climber that afternoon.

Further aerial reconnaissance on June 17 revealed a second backpack and climbing rope near the avalanche debris. Also observed was a fracture line (likely evidence of avalanches) at approximately 13,000 feet on Liberty Ridge. After the recon flight, two rangers were inserted on Curtis Ridge (7,400 feet) to continue observations with a telescope and support recovery operations the following day.

On the morning of June 18, a helicopter inserted two rangers near the 9,000-foot level on the Carbon Glacier. They quickly located the body and the two backpacks and prepared them for removal. After the recovery, the rangers continued ground searching using avalanche transceivers. Their efforts were focused on the area near the backpacks and recovered body but no further clues were found. The ground team was removed after an hour of search, due to safety considerations.

A subsequent aerial search on June 18 revealed more evidence approximately 50 yards west of the recovered climber. Rangers were then inserted onto the glacier to investigate and dig through the snow debris. Nothing more was found and aerial searching resumed. The primary aerial search area consisted of Liberty Ridge, Liberty Wall, Willis Wall and the likely "fall lines" off of the Liberty Ridge climbing route. These were strongly considered to be the most likely areas in which to find clues.

On June 19, an Oregon Army National Guard Chinook helicopter with NPS Rangers conducted a further aerial search. No new clues were detected.

On June 22, a private contract ship provided additional aerial search. During that flight, a climbing harness, pulley, ice axe, and carabiners were spotted near 9,400 feet on the Carbon Glacier. Those clues were located near the avalanche debris cone below Liberty Wall. These items were not retrieved.

On July 13, a climber reported seeing a large blue object on the Carbon Glacier near 9,300 feet while he was climbing Liberty Ridge. Three climbing rangers were dispatched via the ground to investigate the report on July 14.

At 12:00 on July 15, those rangers found the remains of a climber on the Carbon Glacier at 9,300 feet elevation. A contract helicopter inserted two rangers near the site.

The body was successfully recovered from the mountain via long line at 19:00 and was transferred to the Pierce County Medical Examiner's office at 20:00.

ANALYSIS

The obvious fracture line noted below the bergschrund on Liberty Wall was direct evidence of a large slab avalanche whose crown appeared to extend halfway to Ptarmigan Ridge, some 820 feet. The crown was observed from the air only, appearing to vary in thickness from about one to three feet. Whether or not this crown belonged to the avalanche that swept the climbers to their deaths is uncertain, as a smaller slide subsequently overrun by this larger slide is possible. Observations during the search found that large avalanches had run on other slopes in the general vicinity of Liberty and Ptarmigan Ridges following the storm. As there had been no climbers on some of these slopes it is probable these were naturally triggered.

Inadequate rescue equipment

Upon registration, the climbers indicated that they would have avalanche transceivers with them. Neither climber was wearing a transceiver when the slide occurred. One transceiver was found (in the "off" position) in a recovered pack.

APPENDIX A
ACCIDENT
INDEX

ACCIDENTS

Snowy Torrents Number	Page	State	Activity	# Caught	# Killed	Avalanche Character
19961111	26	MT	Backcountry Tourer	1	0	Persistent Slab
19961206	27	UT	Snowmobiler	2	0	
19961207a	28	UT	Snowmobiler	3	0	Persistent Slab
19961207b	28	UT	Snowmobiler	3	1	Persistent Slab
19961223	30	WA	Climber	2	2	
19961226	31	UT	Backcountry Tourer	1	1	Wind Slab
19961228	33	WA	Hiker	3	3	
19970101	34	MN	Snowplayer	4	0	
19970111a	35	ID	Snowmobiler	1	1	
19970111b	36	UT	Backcountry Tourer	3	3	Persistent Slab
19970117	37	AK	Hunter	1	1	
19970125	38	UT	Climber	2	1	Wet Slab
19970201	39	ID	Snowmobiler	1	1	Persistent Slab
19970221	41	MT	Snowmobiler	1	1	
19970303	42	WY	Others at Work	2	2	Persistent Slab
19970308	43	ID	Snowmobiler	1	1	
19970311	43	CO	Sidecountry Rider	1	0	Loose Wet
19970411	44	AK	Snowmobiler	1	1	Cornice fall
19970606	45	AK	Climber	1	1	
19970705	46	CO	Climber	2	1	Wet Slab
19971109	48	AK	Backcountry Tourer	2	1	Persistent Slab
19971122	50	UT	Backcountry Tourer	2	0	Persistent Slab
19971123	51	NH	Hiker	1	0	
19971124	53	AK	Hiker	1	1	
19971230	56	CO	Snowshoer	1	1	Persistent Slab
19980103a	57	ID	Snowmobiler	1	1	Persistent Slab
19980103b	57	MT	Snowmobiler	4	1	
19980103c	58	MT	Climber	1	1	
19980111a	59	MT	Snowmobiler	1	0	
19980111b	60	WY	Snowmobiler	1	1	
19980117a	61	UT	Snowmobiler	1	1	
19980117b	61	UT	Snowmobiler	1	1	
19980118a	62	MT	Snowmobiler	3	3	
19980118b	62	MT	Snowmobiler	1	1	
19980118c	63	WA	Snowmobiler	1	1	Persistent Slab
19980121	64	CO	Backcountry Tourer	1	1	Persistent Slab

CALLOUTS

No rescue equip.	Inadequate rescue equip.	Traveling alone	More than one person on slope	High danger	In runout	Terrain trap	"Red flag" indications	Lack of training
		X						
X			X					
X			X					
X				X				
				X				
		X		X				
X				X	X			
X			X					
X								
				X	X			
		X						
X					X			
						X		
					X			
X			X					
						X		
						X		
	X		X					X
			X		X		X	
X							X	
	X					X		
X					X			
X								
			X					
	X							
	X							X
X								
X								
X								
	X		X					
X								
	X			X				
		X				X		

Snowy Torrents Number	Page	State	Activity	# Caught	# Killed	Avalanche Character
19980124	67	MT	Snowmobiler	1	1	Persistent Slab
19980129	69	MT	Sidecountry Rider	1	0	Wind Slab
19980211	70	CA	Backcountry Tourer	1	1	Cornice fall
19980222	70	ID	Snowmobiler	1	1	Persistent Slab
19980301	72	CO	Backcountry Tourer	2	1	Persistent Slab
19980308	74	CO	Sidecountry Rider	1	1	Persistent Slab
19980326	75	MT	Snowmobiler	1	0	Storm Slab
19980401	76	CO	Hiker	2	1	Persistent Slab
19980419	77	CO	Snowshoer	2	1	Wind Slab
19980420	79	AK	Heliskier	2	1	Cornice fall
19980426	79	AK	Snowmobiler	1	1	Persistent Slab
19980531	80	OR	Climber	3	1	Wind Slab
19980611	82	WA	Climber	10	1	Loose Wet
19981107	86	UT	Backcountry Tourer	5	1	Persistent Slab
19981115	87	MT	Hunter	1	1	Persistent Slab
19981230	88	MT	Snowmobiler	1	1	
19990101	88	MT	Snowmobiler	1	0	
19990102	89	UT	Backcountry Tourer	2	2	Cornice fall
19990104	90	WY	Snowmobiler	1	1	
19990118	91	WA	Sidecountry Rider	1	1	Wind Slab
19990119	92	WY	Inbounds Rider	1	1	
19990123	92	CO	Sidecountry Rider	2	1	Persistent Slab
19990129a	94	OR	Backcountry Tourer	1	1	
19990129b	95	UT	Snowmobiler	1	1	Persistent Slab
19990130	96	CO	Snowmobiler	1	1	Persistent Slab
19990206a	98	CO	Backcountry Tourer	4	3	Deep Persistent Slab
19990206b	101	CA	Snowplayer	4	1	
19990206c	102	UT	Hiker	1	1	Persistent Slab
19990214	103	WA	Sidecountry Rider	2	2	Deep Persistent Slab
19990306	104	MT	Snowmobiler	1	0	Persistent Slab
19990312	106	AK	Inbounds Rider	2	0	Cornice fall
19990321	106	AK	Snowmobiler	13	6	Deep Persistent Slab
19990403	111	AK	Snowmobiler	1	1	
19990406	111	CO	Backcountry Tourer	1	0	Persistent Slab
19990407	113	CO	Backcountry Tourer	1	1	Persistent Slab
19990415	114	AK	Others at Work	1	1	
19990416	115	AK	Snowmobiler	7	1	

No rescue equip.	Inadequate rescue equip.	Traveling alone	More than one person on slope	High danger	In runout	Terrain trap	"Red flag" indications	Lack of training
								x
						x		
			x			x		
x			x					
		x						
	x		x					
x								
x								
x								
x				x				
						x		
x					x			
		x						
					x			
x								
x								
x		x		x		x		
x				x		x	x	
x						x		
					x			
			x					x
x			x	x				
x								
	x							
	x		x					
	x		x		x		x	
x								
x								
		x						
					x			
					x			

Snowy Torrents Number	Page	State	Activity	# Caught	# Killed	Avalanche Character
19990427	115	AK	Heliskier	1	1	Persistent Slab
19990430	117	AK	Climber	3	1	
19990514	118	AK	Hiker	2	1	Loose Wet
19991126	120	MT	Sidecountry Rider	2	1	Persistent Slab
19991214	121	CO	Backcountry Tourer	1	1	Persistent Slab
19991218	123	CO	Hiker	2	1	Wind Slab
19991221	124	CO	Backcountry Tourer	1	1	Storm Slab
19991226	126	AK	Snowmobiler	1	1	Storm Slab
20000111	128	UT	Sidecountry Rider	2	2	Deep Persistent Slab
20000116	129	WA	Sidecountry Rider	1	1	Persistent Slab
20000123	132	CO	Hiker	3	1	Persistent Slab
20000125a	134	CO	Sidecountry Rider	1	1	Persistent Slab
20000125b	135	CO	Backcountry Tourer	1	1	Persistent Slab
20000126	136	AK	Resident	5	1	
20000201	138	AK	Highway Personnel	3	1	Wind Slab
20000219a	140	ID	Snowmobiler	6	1	Persistent Slab
20000219b	141	NY	Backcountry Tourer	4	1	Storm Slab
20000220	142	NH	Backcountry Tourer	2	1	Wind Slab
20000317	144	CO	Sidecountry Rider	2	2	Deep Persistent Slab
20000319	147	ID	Snowmobiler	1	1	Wind Slab
20000322	148	MT	Snowmobiler	1	1	Persistent Slab
20000408a	149	AK	Snowmobiler	1	1	Persistent Slab
20000408b	150	AK	Backcountry Tourer	2	1	
20000421	152	CO	Sidecountry Rider	2	1	
20001127	156	WY	Hunter	1	1	Persistent Slab
20001201	156	WY	Backcountry Tourer	1	1	Persistent Slab
20001209a	158	AK	Snowmobiler	1	1	Persistent Slab
20001209b	159	WY	Backcountry Tourer	1	1	Persistent Slab
20001214	160	UT	Snowmobiler	1	1	Persistent Slab
20001217	161	MT	Snowmobiler	2	2	Persistent Slab
20001225	163	WY	Backcountry Tourer	1	1	Persistent Slab
20001229	164	CO	Backcountry Tourer	1	1	Persistent Slab
20001231	165	MT	Hiker	4	2	Persistent Slab
20010117	167	MT	Snowmobiler	1	1	Persistent Slab
20010129	168	WA	Hiker	2	1	Persistent Slab
20010203	170	AK	Snowmobiler	6	2	Deep Persistent Slab
20010206	173	WY	Sidecountry Rider	1	1	

No rescue equip.	Inadequate rescue equip.	Traveling alone	More than one person on slope	High danger	In runout	Terrain trap	“Red flag” indications	Lack of training
						X		
			X			X		
X			X					
			X			X		
	X							
			X			X		
		X		X				
X				X				X
X								
	X							
X				X				X
X				X		X		
X		X		X		X		
X			X					
X			X					
				X			X	
					X			
X								
			X					
			X					
		X						
	X	X						
	X		X					
		X				X		
X								X
X			X	X		X		
						X		
X		X						
X			X				X	
X						X		
	X		X					
		X						

Snowy Torrents Number	Page	State	Activity	# Caught	# Killed	Avalanche Character
20010217	174	WA	Snowmobiler	1	1	Storm Slab
20010221	175	CA	Sidecountry Rider	2	2	Storm Slab
20010223	176	WY	Sidecountry Rider	1	1	Persistent Slab
20010225	177	CO	Backcountry Tourer	1	1	Persistent Slab
20010227	179	UT	Sidecountry Rider	4	1	Persistent Slab
20010303	181	WY	Snowmobiler	2	1	
20010310	181	UT	Snowmobiler	3	2	Persistent Slab
20010318a	182	CO	Backcountry Tourer	1	1	Storm Slab
20010318b	183	AK	Snowmobiler	2	1	
20010403	184	CO	Snowmobiler	1	1	Persistent Slab
20010404a	185	MT	Snowmobiler	1	1	Persistent Slab
20010404b	186	MT	Backcountry Tourer	1	1	Persistent Slab
20010411	188	WA	Snowmobiler	1	1	
20010428	189	UT	Climber	2	2	Glide
20011111	196	AK	Hiker	2	1	Persistent Slab
20011128	197	CO	Backcountry Tourer	2	1	Deep Persistent Slab
20011212	201	AK	Snowmobiler	3	1	
20011223	202	AK	Snowmobiler	1	1	
20011224	203	AK	Snowmobiler	1	1	
20011231	204	MT	Snowmobiler	1	1	Persistent Slab
20020112	205	AK	Snowmobiler	3	2	Cornice fall
20020126	206	MT	Snowmobiler	5	4	Deep Persistent Slab
20020131a	211	UT	Backcountry Tourer	1	1	Persistent Slab
20020131b	213	MT	Snowmobiler	1	0	Persistent Slab
20020201	214	CO	Inbounds Rider	1	1	Loose Dry
20020206	215	CO	Backcountry Tourer	1	1	Persistent Slab
20020210	217	MT	Snowmobiler	2	1	Persistent Slab
20020216	218	MT	Snowmobiler	3	2	Persistent Slab
20020224	220	CO	Snowmobiler	1	1	Persistent Slab
20020308	223	CA	Sidecountry Rider	3	1	Cornice fall
20020312	224	ID	Snowmobiler	1	1	Cornice fall
20020314a	225	CO	Sidecountry Rider	1	1	Persistent Slab
20020314b	226	CO	Backcountry Tourer	5	1	Persistent Slab
20020315	228	CO	Sidecountry Rider	2	1	Persistent Slab
20020316a	230	MT	Snowmobiler	2	1	Persistent Slab
20020316b	231	UT	Sidecountry Rider	2	2	Persistent Slab
20020317	233	CO	Snowmobiler	3	1	

No rescue equip.	Inadequate rescue equip.	Traveling alone	More than one person on slope	High danger	In runout	Terrain trap	"Red flag" indications	Lack of training
	X							
X						X		
X			X			X		
X			X					
	X					X		
	X				X			
		X				X	X	
X								
	X							
	X							
	X		X					
X			X			X		
			X					
	X		X					
				X				
	X							
X		X						
			X	X				
		X						
	X							
		X						
		X						
			X					
X								
X			X				X	X
	X							
		X				X		
X		X				X		
			X					
X								
			X					
	X							
X								

Snowy Torrents Number	Page	State	Activity	# Caught	# Killed	Avalanche Characte
20020318	234	WY	Backcountry Tourer	1	1	
20020322	234	MT	Snowmobiler	1	1	Persistent Slab
20020328	237	AK	Backcountry Tourer	1	0	Persistent Slab
20020331	239	AK	Hiker	3	2	Wet Slab
20020613	240	AK	Climber	3	3	
20021129	244	NH	Climber	7	2	
20021215	246	NV	Sidecountry Rider	1	1	Storm Slab
20021226	249	WY	Snowmobiler	1	1	
20021228	250	ID	Snowmobiler	2	1	
20021229	250	WA	Backcountry Tourer	4	1	Persistent Slab
20030104	252	WY	Backcountry Tourer	1	1	Persistent Slab
20030105	253	WY	Snowmobiler	2	1	Persistent Slab
20030122	253	MT	Snowmobiler	1	1	Persistent Slab
20030125	255	WY	Snowmobiler	1	1	
20030129	256	WY	Backcountry Tourer	1	1	Persistent Slab
20030201	257	MT	Snowmobiler	2	1	
20030202	258	MT	Snowmobiler	1	1	Persistent Slab
20030209	259	AK	Backcountry Tourer	2	1	
20030210	260	WY	Inbounds Rider	2	1	
20030215	261	UT	Backcountry Tourer	1	1	Persistent Slab
20030217	263	CO	Climber	2	1	Persistent Slab
20030222a	265	CO	Backcountry Tourer	3	1	Persistent Slab
20030222b	267	ID	Backcountry Tourer	1	1	Persistent Slab
20030222c	268	ID	Snowmobiler	5	1	
20030224	269	WY	Snowmobiler	1	1	
20030305	270	CO	Snowmobiler	1	1	Deep Persistent Slab
20030309a	272	CO	Snowmobiler	1	1	Deep Persistent Slab
20030309b	274	MT	Snowmobiler	3	1	
20030320	275	CO	Backcountry Tourer	2	1	Persistent Slab
20030322	277	CO	Snowmobiler	1	1	Persistent Slab
20030410	278	AK	Guided Client	1	1	Persistent Slab
20030426	280	CA	Snowmobiler	1	1	Persistent Slab
20031212	282	WA	Hiker	3	1	Storm Slab
20031213	284	WA	Hiker	2	1	
20031217	286	WA	Snowmobiler	1	1	Persistent Slab
20031226	288	UT	Backcountry Tourer	5	3	Storm Slab
20040101	290	CA	Backcountry Tourer	2	1	

No rescue equip.	Inadequate rescue equip.	Traveling alone	More than one person on slope	High danger	In runout	Terrain trap	"Red flag" indications	Lack of training
		X						
						X		
X			X			X		
X			X					
X								
X								
X				X				
			X					
X								
	X	X						
	X		X					
		X						
	X			X				
X				X				
	X							
X								
	X							
X								
	X							
	X							
X				X				
			X	X				
			X	X				
X								
X								
X								
X				X		X		
	X							
X			X	X				
	X							

Snowy Torrents Number	Page	State	Activity	# Caught	# Killed	Avalanche Character
20040102	291	ID	Resident	2	2	Storm Slab
20040122	295	AK	Others at Work	1	1	Roof
20040131	296	WY	Backcountry Tourer	1	1	Persistent Slab
20040226	297	UT	Hiker	1	1	Storm Slab
20040228a	299	ID	Snowmobiler	1	1	Persistent Slab
20040228b	300	AK	Climber	1	1	Cornice fall
20040305	301	WA	Snowmobiler	1	1	
20040306	301	ID	Snowmobiler	1	1	
20040310	302	CO	Snowmobiler	1	1	Persistent Slab
20040320	304	CO	Climber	2	1	Persistent Slab
20040409	306	CO	Snowshoer	1	1	Deep Persistent Slab
20040410	309	AK	Snowmobiler	3	1	Deep Persistent Slab
20040426	310	WA	Backcountry Tourer	1	1	Wet Slab
20040613	311	WA	Climber	2	2	
TOTAL				**376**	**220**	

No rescue equip.	Inadequate rescue equip.	Traveling alone	More than one person on slope	High danger	In runout	Terrain trap	"Red flag" indications	Lack of training
				X				
		X						
X						X		
X								
	X		X					
X			X					
		X						
	X							

APPENDIX B
GLOSSARY

Alpha Angle —The angle between the horizontal and a line drawn from the highest point of the crown face to the toe of the debris. Alpha can be measured for an individual avalanche (α_i). Extreme values of alpha (α_e) can be determined from historical records, tree ring data, or direct observation. Minimum values of alpha (longest runout length) can also be calculated for a specific return period (α_{10}, α_{50}, α_{100}). Also termed the angle of reach.

Aspect—The exposure of the terrain as indicated by compass direction of the fall line (relative to true north). A slope that faces north has a north aspect.

Avalanche, Snow—A mass of snow sliding, tumbling, or flowing down an inclined surface that may contain rocks, soil, vegetation, or ice.

Avalanche Danger Scale—A categorical estimation of the avalanche danger. In the U.S., a five level scale is used for backcountry recreational users.

Avalanche Path—A terrain feature where an avalanche occurs. An avalanche path is composed of a starting zone, track, and runout zone.

Bed Surface—The surface over which fracture and subsequent avalanche release occurs. The bed surface is often different than the running surface over which the avalanche flows through the track. A bed surface can be either the ground or a snow/ice surface.

Caught—A category of the avalanche toll for an accident. A person is caught if they are touched and adversely affected by the avalanche. People performing slope cuts are generally not considered caught in the resulting avalanche unless they are carried downhill.

Collapse—When fracture of a lower layer causes an upper layer to fall, producing a displacement at the snow surface. The displacement may not always be detectable with the human eye. A collapse in the snowpack often produces a whumpfing sound.

Completely Buried—A category of the avalanche toll for an accident. A person is completely buried if they are completely beneath the snow surface when the avalanche stops. Clothing or attached equipment is not visible on the surface.

Concave Slope—A terrain feature that is rounded inward like the inside of a bowl (i.e. goes from more steep to less steep).

Convex Slope—A terrain feature that is curved or rounded like the exterior of a sphere or circle (i.e. goes from less steep to more steep).

Cornice—A mass of snow that is deposited by the wind, often overhanging, and usually near a sharp terrain break such as a ridge.

Crown—The snow that remains on the slope above the crown face of an avalanche.

Crown Face—The top fracture surface of a slab avalanche. Usually smooth, clean cut, and angled 90 degrees to the bed surface. *Also see fracture line.*

Crystal—A physically homogeneous solid in which the internal elements are arranged in a repetitive three-dimensional pattern. Within an ice lattice the internal elements are individual water molecules held together by hydrogen bonds. Usually synonymous with grain in snow applications (see definition for grain), although the term grain can be used to describe multi- crystal formation.

Danger, Avalanche—The potential for an avalanche(s) to cause damage to something of value. It is a combination of the likelihood of triggering and the destructive size of the avalanche(s). It implies the potential to affect people, facilities or things of value, but does not incorporate vulnerability or exposure to avalanches. Avalanche danger and hazard are synonymous and are commonly expressed using relative terms such as high, moderate and low.

Debris, Avalanche—The mass of snow and other material that accumulate as a result of an avalanche.

Density—A mass of substance per unit volume. The International System of Units (SI) uses kg/m^3 for density.

Deposition, Wind—The accumulation of snow that has been transported by wind.

Exposure—An element or resource (person, vehicle, structure, etc…) that is subject to the impact of a specific natural hazard.

Failure—A state of stress or deformation that meets a specific criterion. Many criteria for failure exist, but the most commonly used criteria for snow are: 1) the point at which shear stress in a weak layer equals the shear strength, 2) the point at which shear deformation increases while the strength of the weak layer decreases, 3) sudden excessive plastic deformation, 4) during a stability test, the loading step at which the test column fractures. Failure is a precursor to fracture, but fracture (and slab release) may or may not occur after failure. To avoid confusion, the criterion should always be specified when discussing failure.

Fall line—The natural downhill course between two points on a slope.

Flank—The snow to the sides of a slab avalanche, which remains after the release.

Fracture—The process of separating a solid body into two or more parts under the action of stress. The result of the fracture process is variously described depending on stress mode(s), scale, material type, and other variables. Nomenclature includes cracks, breaks, slip regions, dislocations, and ruptures. Occasionally, the word fracture is also used to denote the result of the fracture process (e.g. fracture line profile, fracture character, etc.)

Fracture Line—The remaining boundary of a slab after an avalanche has occurred. Also see definitions for crown face, flank and stauchwall.

Full Profile—A complete snow profile observation where grain size, grain type, interval temperature, layer density and layer hardness are measured and recorded in addition to stability information.

Glide—Downhill slip of the entire snowpack along the ground or firm interface.

Grain—The smallest distinguishable ice component in a disaggregated snow cover. Usually synonymous with crystal in snow applications. The term grain can be used to describe polycrystal formations when the crystal boundaries are not easily distinguishable with a field microscope.

Hang Fire—Snow adjacent to an existing fracture line that remains after avalanche release. Hang fire typically has a similar aspect and incline to the initial avalanche.

Hard Slab—A snow slab having a density equal to, or greater than 300 kg/m3 prior to avalanching.

Hazard, Avalanche—The potential for an avalanche(s) to cause damage to something of value. It is a combination of the likelihood of triggering and the destructive size of the avalanche(s). It implies the potential to affect people, facilities or things of value, but does not incorporate vulnerability or exposure to avalanches. Avalanche danger and hazard are synonymous and are commonly expressed using relative terms such as high, moderate and low.

Incline—The steepness of a slope. The acute angle measured from the horizontal to the plane of a slope. Also termed slope angle.

Injured—A category of the avalanche toll for an accident. A person is considered injured if they require medical treatment after being caught, partially buried-not critical, partially buried-critical, or completely buried in an avalanche.

Isothermal—The state of equal temperature. In an isothermal snow cover there is no temperature gradient. Seasonal snow covers that are isothermal are typically 0°C.

Layer, Snow—An element of a snow cover created by a weather, metamorphic, or other event.

Loose-Snow Avalanche—An avalanche that releases from a point and spreads downhill entraining snow. Also termed a point-release avalanche or a sluff.

Mitigation, Avalanche Hazard—To moderate the frequency, timing, force, or destructive effect of avalanches on people, property, or the environment through active or passive methods.

Partially Buried—Critical—A category of the avalanche toll for an accident. A person is partially buried–critical if their head is below the snow surface when the avalanche stops but equipment, clothing and/or portions of their body are visible.

Partially Buried—Not Critical—A category of the avalanche toll for an accident. A person is partially buried–not critical if their head was above the snow surface when the avalanche stops.

Point-Release Avalanche—See loose snow avalanche or sluff.

Precipitation Intensity—A measurement of the water equivalent that accumulated during a defined time period (usually 1 hour).

Remote Trigger—When an avalanche releases some distance away from the trigger point.

Risk—The effect of uncertainty on objectives (ISO 31000: 2009). Avalanche Risk is the probability or chance of harm to a specific element at risk, determined by the element's exposure and vulnerability to the avalanche hazard (Statham, 2008). In common usage, risk is a broad construct that relates uncertainty to outcome, often mediated by decision making or a diagnostic tool.

Running Surface—The surface over which an avalanche flows below the stauchwall. This surface can extend from the stauchwall, through the track, and into the runout zone. The running surface can be composed of one or more snowpack layers.

Runout Zone—The portion of an avalanche path where the avalanche debris typically comes to rest due to a decrease in slope angle, a natural obstacle, or loss of momentum.

Settling, Settlement—The slow, internal deformation and densification of snow under the influence of gravity. A component of creep.

Slab—A cohesive snowpack element consisting of one or more snow layers.

Slab Avalanche—An avalanche that releases a cohesive slab of snow producing a fracture line.

Slope Angle —The acute angle measured from the horizontal to the plane of a slope.

Sluff—A loose snow avalanche or point release avalanche.

Snow Profile—A pit dug vertically into the snowpack where observations of snow cover stratigraphy and characteristics of the individual layers are observed. Also used to describe data collected by this method at an individual site.

Soft Slab—A snow slab with a density less than 300 kg/m^3.

Spatial Variability—The variation of physical properties across the physical extent, or various spatial scales, of a material. Typical scales in snow avalanche research and practice include the continental scale (defining variations in snow and avalanche climates), the regional scale (such as regions covered by backcountry avalanche advisories), the scale of individual mountain ranges (of various sizes), and the scale of individual slopes. Physical properties investigated vary, but include weak layer shear strength, stability test scores, penetration resistance, microstructural parameters, layer continuity, snow water equivalent, snow depth, and other characteristics.

Stability—1) A property of a system where the effects of an induced disturbance decrease in magnitude and the system returns to its original state. 2) For avalanche forecasting stability is the chance that avalanches do not initiate. Stability is analyzed in space and time relative to a given triggering level or load.

Starting Zone—The portion of an avalanche path from where the avalanche releases.

Stauchwall—The downslope fracture surface of a slab avalanche.

Strength—1) The ability of a material to resist strain or stress. 2) The maximum stress a snow layer can withstand without failing or fracturing.

Sympathetic Trigger—When an avalanche triggers another avalanche some distance away. The second avalanche releases due to the disturbance of the first.

Temperature—Often defined as the condition of a body that determines the transfer of heat to or from other bodies. Particularly, it is a manifestation of the average translational kinetic energy of the molecules of a substance due to heat agitation. Also, the degree of hotness or coldness measured on a definite scale.

Temperature Gradient—The change in temperature over a distance. Expressed in units of degrees per length (i.e. °C/m).

Test Profile—A snow profile where selected characteristics of the snowpack are observed and recorded. Stability tests are typically conducted in a test profile. *Also see full profile.*

Track—The portion of an avalanche path that lies below the starting zone and above the runout zone.

Trigger—The mechanism that increases the load on the snowpack, or changes its physical properties to the point that fracture and subsequent avalanching occurs.

Trigger Point—The area where a trigger is applied.

Wind Sensor—An instrument that measures both wind speed and direction.

Wind Slab—A dense layer(s) of snow formed by wind deposition.

Whumpf—*See collapse.*

APPENDIX C
AVALANCHE
EVENT CHARACTERISTICS

TABLE 1 Avalanche Type

CODE	AVALANCHE TYPE
L	Loose-snow avalanche, comprised of dry, incohesive snow
WL	Wet loose-snow avalanche, comprised of wet, incohesive snow
WS	Wet slab avalanche, where the weak layer and often slab were wet or moist snow
SS	Soft slab avalanche, with average slab densities less than 300 kgm^-3, usually identified by rounded, small debris
HS	Hard slab avalanche, with average slab densities equal to or greater than 300 kgm^-3, usually identified by angular blocks of debris
R	Roof avalanche, where the snow slab slid off a structure

TABLE 2 Avalanche Trigger (u designates unintentional trigger)

CODE	CAUSE OF AVALANCHE RELEASE
ACu	Triggered by human-induced cornice fall
AFu	Triggered by person on foot
ALu	Triggered by person on snowshoes
AMu	Triggered by snowmobile
ARu	Triggered by snowboarder
ASu	Triggered by skier
N	Natural trigger, usually weather

TABLE 3 Avalanche Size—Relative to Path

CODE	AVALANCHE SIZE
R1	Very small
R2	Small
R3	Medium
R4	Large
R5	Major or maximum

TABLE 4 Avalanche Size—Destructive Force

CODE	AVALANCHE DESTRUCTIVE POTENTIAL
D1	Relatively harmless to people.
D2	Could bury, injure, or kill a person.
D3	Could bury and destroy a car, damage a truck, destroy a wood frame house, or break a few trees.
D4	Could destroy a railway car, large truck, several buildings, or substantial amount of forest.
D5	Could gouge the landscape. Largest snow avalanche known.

TABLE 5 Avalanche Bed Surface

CODE	BED SURFACE
I	The avalanche released at the new snow/old snow interface.
O	The avalanche released within the old snow.
G	The avalanche released at the ground.

APPENDIX D
AVALANCHE
REPORTING FORM

American Avalanche Association
Forest Service National Avalanche Center
Avalanche Incident Report: Short Form

Occurrence Date:(YYYYMMDD)__________________ **Time:**(HHMM) ______________

Reporting Party Name and Address: ____

Avalanche Characteristics:
Type:______ Aspect:__________
Trigger _____ Slope Angle:_________
Size: R__/D__ Elevation:___________ m / ft
Sliding Surface (check one):
In new New/old In old Ground

Location:
State:____ County:______________ Forest:_______________
Peak, Mtn Pass, or Drainage:_______________________
Site Name:_______________________
Lat/Lon or UTM:_______________________
Datum:_______________________

Group	Number of People	Time Recovered	Duration of Burial	Depth to Face ☐☐☐ m ☐ ft
Caught				
Partially Buried—Not-critical				
Partially Buried—Critical				
Completely Buried				

Number of people injured:___________ Number of people killed:________

Dimensions ☐☐ m ☐ ft	Average	Maximum
Height of Crown Face		
Width of Fracture		
Vertical fall		

Snow	Hardness	Grain Type	Grain Size
Slab			
Weak Layer			
Bed Surface			

Thickness of weak layer:______________ mm / cm / in

Burial involved a terrain trap? ☐ no ☐ yes→type:____________________ Number of people that crossed start zone before the avalanche: ______
Location of group in relation to start zone during avalanche: ☐high ☐middle ☐low ☐ below ☐ all ☐ unknown Avalanche occurred during: ☐ ascent ☐

Subject	Name	Age	Gender	Address	Phone	Activity
1						
2						
3						
4						
5						

Equipment Carried
1 2 3 4 5
☐☐☐☐☐ transceiver
☐☐☐☐☐ shovel
☐☐☐☐☐ probe pole
☐☐☐☐☐ ________

Experience at Activity
1 2 3 4 5
☐☐☐☐☐ unknown
☐☐☐☐☐ novice
☐☐☐☐☐ intermediate
☐☐☐☐☐ advanced

Avalanche Training
1 2 3 4 5
☐☐☐☐☐ unknown
☐☐☐☐☐ none
☐☐☐☐☐ some
☐☐☐☐☐ advanced

Signs of Instability Noted by Group
☐ unknown
☐ none
☐ recent avalanches
☐ shooting cracks
☐ collapse or whumphing

Injuries Sustained
1 2 3 4 5
☐☐☐☐☐ none
☐☐☐☐☐ first aid
☐☐☐☐☐ doctor's care
☐☐☐☐☐ hospital stay

Extent of Injuries or Cause of Death
1 2 3 4 5
☐☐☐☐☐ asphyxiation
☐☐☐☐☐ head trauma
☐☐☐☐☐ spinal injury
☐☐☐☐☐ chest trauma
☐☐☐☐☐ skeletal fractures

Damage Number of Vehicles Caught:__________ Number of Structures Damaged:__________ Estimated $ Loss:________________

Accident Summary Include: events leading to accident, group's familiarity with location, objectives, route, hazard evaluation, etc.

Rescue Summary Include: description of initial search, report of accident, organized rescue etc.

Rescue Method:
1 2 3 4 5
☐☐☐☐☐ self rescue
☐☐☐☐☐ transceiver
☐☐☐☐☐ spot probe
☐☐☐☐☐ probe line
☐☐☐☐☐ rescue dog
☐☐☐☐☐ voice
☐☐☐☐☐ object
☐☐☐☐☐ digging
☐☐☐☐☐ other____

Attach additional pages as needed. Include: weather history, snow profiles, reports from other agencies, diagram of site, and any other supporting information.

Please send to: CAIC; 325 Broadway WS1; Boulder, CO 80305; caic@state.co.us
Voice:(303) 499-9650 www.colorado.gov/avalanche

American Avalanche Association
Forest Service National Avalanche Center
Avalanche Accident Report: Long Form

Please send to:
Colorado Avalanche Information Center
325 Broadway WS1
Boulder, CO 80305
voice: (303) 499-9650, email: caic@state.co.us, web: www.colorado.gov/avalanche

Occurrence Date:____________________ **Time:**______________

Report Author(s):

Name:____________________ Affiliation____________________

Address: ____

Phone:__________________ Fax:____________ Email:__________________

Location:

State:______ County:________________ Region:_________ Forest:________________

Geographic Area (mountain range, mountain pass, drainage, or feature):____________________

Site Name:____

Lat/Lon or UTM:__________________________ Elevation: ☐ above treeline ☐ near treeline ☐ below treeline

Datum:____________________________

Summary	Caught	Partially Buried Not-critical	Partially Buried Critical	Completely Buried	Injured	Killed	Vehicles Damaged	Structures Damaged
Number								

Weather Fill in the weather chart of the five days prior to the accident. Use 24 hr averages or trends for wind speed and direction.

Weather station(s): Location____________________ Lat/Lon or UTM:__________ Elevation:________ m / ft

Date						Day of Accident
Max						
Min						
24						
24W						
Wind Speed						
Wind Dir						

Avalanche Conditions Attach most recent avalanche advisory

Nearest Avalanche Center: __________ Accident outside of forecast	Avalanche Danger Rating: Low, Moderate, Considerable, High, Extreme	Recent Avalanche Activity
Avalanche warning in effect? yes no		

Snowpack Describe the state of the snowpack. Include season history, snow profiles, and prominent features as necessary.

Section I: Group Information

Fill in the following tables. Some of the fields can be checked yes or left blank. Attach additional pages and reports from other agen-cies as necessary.

Subject	Name	Age	Gender	Address	Phone
1					
2					
3					
4					
5					

Skill Level	Activity	Years at Activity	Rank skill level as novice, intermediate, advanced, or expert.		Years Traveling in Avalanche Terrain	Avalanche Education Level
			Activity Skill Level	Accessed Local Avalanche Advisory		
1						
2						
3						
4						
5						

Rescue Equipment Carried	Transceiver Make and Model	Shovel	Probe Pole	Releasable Bindings	Other	Snowmobile: Rescue Equipmen Carried on Perso
1						
2						
3						
4						
5						

Injuries or Cause of Death	Unknown	None	First-Aid Necessary	Doctor's Care Needed	Hospital Stay Required	Asphyxia	Head Injury	Chest Injuries	Spinal Injury	Hypothermia	Skeletal Fracture	Other	Fat
1													
2													
3													
4													
5													

Comments

Section II: Avalanche Path and Event Information

Fill in the following tables. Some of the fields can be checked yes or left blank. Attach additional pages, fracture line profiles, and reports as necessary.

Avalanche Characteristics

Type:____________ Trigger:______________ Size: R1 R2 R3 R4 R5 / D1 D2 D3 D4 D5

Sliding Surface (check one): Within new snow New/old interface Old snow layer Ground Avalanche stepped down into old snow layers.

Distance from trigger to crown face:______________________ m ft

Comments:

Dimensions ☐ m ☐ ☐ft	Average	Maximum	Measured
Height of Crown Face			
Width			
Vertical fall			

Snow	Hardness	Grain Type	Grain Size	Thickness
Slab				
Weak Layer				
Bed Surface				

Start Zone

Elevation: ___________m / ft

Average Slope Angle (°) :________

Maximum Slope Angle (°) :_______

Aspect:_________

Ground Cover: Smooth, Rocky, Glacier, Dense Forest, Open Forest, Brush, Grass, Unknown

Location of Crown Face: Ridge, Cornice, Mid-slope, Convex Roll, Concave Slope, Rocks, Unknown

Snow Moisture: Dry, Moist, Wet

Vegetation:____

Track

Open Slope Average Slope Angle (°):___________

Confined Aspect:___________

Gully

Snow Moisture: Dry Moist Wet

Runout

Elevation: ___________m / ft

Average Incline (°) :________

Aspect:_________

Ground Cover: Smooth, Rocky, Glacier, Dense Forest, Open Forest, Brush, Grass, Unknown

Snow Moisture: Dry, Moist, Wet

Debris Type (check all that apply): Fine, Blocks, Hard, Soft, Rocks, Trees, ________, ________

α_i (°) :__________

☐α_e (°) :_________

Debris Density:_________ kg/m^3

Terrain Trap: no yes

Terrain Trap Type:________________

Vegetation:_______________________________

Comments

Section III: Accident Description

Fill in the following sections with available information. Attach additional pages, statements, witness accounts, and other reports as necessary.

Events Leading Up to the Avalanche

Include objectives of party, departure point, route taken, familiarity with area, and encounters with other groups, location of party at time of avalanche, etc.

Location of group in relation to start zone at the time of avalanche release: high middle □low below all unknown

Slope angle at approximate trigger site:________°

Avalanche Danger Evaluation

Number of snowpit observations :____

Signs of Instability Observed:

none unknown
some cracking shooting cracks
whumphing hollow sounds
recent avalanche activity

Stability Tests Performed:

yes
no
unknown

Location of observations:________________

Test Results

Comments

Witnesses	Name	Address	Phone
1			
2			

Accident Diagram

On a separate page or on a photograph, draw a diagram of the accident scene. Include avalanche boundaries, prominent rock and/or trees, the location of all party members before the avalanche, and the location of people, machines and equipment after the avalanche

Section IV: Rescue

Fill in the following sections with available information. Attach additional pages, statements, witness accounts, and other reports as necessary.

Rescue Chronology

First Report	Response					
Reporting Party: ____________	Agency	Time Dispatched	Time on Scene	Method of Travel	Number of Rescuers	Equipment
Report Method: ____________						
Time Reported: ____________						

Recovery

For Body Position use: Prone/Face Down, Supine/On Back, On Side, Sitting, Standing
For Head Position use: Up Hill, Down Hill, Sideways

Subject	Caught	Partially Buried - Non-critical	Partially Buried - Critical	Completely Buried	Depth to Face m ft	Time Recovered	Length of Burial	Body Position	Head Position
1									
2									
3									
4									
5									

Recovery Method

For a transceiver recovery, include make and model of transceiver used by searcher. If an object on the surface was used as a clue, list the object.

Subject	Self Rescue	Companion	Organized	Voice	Object	Transceiver	Spot Probe	Probe Line	Rescue Dog	Digging
1										
2										
3										
4										
5										

Rescue Description

List pertinent events that occurred during the rescue. Include additional pages of dispatch notes, statements, and agency reports as needed.

Section V: Damage

Fill in the following sections with available information. Attach additional pages, statements, witness accounts, and other reports as necessary.

Vehicles in Avalanche Fill in the table below. Describe and/or estimate the cost of the damage to each vehicle caught in the avalanche.

Type	Partially Buried	Completely Buried	Damage	Replacement Cost

Structures Damaged Fill in the table below. Describe and/or estimate the cost of the damage to each structure affected by the avalanche.

Type	Construction Type	Damage	Destroyed	Replacemer Cost

Total Loss Estimate the cost of the damage caused by the avalanche. $____________________

Rescue Cost Estimate the cost of rescue. $____________________

Economic Effects List economic effects not included in the above tables (road closed, ski area closed, mine closed, change in policy, etc.)

Additional Comments and Recommendations

APPENDIX E
REFERENCES
CITED

HOW TO USE THIS BOOK

[1]American Avalanche Association. *Snow, Weather, and Avalanches: Observation guidelines for avalanche programs in the United States* (3rd ed). Victor, ID: 2016.

[2]Logan, Spencer and Ethan Greene. 2016. The avalanche character frequency of reported avalanche events in Colorado, USA, 2011-2016. Proceedings, 2016 International Snow Science Workshop, Breckenridge, Colorado.

1996-97 SEASON

[1]Palmer, Jim. "Tragedy averted as three are rescued after being buried in snow Monday." *Pope County Tribune*, January 13, 1997.

[2]Sanderson, Ward. "Searchers recover body of avalanche victim: friends riding nearby triggered snow slide that buried snowmobiler." *The Spokesman-Review*, March 10, 1997.

[3]Martin, Eric. "Avalanche, warm weather, Alaska, Mount Hunter, Moonflower Buttress." *Accidents in North American Mountaineering* (1998).

1997-98 SEASON

[1]Fredston, Jill and Doug Fesler. "Untitled report." Unpublished report, Alaska Mountain Safety Center in Colorado Avalanche Information Center archives, 1997.

[2]Rider, Jane. "Two avalanches kill snowmobiler, hiker." *Missoulian*, January 4, 1998.

[3]Haines, Joan. Bozeman Daily Chronicle.

[4]Clark, Maureen. "Snowmobiler dies after being hit by avalanche." *Alaska Dispatch News*, April 28, 1998.

[5]Richard, Terry. "Slide no surprise, experts say." *The Oregonian.*

[6]Blanck, John, Al Cooke, Josh Lockerby, Alan Proffitt, Dave Sauerbrey, Larry Stadler, and Ian Wade. "Avalanche, poor protection, Oregon, Mount Hood, West Crater Rim." *Accidents in North American Mountaineering* (1999).

1998-99 SEASON

[1]Backus, Perry. *Montana Standard.*

[2]Fredston, Jill and Doug Fesler. *Snow Sense: A Guide to Evaluating Snow Avalanche Hazard, 5th Ed.* Anchorage: Alaska Mountain Safety Center, Inc., 2011.

[3]White, Jeanette. "Snowboarder from Spokane dies in avalanche." *The Spokesman-Review*, January 31, 1999.

[4]Watzman, Nancy. "Swept away." *Westword*, April 22, 1999.

[5]Lieberman, Steve. "Three survive, one die in lengthy avalanche burial." Avalanche.org.

[6]Aho, K., L. Rushkin, and N. Phillips. "Avalanche hits Alyeska ski run, officials say no one badly hurt." *Anchorage Daily News*, April 13, 1999.

[7]Fesler, Doug and Jill Fredston. "Turnagain Pass, Alaska Avalanche Accident." Avalanche.org. April 4, 1999.

[8]Manning, Elizabeth. "Loved ones find snowmobiler." *Alaska Dispatch News*, April 5, 1999.

[9]Porco, Peter. "Snowmachiner missing after avalanche." *Anchorage Daily News*, April 17, 1999.

[10]Kowalski, Robert. "Avalanche kills snowboarding pair." *Anchorage Daily News*,

[11]Medred, Craig. "Climber dies in avalanche." *Anchorage Daily News.*

[12]Phillips, Natalie. "Avalanche claims hiker." *Anchorage Daily News*, May 18, 1999.

1999-00 SEASON

[1]Fredston, Jill. *Snowstruck: In the Grip of Avalanches.* San Diego: Harcourt Books, 2005.

[2]Philips, Natalie and Craig Medred. "With no time to escape, workers braced for slide." *Anchorage Daily News*, February 2, 2000.

[3]Badger, T.A. "Alaska avalanche victims rescued." *Associated Press*, February 2, 2000.

[4]The Enterprise Staff. "Avalanche kills Lake Placid man." *Adirondack Daily Enterprise*, February 21, 2000.

[5]O'Harra, Doug. "Body of avalanche victim found." *Anchorage Daily News*, April 10, 2000.

[6]"Skiers caught in Talkeetna slide ID'd." *Anchorage Daily News*, April 10, 2000.

2000-01 SEASON

[1]Fredston, Jill. "Accident Report: East Fork Matanuska Headwaters, Alaska." *Avalanche.org*, February 7, 2001.

[2]Tremper, Bruce. "Untitled report." Unpublished report, Utah Avalanche Center, May 29, 2001.

2001-02 SEASON

[1]Medred, Craig. "Search for avalanche victim was search for friend." *Anchorage Daily News*, December 14, 2001.

[2]Hooper, Troy. "Ashcroft skier was a senior scientist at CSU." *Aspen Daily News*, March 18, 2002.

[3]Schaerer, Peter and David McClung. *The Avalanche Handbook, Third Edition.* Seattle: Mountaineers Books, 2006.

2002-03 SEASON

[1]Laine, Kristin. "White Nightmare." *Rock and Ice*, December 2002.

[2]Thuermer, Angus M. "Slide kills Michigan snowmobiler." *Jackson Hole News & Guide*, January 30, 2003.

[3]Lipsher, Steve and Kieran Nicholson. "Avalanche victim recovered." *Denver Post*, February 19, 2003.

[4]Lipsher, Steve. "Body of avalanche victim recovered." *Denver Post*, March 7, 2003.

2003-04 SEASON

[1]Judd, Ron C. "A mountain, an avalanche, and amazing grace." *Seattle Times*, February 22, 2004.

[2]Judd, Ron C. "An avalanche and a miracle that saves two students' lives." *Seattle Times*, February 23, 2004.

[3]Hyde, Jesse. "Pain and guilt linger a year after avalanche." *Deseret Morning News*, December 26, 2004.

[4]Boone, Rebecca. "Avalanche survivors recount snow 'explosion.'" *Associated Press*, January 6, 2004.

[5]Brown, Andrea. "Safety didn't save climber in avalanche." *The Gazette*, March 23, 2004.

[6]"Avalanche surprises snowmachiners." *Anchorage Daily News*, April 14, 2004.

[7]Kessler, Glenn. "Avalanche Incident Summary Washington State, Mount Rainier, Liberty Ridge—June 13, 2004." Northwest Avalanche Center, 2004.

About the Authors

Knox Williams got his Master's Degree in Atmospheric Science from Colorado State University in 1970. That same year, he began a career in avalanche science and research with the U.S. Forest Service Avalanche Research Project in Fort Collins, Colorado. In 1983, he was a co-founder of the Colorado Avalanche Information Center and was its Director until retiring from the position in 2005. He retired from full-time work following one year as a forecaster at the Northwest Avalanche Center based in Seattle. Knox was an instructor at the National Avalanche School from 1971 to 2015 and is a past president of the American Avalanche Association. Knox authored and co-authored two previous volumes of *The Snowy Torrents*.

Spencer Logan learned to ski at a now-defunct ski hill in northern Colorado. He began learning about avalanches in northern Utah, and worked several winters as an avalanche forecaster. Spencer earned his Master's Degree in Earth Science from Montana State University, where he examined changes in avalanche weak layers through time. Knox hired him as a forecaster at the Colorado Avalanche Information Center in 2004, one of Knox's last hires. Since 2008, he has maintained the CAIC's archive of US avalanche accidents, which has allowed him to co-author research papers about avalanche accidents in scientific journals and conference proceedings.